THE HANDBOOK OF
BRITISH MAMMALS

THE HANDBOOK OF
BRITISH MAMMALS

EDITED FOR THE MAMMAL SOCIETY
OF THE BRITISH ISLES BY

H. N. SOUTHERN

ILLUSTRATED BY

ROBERT GILLMOR

CETACEA BY ERIK THORN

BLACKWELL
SCIENTIFIC PUBLICATIONS
OXFORD

PRINTED IN GREAT BRITAIN IN THE CITY OF OXFORD
AT THE ALDEN PRESS
AND BOUND BY THE KEMP HALL BINDERY

Contents

v

PART II

A SYSTEMATIC ACCOUNT OF BRITISH MAMMALS

* Responsibilities in sections of composite authorship are noted in Editor's Acknowledgments.

List of Illustrations

TEXT-FIGURES

PHOTOGRAPHS
between pages 186-187

Preface

It seems extraordinary that this should be the first complete Handbook of British Mammals to be published in this country. The need has always been there and was in part met by Barrett-Hamilton and Hinton in the early years of this century but the past 40 or 50 years have seen enormous advances in our knowledge of our native mammals—and an ever-increasing demand from the ever-increasing number of those interested for an up-to-date definitive handbook. Nobody knows how many these are but there are several thousand professional biologists, something in the nature of 80,000–100,000 members of national and local Natural History Societies and of course many thousands more who make a point of listening to or looking at sound or television programmes on natural history. This book is designed for all interested in British mammals, to be an essential tool for the professional zoologist and amateur naturalist alike and to show those whose interest has been aroused by wireless or television how they can take the next step of learning how to watch and study the animals which are all round us.

It is, moreover, unique in so far as all concerned, editor, contributors and the Mammal Society which sponsored it, have waived rights to royalties in order that it can be sold as cheaply as possible. The Mammal Society owes a great debt of gratitude to all those, each one an expert in his own field, who have given so much time to the compilation of this book and I am sure that the present and future generations of naturalists will feel the same.

Cranbrook

Introduction

L. HARRISON MATTHEWS F.R.S.
Chairman of the Mammal Society of the British Isles, 1955–1962

This book has had a long gestation. It was conceived in 1955 at the Exeter conference of the Mammal Society of the British Isles, then in its infancy, as a work of collaboration between its members. It is one thing, however, to plan such a book, but quite another to bring it to completion. Authors are often optimistic about the time necessary to write their contributions so that their target dates are sometimes passed with their manuscripts still unfinished; when a book has many authors the speed of producing it depends upon the speed of the slowest. The task of collecting and collating the contributions is great, and during the course of the work it has fallen more and more upon the shoulders of H.N.Southern, who has not only written many of the sections himself but has re-written much of the material supplied by others in order to secure some uniformity of style and treatment.

Those who have looked forward to the publication of this book for so long will not, I think, be disappointed, and will agree that though its making has been protracted it has been well worth the lengthy wait. As a guide to the British mammals it contains practically everything that is known of them at the time of publication; a careful perusal of the systematic section shows how much is yet to be discovered about many aspects of their biology. A very useful feature of this section is the information given under the headings of families and genera about related forms in other parts of the world, thus enabling the reader to see our native species in proper perspective with relation to the world fauna.

The general sections in Part I are designed to give the naturalist an introduction, both theoretical and practical, to the study of mammals and to help him with a full account of the best methods of observation and research. They remind me strongly of that splendid book on birds that now seems to be generally forgotten, Elliot Coues's *Field and General Ornithology*, which was an inspiration to so many birdmen of the last century. Everything that may be useful to the student of our mammals has been included in these general chapters, which will surely provide fascinating reading for amateur and specialist alike.

I hope this book will have a wide circulation among British naturalists and that in due course further editions will be required. All the contributors expect that those later editions will be greatly expanded to contain the new information that this foundation will help our colleagues to seek out in the field and the laboratory. As Elliot Coues said, 'the true ornithologist goes out to study birds alive and destroys some of them simply because that is the only way of learning their structure and technical characters ... the (mere collector) knows that Nature is beautiful, as even a corpse may be; the naturalist catches her sentient expression and knows how beautiful she is!' These words apply with equal force to the study of mammals, as does his concluding remark—'Aim high!—press on, and leave the halfway house of mere collectorship far behind in your pursuit of a delightful study...' The study of mammals is in many ways technically more difficult than that of birds, but it is equally delightful. Aim high and press on!

Editor's Acknowledgments

The Handbook of British Mammals as it now appears, is very like an iceberg because most of the efforts that have produced it are hidden below the surface. A brief note about its history will be the most direct introduction to the acknowledgment of the various shares in its production.

At the first meeting of what was to become the Mammal Society, called on the initiative of T.J.Pickvance and G.B.Hindle, at Birmingham in 1954 our first chairman, A.N.Worden, suggested, in a light-hearted moment, that the Society might take as one of its long-term aims, the production of a definitive *Handbook of British Mammals* to emulate, or to outstrip, the *Handbook of British Birds* and to fill a gap which has been significantly vacant since the unfinished *History of British Mammals*, begun by G.E.H. Barrett-Hamilton and continued by M.A.C.Hinton, had ground to a halt at the end of World War I.

A year later, our second chairman L.Harrison Matthews, outlined a practical scheme for an introductory book on the field study of British mammals to be produced as an inexpensive paper-back, which would stimulate both amateurs and professionals to revive field work on mammals. A Scientific Committee was formed, whose members were to co-operate in this immediate project under the joint editorship of the Scientific Secretary (the present Editor) and L.Harrison Matthews.

A plan was drawn up but the manuscript of the book was slow to accumulate and it was not until 1961 that the complete work had taken shape. By then it was obviously no longer an introductory work but had pushed ahead towards the target originally suggested by A.N.Worden of being a definitive *Handbook of British Mammals*. Furthermore, the addition of a general section (Part I) on the lines suggested by L.Harrison Matthews made it

B xvii

possible to go beyond the limited objective of a reference book (Part II) and to discuss the features and importance of mammals as biological subjects and the ways in which they can be studied in the field. As time went on the editorial work fell more and more upon the shoulders of the present Editor and L.Harrison Matthews has felt that his name ought to be withdrawn as joint editor.

Much re-writing has been necessary as the character of the book shifted from an introductory to a comprehensive work and this has largely fallen to the Editor to do. Fortunately the library of the Bureau of Animal Population at Oxford, with its excellent collection of literature on mammals, has been at hand throughout and this has made it possible to cover the ground fully, and also to add what is known about British species (or those most closely related to them) outside the British Isles.

Responsibility for most of the chapters in Part I is easily assigned as denoted in the Contents pages. The exceptions are Chapters 2 and 6. Most of chapter 2 was, in fact, written by the Editor, but significant contributions in the form of notes were made by Mrs Vizoso (Monica Shorten), Raymond Hewson, K.M.Backhouse, M.Blackmore and F.J.Taylor Page.

Apart from the section specially written by G.B.Corbet, responsibility for the material in chapter 6 is more difficult to assign. A particular debt is owing to D.A.Kempson, Principal Technician at the Bureau of Animal Population, not only for contributing large parts of the sections on photography, on technical aids to observations and on tape recorders but for reading the whole chapter and supplying much information about what apparatus to buy and where to buy it. Others who have helped with this chapter are K.M.Backhouse and Mrs Vizoso.

The chapter on Wild Mammals and the Law was one of the earliest contributions to be received and, since Miss Worrall was no longer available to bring it up to date, this task has been performed by J.D.Westlake and H.V.Thompson, to whom the gratitude of the Mammal Society is due.

Part II is much more complicated and, in fairness to all who have contributed, it is necessary to go into some detail. The connecting paragraphs dealing with families and genera and showing the British fauna against its world background have mostly been supplied by the Editor.

Insectivora. The whole of this section, including the introduction to the order and the Field Identification Characters, was drafted by W.P.Crowcroft and Miss G.K.Godfrey (Mrs Crowcroft) early on. After they had left for Australia the Editor undertook the task of adding the considerable amount of knowledge that had accumulated and of rewriting most of it accordingly.

Chiroptera. M.Blackmore is responsible for the whole of this section.

Lagomorpha. All of this section was written by the Editor with the exception of the part dealing with the Rabbit, which was outlined by A.N.Worden and written by H.V.Thompson.

Rodentia. This was, perhaps, the most complicated section of all and was under the general supervision of the Editor and Ian Linn.

The introduction to the order was written by the Editor and the Field Identification Characters by him and Ian Linn together.

The squirrels in their entirety are the work of Mrs Vizoso.

The smaller voles were done by the Editor and Ian Linn; D.H.Chitty kindly read through the section on the Short-tailed Vole. The Water Vole was drafted by H.V.Thompson and later rewritten and much enlarged by the Editor. The two species of *Apodemus* were treated by the Editor and Ian Linn, with help on the Yellow-necked Mouse from the Earl of Cranbrook, while the Harvest Mouse, the House Mouse and both rats were treated by the Editor alone. H.V.Thompson wrote about the Edible Dormouse and the Editor about the Common Dormouse. H.G.Hurrell and Miss Elaine Hurrell contributed valuable comments on the latter. Lastly, R.A.Davis wrote the section on the Coypu.

Cetacea. F.C.Fraser is entirely responsible for this section.

Carnivora. A troublesome section because there is no single expert to deal with all of it. H.R.Hewer, who was responsible, with K.M.Backhouse, for the subdivision Pinnipedia, most kindly stepped in and took over the organization of the order including the introduction. J.D.Lockie also read the whole section and made many additions and suggestions.

The Fox was first drafted by H.V.Thompson, the Marten by H.G.Hurrell, the Stoat and Weasel by Mrs Vizoso and Colin Matheson, the Polecat by Colin Matheson, and the Wild Cat by L.Harrison Matthews. All these sections were re-written to a greater or less degree by the Editor, adding especially information from outside the British Isles. The Badger is entirely the work of E.G.Neal and the Otter was first drafted by the Editor from Miss

Marie Stephens's report and afterwards much modified by H.G. Hurrell and Miss Elaine Hurrell. The short section on the American Mink was produced jointly by Ian Linn, the Editor and J.H.F.Stevenson.

Perissodactyla and Artiodactyla. This whole section was written by F.J.Taylor Page and the part on Red Deer commented upon by V.P.W.Lowe.

Various small sections on species now extinct in the British Isles were written by Colin Matheson. In addition to this, many sections benefited from circulation at various stages, each critic adding and modifying from his special branch of knowledge. I should particularly like to thank people who have allowed current research to be quoted. Where unpublished theses are available these have been cited in the Bibliography.

Coming to more general acknowledgments, a special debt of gratitude is owed to the Bureau of Animal Population and its Director Charles Elton. Not only were the facilities of its library and the help of its librarians of vital assistance to the Editor but considerable secretarial help was also made available. In the last stages Miss Wendy Welsh (Mrs Harrison) laboured hard and carefully at a difficult typescript.

The Mammal Society is particularly indebted to Robert Gillmor who has worked with such imagination, skill and accuracy upon the bulk of the line drawings. The original intention, when a paperback was contemplated, was to illustrate each British species with a line drawing portrait and the illustrations of Cetacea by Erik Thorn carried out this intention admirably. When we were released from this requirement, the policy was switched to illustrating diagnostic detail foremost, especially small structural minutiae, and then to show some of the characteristics of mammals as a group and general drawings of some British mammals which are difficult for the beginner to separate. Robert Gillmor entered into the spirit of this treatment with enthusiasm. Gratitude is also due to all those people who assisted Mr Gillmor with material, specially to the Zoological Society of London; to the Comptroller of Woburn Estates, and to the Head Deer Keeper, D.Talbot; to W.G.Kingham who gave permission for sketches to be made of his private collection of live British mammals; to the British Museum (Natural History); to G.Kinns and M.Blackmore for the loan of photographs and to others who have helped with critical advice in their special groups; to R.G.Schardt for the loan of equipment; and to M.G.Hardy who has been particularly helpful in general discussion about the illustrations. L.Harrison Matthews and H.R.Hewer have given valuable help over the illustrations of the carnivores. The assistance of D.A.Kempson in producing photographic copies of the drawings for circulation and criticism is gratefully acknowledged.

The graphs and maps among the text-figures have been drawn with great care by Tony Dunford.

A word must also be said about the arrangement and typography of the Handbook. We are especially grateful to Blackwell Scientific Publications for their care and patience in these matters, in particular to their production manager Mr J.L.Robson. Robert Gillmor and M.L.Twyman have made valuable comments. Blackwell Scientific Publications have taken all this in their stride and over every aspect and stage of the production of the book have been most helpful and enthusiastic.

In particular the publishers have met the desire of the Mammal Society's Committee that the price of the book should be kept reasonably low. Towards this end the Committee decided to forego some royalties, and Blackwell Scientific Publications have been most painstaking in producing a book of high quality at the lowest possible price.

The whole burden of collecting, selecting and arranging the photographic illustrations has been undertaken by H.R.Hewer and his help in this way during the last hectic year of seeing the book through the press has been particularly appreciated.

There are many other people who should be thanked but the list grows and the reader will be impatient to get to the book. I hope all these will forgive being lumped in one large and collective 'thank-you'.

After all this effort acknowledged it may well seem graceless to ask for more help, but there must be many mistakes and omissions in a book of this kind and readers would do a great service by noting each one that they discover and informing me, c/o The Mammal Society, Institute of Biology, 41 Queen's Gate, London S.W. 7.

THE BIOLOGY OF BRITISH MAMMALS

CHAPTER I

What is a Mammal?

L. HARRISON MATTHEWS

Know then thyself, presume not God to scan,
The proper study of mankind is man.

As man is one of the mammals and flatters himself that he is the best of them, it is appropriate that he should enlarge Pope's advice and extend his studies to include what he regards as his inferior relations. In the British Isles there are fewer species of mammals than of birds, yet they are equally common and widespread though much less frequently seen. The ease with which birds can escape danger because they can fly gives them a confidence and indifference to observation which the earth-bound mammals cannot share—they must ever seek concealment, and consequently the majority are active mainly by night. Although the study of mammals in the field presents many difficulties to naturalists, it is a very rewarding occupation, for we have comparatively little detailed knowledge of the lives of mammals, as perusal of these pages will show. The mammals offer a wide field for the winning of new knowledge about animals, and the long neglect which they have suffered—or enjoyed—in Britain is now only beginning to be rectified. This book, written by members of the Mammal Society of the British Isles, a society only nine years old, is an attempt to present a summary of all that is known about British wild mammals as a foundation for further work.

The mammals as a whole have had their day and, like many another group of animals before them, they are a dwindling race. In the whole world there are living today about 4,500 species of mammals, whereas birds number about 8,600, fishes about 23,000, insects 700,000 and even the Protozoa about 30,000. Simpson (1945) notes that all the orders of mammals, except the rodents and perhaps the higher artiodactyls (the cloven-hoofed ruminants)

3

have declined in *numbers* since the Miocene and Pliocene periods when they were at their peak. He lists the 32 orders of mammals of which 14 (44 per cent) are extinct, the 257 families of which 139 (54 per cent) are extinct and the 2,864 genera of which 1,932 (67 per cent) are extinct. The natural decline in numbers that has been going on for several million years has been enormously accelerated during the last century and a half, and in spite of strenuous efforts at conservation there is no sign yet that the pace is slackening.

Mammals, like the birds, reptiles, amphibians and fishes, are vertebrates, animals with backbones made up of more or less similar joints; and together with the birds they are distinguished from the rest by being warm-blooded. There are, however, few characters that are absolutely diagnostic of mammals, for there are exceptions to many features that are almost universal; one of the few universal ones is that from which they take their name, the possession of mammary glands which produce milk for the nourishment of the young. Among others are the possession of three small bones, the auditory ossicles in the middle ear which transmit vibrations from the ear drum to the inner ear, and the formation of each half of the lower jaw from a single bone. Typically mammals are four-limbed, warm-blooded vertebrates covered with hair, which bring forth living young—but the whales are naked (though some do possess a few hairs) and have no hind limbs; and the echidna and platypus lay eggs. There are similar exceptions to other widely shared features.

The mammals have become adapted to living in most of the possible environments on the surface of the globe below the permanent snow line, from the high Arctic to the tropics, and from mountain streams to rivers, lakes and the great oceans. The adaptation to so many different environments is correlated with an enormous range of differentiation in body form and size, and in habits, food and behaviour—elephants, mice, whales, armadillos, lions, monkeys, giraffes. Yet comparative anatomy shows that all these diverse forms are modifications, by enlargement and development here, and diminution or complete loss there, of a single basic pattern.

This pattern can be imagined as a mammal of medium or small size covered with hair, with the head set on the trunk by a neck of moderate length, with a tail, with four limbs each of which ends in five digits armed with short claws, and with the palms of the fore limbs and the soles of the hind applied to the ground in walking. On the head the nostrils open at the end of the snout, the eyes are at the sides, and the ears, provided with pinnae or external flaps, lie behind them.

The body is supported by the internal skeleton which consists of the backbone or vertebral column made up of numerous individual *vertebrae* (seven of which form the neck), of the skull, the ribs and the limb bones. The skull consists of numerous bones closely fitted together (Fig. 1) and is divisible into two parts, the facial region comprising the snout and jaws, and the *cranium*—a box containing the brain. The brain is continuous with the spinal cord or *marrow* running the length of the body in a tube formed by the vertebrae. The ribs are jointed to a number of the vertebrae behind the neck, and encircle the body to meet and join the breast bone, or *sternum*, on the under surface, forming a cage, the chest or *thorax*, in which the heart and lungs are protected. The contraction and expansion of the chest help to expel air from the lungs and to draw a further supply into them in breathing. Behind the thorax the vertebrae carry no ribs, but some of them are fused together to form the *sacrum* which gives a firm anchorage to the bones supporting the hind limbs; behind the sacrum the vertebrae diminish progressively in size to the tip of the tail.

The skeleton of the limbs consists of the *long bones* and the limb *girdles* supporting them. The girdle of the fore limb is made up on each side of the body by a shoulder blade or *scapula* bearing a ball and socket joint at its lower end and a collar bone or *clavicle* which connects the lower end of the scapula to the front end of the sternum. The girdle of the hind limb is more firmly fixed to the vertebral column at the sacrum; it is made up of three bones on each side, the *ilium, ischium* and *pubis*, fused into a single structure which together with the sacrum is termed the *pelvis*. The pelvis forms a complete ring of bone through which the intestine, the sex and urinary ducts, and other structures pass; on its outer side the pelvis bears a ball and socket joint. The long bones of the fore and hind limbs resemble each other: first there is a single bone with a rounded end fitting into the socket of the girdle (upper arm, *humerus*; thigh, *femur*) and hinged at its lower end are two bones (forearm, *ulna* and *radius*; shin, *tibia* and *fibula*). Then follow the wrist or ankle bones (*carpals* or *tarsals*) two rows each of five

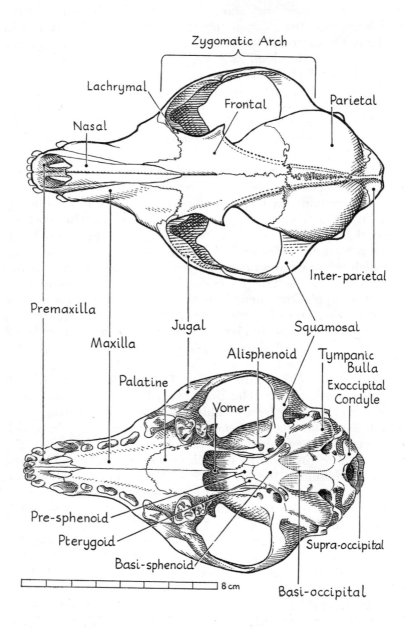

Zygomatic Arch

Lachrymal

Frontal

Parietal

Nasal

Premaxilla

Maxilla

Jugal

Squamosal

Inter-parietal

Palatine

Alisphenoid

Tympanic Bulla

Vomer

Exoccipital Condyle

Pre-sphenoid

Pterygoid

Basi-sphenoid

Supra-occipital

Basi-occipital

8 cm

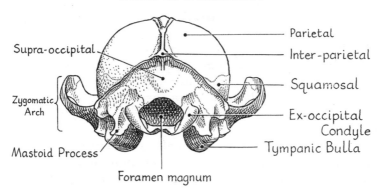

Supra-occipital

Zygomatic Arch

Mastoid Process

Foramen magnum

Parietal

Inter-parietal

Squamosal

Ex-occipital Condyle

Tympanic Bulla

FIG. 1. Skull of Fox (*Vulpes vulpes*) from above, below and behind, showing general topography and bones.

surrounding a larger central one, and all fitting closely together. These support the elongated *metacarpal* (hand) or *metatarsal* (foot) bones each of which supports typically three *phalanges* (finger or toe bones) progressively diminishing in size. The bones of the skeleton are fixed together by strong ligaments which, however, are sufficiently elastic to allow the necessary movement. The joints are lubricated by the interposition between the moving surfaces of small envelopes containing slippery fluid (if they are irritated and become over-filled conditions such as 'tennis elbow' and 'housemaid's knee' are produced).

The movements of the limbs and of the rest of the body are effected by the muscles, the 'meat' of the butcher. Each muscle is built up from innumerable elongated cells which have the property of shortening or contracting when stimulated. Most muscles are attached by each end to different bones, so that when they contract they make the bones move in relation to each other; the ends of many muscles are attached to bones by means of tendons so that the effective pull is transmitted to a distant site.

The brain and spinal cord, already mentioned, form the *central nervous system* and are connected with all parts of the body by the nerves which ramify to and from them. The nerves transmit stimuli from the eye, ear, nose, touch- and temperature-receptors in the skin, and all the other sense organs, to the central nervous system. They also carry outgoing stimuli to the muscles which respond by movement, and to all the other 'effector' organs such as glands, the heart, stomach, intestines and many more. Other nerve networks, the sympathetic and para-sympathetic are connected with the central nervous system.

The thorax contains, within the cage of the ribs, the lungs and heart which are shut off from the hinderpart of the body, the abdomen, containing the digestive and other organs, by the *diaphragm* or midriff which is a thin sheet of tendon and muscle that helps in breathing by enlarging or compressing the cavity of the thorax.

When food is swallowed it passes along the gullet or *oesophagus*, a tube that runs through the thorax and penetrates the diaphragm to reach the abdomen. There it joins the stomach, a comparatively large bag in which the first stages of digestion take place under the influence of the acid and digestive ferments produced in it. Thence it passes into a long narrow tube, the small intestine, which packs into the abdomen through being folded into many coils. The small intestine receives the bile from the liver, and digestive secretions from the pancreas, and also produces digestive juices from its own lining. Under the influence of these agents the food is reduced to fine particles and finally dissolved so that the nourishment it affords can be taken up through the lining of the intestine and be passed into the blood for distribution round the body. What is left passes on to a wider and shorter tube, the large intestine, where much water is removed from it, and the residue passes on to the exterior through the rectum and anus.

The blood vessels ramify throughout the body carrying blood *from* the heart in the arteries, and *to* it in the veins. The ultimate branches of the arteries are extremely minute tubes, the capillaries, and they are continuous with the first beginnings of the veins which become larger as more and more tributaries join them on their way to the heart. The blood carries oxygen from the lungs, and food from the intestine, to all parts of the body and removes the carbon dioxide and other waste products of the processes of living to be discharged through the lungs and kidneys. The heart is a muscular bulb continually contracting rhythmically; it contains four communicating chambers connected to each other by openings guarded by valves so that the blood flows only in one direction. On entering the first chamber from the main veins the blood goes to the second and is pumped to the lungs where it loses its carbon dioxide and takes up oxygen; it then returns to the third chamber and thence goes to the fourth from which it is pumped into the main artery and so round the body to the capillaries to return to the heart again through the veins.

The veins bringing nourishment away from the intestine go first to the liver where the blood undergoes a process of 'purification' and where a proportion of the nourishment may be stored. In addition to the arteries and veins there is a complicated network of fine tubes connected with them and ramifying throughout the body carrying a colourless fluid, the lymph. Much of the food absorbed by the intestine is passed into the lymph channels and finally delivered into the main vein from the largest of them.

The lungs are spongy in texture owing to the vast number of small air passages within them. The ultimate ramifications of the passages are minute bags in which the air is separated from the blood in the capillaries by an extremely tenuous membrane through which exchange of gases readily takes place. The smallest channels join to form larger ones, they join others and so on until a single pipe, the *bronchus*, emerges from each lung and joins its fellow to form the *trachea* or windpipe which communicates with the back of the mouth and nose. It is kept open by a series of gristly rings so that it cannot collapse when the breath is drawn in.

The kidneys lying on the back wall of the abdomen remove the nitrogenous waste matter produced by the activity of the body tissues. It is brought to them by the blood every time it makes its circuit round the body. This waste is dissolved in water and passes from each kidney through a tube to the bladder where it accumulates as the urine and is periodically discharged.

In addition to the nervous system, which can be said to control the activities of the body, the ductless or endocrine glands produce substances, the hormones, that are carried by the blood to other parts of the body where they cause specific changes in the 'target organs'. Some of these, the sex hormones, are of great importance in the reproductive cycle and are discussed in a later chapter. The thyroid in the neck, the thymus in the thorax, the pituitary at the base of the brain, the adrenals close to the kidneys are important endocrine glands. The spleen which lies near the stomach in the abdomen is mainly an organ for the manufacture of blood.

The abdomen also contains the reproductive organs, male or female, but the description of them is deferred to the chapter on breeding.

When we observe living animals it is the outside that we see—
the skin and its appendages which are as diverse in their variation
as are the general body form and proportions. The skin is tough
yet flexible and consists of several layers, the outermost of which
is dead and is continually flaking off in small bits and being
replaced by growth from the living layers beneath. It is covered
with minute pits from each of which a hair grows; the hairs, like
the outer layer of the skin, are dead and are produced by the living
cells at the bottom of the pits. A small gland opens into each pit
and exudes a greasy substance that acts as a waterproof dressing
for the hair. The skin of most mammals also contains sweat glands
which exude a watery fluid containing dissolved salts; in some
mammals the glands are numerous and are spread over nearly the
whole surface, in others they are few and confined to definite
parts of the body.

The hair is generally of two sorts, a soft dense woolly underfur,
which is concealed by the longer and coarser guard hairs that
overlap and conceal it unless they are parted. Underfur and guard
hairs often differ in colour, and it is the latter that give the
animal its characteristic colour and pattern. The hairs contain
pigment granules that are incorporated as the hair grows from
the living cells at the bottom of its pit; if they are not produced at
a constant rate the hair may be variegated or ringed—very often
the tips differ in colour from the shaft of the hair. These variations
produce those subtle gradations of colour that make the coats of
many mammals, especially those used by man as furs for clothing,
such beautiful things. There is a wide range in the amount of
underfur; it is abundant in many carnivores and rodents, but
comparatively scanty in dogs and horses. In domestic sheep,
through artificial selection, the underfur has become very long and
curly, and the guard hairs are absent so that a fleece is formed.

The colour of the hair commonly differs in different parts of
the body and thus forms patterns which may be of two sorts, those
that advertise and those that conceal the presence of the animal.
Among the first are patterns facilitating recognition between
members of a species or distinguishing the sexes, and those warning
predators to keep away. A typical warning pattern is carried by
the Skunk, and with reason—the conspicuous head pattern of the
Badger may have a similar meaning. In addition some warning
patterns are used within the species, such as the white scut of the

Rabbit. Concealing patterns are of two sorts—those that blend the animal with its background and those that break up its outline with contrasting colours as in ship-camouflage. Blending patterns are usually reinforced by the underside of the animal being lighter in colour so that the natural shadow of the underparts is neutralized. Nearly all the mammals are colour blind or have poor colour vision, and consequently their colours are dull or neutral in character; it is only in those with colour vision such as the squirrels and monkeys that bright colours other than browns, dull greens, greys, black and white, are found.

In nearly all mammals certain hairs are much longer than those of the general body covering—they are the vibrissae, usually called the whiskers, although they are not the same as the hairs of the same name that adorn the faces of unshaven men. They are tactile organs and are set in extra deep pits which are surrounded with nerve endings so that their slightest movement is signalled to the brain. They are nearly always present on the snout on each upper lip, and they also occur on other parts of the body—above the eyes, under the chin, on wrist and ankle, and less commonly on the sides of the belly. In some mammals some of the hairs are extremely coarse and strong so that they form prickles or spines as on the hedgehog, or long quills as on the porcupine.

Just as hairs are dead products of the skin so too are more robust structures such as nails, claws, hoofs and horns. Nails and claws are constantly worn away at their free ends, the loss being made good by growth at the base from the living cells lining the pocket in the skin from which they protrude. The horns of ruminants such as the ox and sheep are supported by cores of bone attached to the skull and forming part of the skeleton. The core is ensheathed by the horn proper which, like hoof, is a product of the skin. The horns or antlers of deer when fully developed are the equivalent of the bony core alone of the ruminants—they are dead parts of the skull sticking through the skin. During the development of the antlers, however, they are covered with a living skin bearing short soft hairs, the velvet; in this the blood vessels bring the material for forming the bone. When the antler reaches full size the velvet dies and its shrivelled remains are frayed off by the animal against bushes and other low herbage. The horn of the rhinoceros has no core of bone and is thus entirely a product of the skin.

c

The skin lining the mouth is continuous with that of the surface of the body; in origin it is part of it, for they are both derived from the *ectodermal* layer of the embryo whereas the lining of the inner parts of the digestive tube arises from another layer. The teeth, or parts of them, are thus also products of the skin. They consist of hard dentine covered with an even harder enamel, and are derived from pockets of the mouth-lining that penetrate into the tissues below so far that the fully developed teeth fit into sockets in the jaw bones. The teeth, being hard and compact, are the most indestructible part of the body and are very important in the study of mammals, partly because they are often the only remains of extinct and fossil forms available to us, and partly because they are very distinctive in the different orders of mammals and hence one of the chief characters used in classification. The main types of mammalian skulls and dentition found in the British Isles are illustrated in Fig. 2.

The basic purpose of classification is to give all the animals names so that we know what creatures we are talking about, and to arrange them systematically by grouping together species that resemble each other closely and separating those that do not. The resemblances and differences between species are real, but their systematic arrangement is a matter of opinion because we do not know the exact relationships of one to another. Classification attempts to show the probable evolutionary relationships of animals, but it cannot show the family tree when dealing only with living animals because they all represent the topmost twigs of the tree. The lower branches and trunks can only be sketched in with what we can learn from the imperfect fossil record, of which teeth form a large part.

In most mammals the teeth of an individual are not all similar, the dentition is *heterodont* and is typically divided into the front biting teeth or incisors, the eye teeth or canines, and the grinding teeth, subdivided into premolars and molars. In many vertebrates the teeth are replaced throughout life as they are broken or worn out, but in the mammals there is only one replacement of some of the teeth, and not always that. The replacement generally occurs during youth and may be connected with the increasing size of the jaws as they grow, for teeth once fully formed cannot grow. This suggestion, however, is not supported by the many examples of mammals in which the first teeth are rudimentary and are lost in infancy, or even before birth, as in bats and seals. Even in mammals in which the first or milk teeth are fully functional for some time not all of the second or permanent teeth are preceded by milk teeth. The milk dentition consists only of incisors, canines and premolars; the true molars belong to the permanent set and have no predecessors.

The incisors are usually not more than three on each side of each jaw; they are typically small and chisel-shaped and have single roots. The canines, one on each side in each jaw are generally large and pointed, and have single roots; although they are particularly conspicuous in the carnivores they are well developed in many other mammals. When the jaw is closed the lower canines always fit in front of the upper ones, a fact often overlooked by artists when they try to make a drawing of some carnivore look very fierce. The premolars and molars each typically have several points or cusps, and it has been shown that their pattern has been derived from a tooth in which a main central cusp has a smaller one in front and behind. In the course of evolution the smaller cusps have increased in size and shifted in position so that they often lie beside the main cusp. A further complication is introduced by the formation of additional cusps on the heel or talon at the back of the tooth where the exposed surface is separated from the root by the ridge or *cingulum* at the level of the gum. The premolars generally have two roots, the molars at least three. There is, however, great variation from the basic pattern in the form of all the teeth in the different orders of mammals.

There is a similar variation in the number of teeth in each category, but the number remains constant in any one species and is thus a useful character in defining it. The number of teeth is conveniently shown in an abbreviation known as the dental formula. We have thirty-two teeth; on each side of the upper and lower jaws we have two incisors, one canine, two premolars and three molars.

Our dental formula is therefore

$$ i \frac{2\text{-}2}{2\text{-}2}, \quad c \frac{1\text{-}1}{1\text{-}1}, \quad pm \frac{2\text{-}2}{2\text{-}2}, \quad m \frac{3\text{-}3}{3\text{-}3} - 32 $$

or more simply, counting one side only $i \frac{2}{2}, \quad c \frac{1}{1}, \quad pm \frac{2}{2}, \quad m \frac{3}{3}$

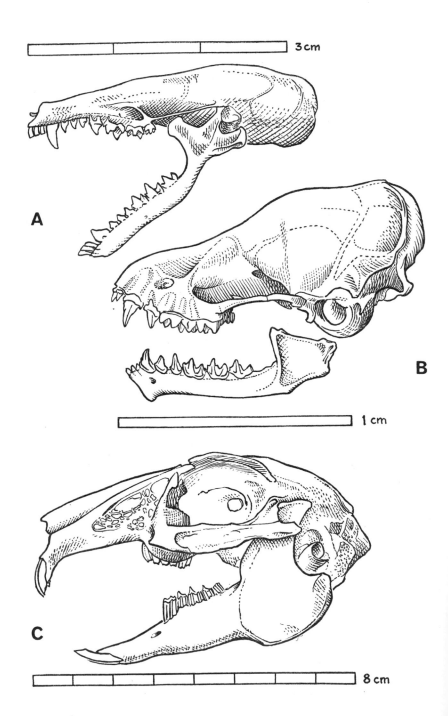

A

B

3 cm

1 cm

C

8 cm

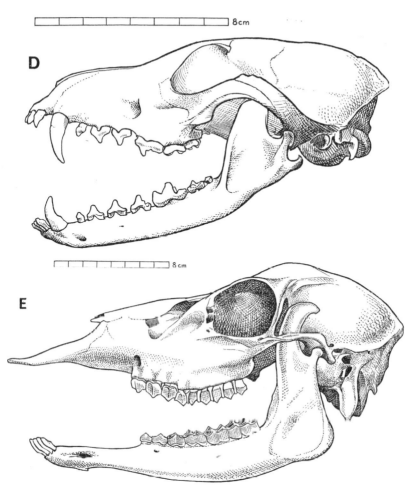

FIG. 2. Types of mammalian skulls: (*a*) Mole (*Talpa europaea*), (*b*) Pipistrelle Bat (*Pipistrellus pipistrellus*), (*c*) Rabbit (*Oryctolagus cuniculus*), (*d*) Fox (*Vulpes vulpes*) and (*e*) Fallow Deer (*Dama dama*).

or, most abbreviated of all $\dfrac{2.1.2.3}{2.1.2.3}$.

Similarly the dental formula of the cat is $\dfrac{3.1.3.1}{3.1.2.1}$

or of the Red Deer $\dfrac{0.1.3.3}{3.1.3.3}$.

Although the type of the dentition is characteristic for each order of mammals the dental formula is not, for it may vary considerably within an order. The character of the dentition in each of the seven orders found in Britain out of the eighteen orders of living mammals may be summarized as follows:

INSECTIVORA The insectivores are regarded as the least specialized mammals, but their dentition is anything but simple. The cheek teeth (premolars and molars) are generally of a modified tuberculo-sectorial type, that is they are provided with three or more pointed cusps adapted for crunching up the bodies of invertebrates. In the premolars, canines and incisors, however, there is great variation, and often a wide divergence from the basic pattern. In the Hedgehog the front incisors are larger than the others and much larger than the canines; in the Mole the lower canine resembles an incisor in position and shape, the first lower premolar resembles a canine, and the canine of the upper jaw has two roots; in the shrews the first incisors are very large and project almost horizontally, the upper being hook-shaped and having two points, the lower often having raised lobes—the other incisors together with the canines and front premolars all have single cusps and resemble each other in size and shape.

CHIROPTERA The incisors are small and those of the upper jaw are reduced in number, being never more than two on each side. The canines are large and the premolars, except the last upper premolar which resembles the molars, are pointed like the canines but are much smaller. The molars bear three main pointed cusps and several minor ones. As all the British bats are exclusively insectivorous their dentition is highly adapted for the capture and fragmentation of insects.

LAGOMORPHA The dentition strongly resembles that of the rodents but has two upper incisors on each side (three in the milk dentition). The second incisors lie immediately behind the first, and are very much smaller. There are no canines and the premolars resemble the molars and form with them a pattern of transverse ridges.

RODENTIA The incisors are reduced to $\frac{1}{1}$; they are very large and have open roots so that they never stop growing. The enamel is absent from the back so that the ends wear to a sharp chisel shape. There are no canines and a wide gap (*diastema*) separates the incisors from the premolars. The cheek teeth vary widely; in some rodents they bear a simple pattern of rounded cusps or a series of ridges, adapted for grinding up seeds and soft vegetable matter, whereas in others they consist of several columns joined by narrow waists so that an extensive grinding surface is formed for dealing with hard grass stems. The more generalized kinds of molar have closed roots, but the specialized ones have open roots so that growth is continuous and compensates for the extreme wear to which they are subjected. In all rodents the premolars are never more than $\frac{2}{1}$ in number, and in many they are completely absent.

CETACEA The toothed whales, porpoises and dolphins differ from all the other mammals in having a *homodont* dentition—all the teeth are alike and they are not differentiated into incisors, canines and cheek teeth. Furthermore, they are often very numerous and far exceed the highest number found in any mammal with heterodont dentition (the Numbat or Banded Anteater of Australia which has a total of fifty-six). The teeth are peg-like, slightly more complex in only a few species, and super-ficially resemble the shape and arrangement of the teeth on the jaws of a fish. In some species they are reduced in number, and in a few they are totally absent at least in the fully adult animals. The homodont dentition is commonly held to be an adaptation for catching slippery and active prey such as fishes and squids, but the toothless species feed upon the same diet. The whalebone whales have no teeth; their mouths are provided with baleen or whalebone which consists of numerous horny plates set crossways and hanging down from the upper jaw. Their inner edges are frayed out into fibres which form a hairy mat through which the sea water is strained to separate the small planktonic animals on which these whales feed.

CARNIVORA The incisors are small but the canines large; the premolars and, even more, the molars are reduced in number, so that some species have only one molar. The last upper premolar and the first lower molar are enlarged as the carnassial teeth. In their most highly developed form, as in the cats, the carnassials are sharp flattened blades that sweep past each other with a scissors action; they cut meat and bone into fragments that can be swallowed whole, for these animals do not chew their food.

ARTIODACTYLA In the cloven-hoofed ungulates there are no upper incisors but the gum forms a hard pad against which the lower incisors bite. The lower incisors are more or less spoon-shaped; at first sight they appear to number four, but the fourth, outer one is really a modified and incisiform canine. The canine of the upper jaw is generally a small *tush* which in the males of some species is a fully developed tusk projecting from the mouth. The premolars and molars are alike and low-crowned; their cusps are arranged so that when they wear in use a number of crescentic ridges are formed. The combined grinding surfaces of the cheek teeth thus make a mill adapted to chewing the cud.

Many mammals live in burrows or dens which form their homes and on which their activities are centred. An individual territory generally surrounds the home, and in many species its boundaries are marked with secretions from special glands so that others are warned not to trespass. The extent of the territory varies greatly between species and may be measured in yards in some small rodents, or in miles in larger animals such as badgers, though wide-ranging animals may go foraging on neutral ground far beyond the bounds of the home territory. Much remains to be discovered about territories and their uses among the British mammals. Even species that live always above ground such as hares and deer have their territories as precisely defined, at least during part of their lives.

In all mammals there is necessarily a close bond between the mother and her young because she must suckle them during infancy. This care often extends beyond the time of weaning so that the young and parent form a family party, as in many rodents. In other species which pair for life, such as the Fox, the father helps in the rearing of the young and is part of the family group. In yet others, family groups combine and form herds as in some of the deer, though in these animals the sexes keep separate except at the breeding season and the herds consist either of adult males or of females with their young of both sexes. In such gregarious animals there is a social structure within the herd in which a dominant place is held by one animal. In extreme form there is a social hierarchy in which the order of precedence is rigidly observed down the scale from the dominant animal in the 'alpha position' to the unfortunate inferior in the 'omega position'.

Mammals, like birds, are descended from the reptiles, though from a very different group, and like the birds they have been able to spread into practically every environment that is possible for an air-breathing vertebrate. They have emancipated themselves from some of the restrictions imposed on the other vertebrates partly by being warm-blooded, and partly by the comparatively enormous size of the fore-brain which gives an enhanced ability for learning so that appropriate reactions can be produced to unusual situations. The cold-blooded reptile is born with a number of 'built in' reactions to various things that can happen to it; so also to a certain extent is the warm-blooded mammal. But in addition to them it has better powers of learning so that much of its behaviour is not instinctive and the result of inheritance, but is learned through imitation of adults during adolescence. The tradition or lore passed from one generation to another, although limited, is of great importance, and appears to increase with an increase in the size of the brain. Only one species has achieved articulate language, and once the way of recording it permanently had been discovered the experience of past generations became the property of all posterity.

All animals are fascinating subjects to those with the patience to study them, and none more than the mammals which, because of the complexity of their structure, physiology and behaviour, are perhaps the most difficult of all. But in addition to these considerations the naturalist finds satisfaction in learning about them because, quite simply, he likes them.

CHAPTER 2

Field Work on British Mammals

H.N.SOUTHERN *

Birds, butterflies and plants, the principal preoccupations of amateur naturalists, need little seeking. The mammals that are left in the British Isles, on the other hand, are secretive and require time and trouble to observe. There are, however, some methods—tricks, if you like—which make observation simpler and this chapter will consider them.

The popularity of birds, as subjects for study, has arisen because the naturalist's leisure for his hobby is nowadays short and cut up into odd, snatched hours. The long period that young naturalists need for the essential grounding of learning to recognize the many species of British birds in the field can easily be compounded from such odd hours, especially if they are spent at places, such as reservoirs or sewage farms, where migrating or wintering masses of birds congregate. This kind of natural history work has a special appeal to those with varied hobbies because, like stamp collecting, it needs little organizing and is intensely pleasurable and rewarding to pursue.

With land mammals the situation is rather different. Identification (bats excepted) is relatively simple, but finding and observing them is much more difficult than with birds. Thus any naturalist, who starts observation on those few of our mammals which are less difficult to find, such as rabbits, hares or squirrels, will quickly find his curiosity concentrating on habits, distribution and behaviour generally. I believe this is not only because the task of identifying our mammals is so speedily done, but because the fact of their being mammals and so more akin to ourselves than birds makes their behaviour more stimulating to think about.

Thus, wherever such study is made possible either by abundant leisure (the 'anecdotal' sections of B.-H.&H. illustrate this

* Partly based on notes by various contributors (see Editor's Acknowledgments).

admirably; so many of the correspondents evidently had un-limited 'time to stand and stare') or by pertinacity and the use of short-cuts to observation, there will be found an even greater satisfaction than in watching the behaviour of birds.

Once we have admitted the disadvantages of most British mammals as objects of study because they are secretive, small and often nocturnal, we can consider some of the counterbalancing advantages.

Consider, in the first place, the senses of wild mammals. Their hearing—within certain ranges—is acute and their sense of smell far more highly developed than in birds, but, once it has become second nature to take note of wind direction and act accordingly, one can often approach very close to a mammal because its sight is poor. As far as we can tell, most of them (the squirrels and Bank Vole are possible exceptions) are colour blind and their eyes respond more to change in the intensity of illumination and so to movement than to the discrimination of objects in their field of view. Often one can come out into a ride in woodland and surprise a Fox, who is instantly on the alert. But, if one stands motionless and quiet and one's scent is blowing away from the Fox, it may halt puzzled and finally resume its normal activities in full view. It is even possible to draw the Fox towards you by squealing like a wounded rabbit.

Small mammals and Badgers have even poorer sight as far as discriminating objects against a background goes and I have had a Badger almost walk into me before he realized that I was a strange and fear-inspiring object in his environment. Similarly, voles can sometimes be watched at very close quarters, if they venture out of cover, while shrews, moles and bats take hardly any notice of an observer at all. Furthermore, all naturalists will have encountered the occasional individual of most species and the occasional species (like the Skomer Bank Vole) which appear to be devoid of any fear. Of course, as with birds, the seasonal waxing and waning of cover means that much more watching can be done in winter. Bare river banks can supply endless entertainment where there is a colony of Water Voles, but in summer far less can be seen. Unless special hides are built, deer are perhaps the most difficult mammals to watch from close quarters because their eyesight is especially acute at detecting movement and Red Deer at any rate inhabit the kind of country in Great Britain where it is difficult—without training—to move without inadvertently showing one's silhouette against the sky. However, all the technique of the skilled stalker is available to anybody keen to learn, and with such large animals a telescope enables detailed observations to be made from a long distance.

There is no question, therefore, that keeping still and alert for what may come along is a much more productive business with mammals than with birds. This is especially so when all the auxiliary indications of approach have been learned, the smell of a Fox (or of woodland deer), the chatter of a vole, the whickering of shrews, the thumping of rabbits and hares, the snuffling of a Badger, the whistling of Otters—all these when recognized instantly make the observer freeze for a possible exciting glimpse of the animal itself.

Most of our mammals carry on their lives in two dimensions only, unlike birds, and many of them are so organized that their journeys from one part of their home range to another are made with the greatest regularity in time and space. Thus, not only do many of them have systems of paths and runways, where they can be awaited with a reasonable hope of their being seen, but the skilled gamekeeper will set his wires upon a rabbit track where the animal reaches its highest point at a single step. Unless it is in a mortal hurry or actually foraging, a Rabbit will place its feet in precisely the same spots each time it passes along a track, leaving marks which can be readily interpreted.

If its home range is known to an animal in such intimate terms of muscle movements, it has the advantage of being able to move about the range without 'seeing' or even 'thinking' where it is going. It is probably by the use of this kinaesthetic sense that a mouse can move through the most bewildering tangle of cover in a flash. This highly stereotyped nature of an animal's journeyings makes it easier to predict where it will go and when. This question has recently been examined for the Short-tailed Vole against the background of the nature of exploratory behaviour (E.Shillito, 1963).

A mammal's sensory equipment, therefore, and the way it comes to intimate terms with the topography of its environment help us in devising ways of watching it.

There is yet a further advantage. Such behaviour cannot be so stereotyped that it fails to respond to changes in the environment.

Alterations in space are quickly learned after initial mistakes: similarly, alterations in time can be used to manipulate the activity rhythms of animals. For small mammals the specific characteristics of the 24-hour activity cycle have been surveyed by Chitty & Southern (1954), by Miller (1955) and by Crowcroft (1954). There is usually a short-term rhythm of 1–3 hours and on top of this there may be a superimposed day–night rhythm. The latter is susceptible to modification and even to complete reversal under laboratory conditions when the hours of light and dark are switched round. Since this activity rhythm is usually also a feeding rhythm, it can often be modified by providing bait at a stated time each day. It is possible in this way to condition Brown Rats so completely that they are practically waiting with their mouths open for the bait at the appointed time. I have often watched 10 or 20 of them feeding quite unconcernedly in broad daylight and within a few yards of me. Naturally, conditioning to place as well as to time is necessary, but once this has been done, it is possible to go a step further with observations and by catching and marking the animals to see the frequency of visits by single animals and the social hierarchy of a visiting group (see e.g. Chitty & Shorten, 1946; J.Kikkawa, unpubl.). Indeed, the method opens up endless opportunities for behaviour studies.

Further extensions of this technique of attracting mammals to the observer suggest themselves. Most of our small rodents will respond to some well-liked bait like oats; for others an appropriate bait can be found, such as acorns for squirrels and salt-licks for deer, or an unlikely one discovered, such as milk for Hedgehogs and honey for Badgers.

Another focal point for study which has been little exploited except in the larger carnivores and bats is the resting or sleeping refuge. Some of our mammals, like the Harvest Mouse and the Dormouse, may build their nests above ground where they can be watched; others like the voles and mice are usually in underground burrows and for these the provision of shelters and nesting boxes offers possible help. Much experimenting is needed to discover the type each species likes, but once this is done plenty of valuable information can be collected. Some tests have been made with Short-tailed Voles by laying sheets of corrugated iron or uralite flat on the grass. When these have become bedded down the voles will shelter beneath them. If a sheet is suddenly lifted, it is often possible to catch the voles by hand before they have bolted. Little else has been done in this way with British mammals, but in the United States deermice (*Peromyscus* spp.) have been successfully induced to use nest-boxes sunk in the ground (Howard, 1949).

Lastly we should always remember that mammals, especially the small ones, are far easier to keep in captivity and observe at close quarters than are birds. The wisest plan is to catch a pregnant female in the wild and let her bear her young in captivity. It is often possible by this means to establish a breeding stock, from which one can select and mate the tamest animals. There are many books on how best to care for captive mammals: perhaps the most complete for general reference is Worden & Lane-Petter (1957). Small mammals have the great advantage over birds that they behave far more naturally in captivity, provided they are given reasonable-sized quarters and appropriate surroundings. This is partly due to their living together far more tolerantly, especially in family groups: nevertheless, too many should not be crowded together or there will be casualties and, with shrews particularly, if several are kept together, they should be given plenty of room to get out of each other's way (see Crowcroft, 1957).

With these general points in favour of mammals in our minds, we can now glance at each group and debate the best ways of setting about studying them. Let us take first the small rodents and start with the Wood Mouse, probably the most abundant and ubiquitous vertebrate animal we have. It lives much of its life underground, though we do not know whether it makes its own burrows. It is fairly strictly nocturnal and when it comes out from its burrow at dusk, forages mainly on the ground, though it is not inexpert at climbing. Being so nocturnal (even moonlight will decrease its activity) it is not so bound to cover as the voles and will readily search the barer parts of the woodland floor as well as open fields.

These habits and characteristics make the Wood Mouse an easy animal to watch at night with a red light. This way of watching nocturnal animals was evolved when I was studying owls. Having experimented with an infra-red telescope, which did indeed enable one to watch in complete darkness (see Southern, Watson & Chitty, 1946) but was clumsy and noisy, I next tried using visible red light because the nocturnally adapted eye reacts mainly to the blue and green end of the spectrum and is presumably almost blind to red. This presumption turned out to be well founded. The only apparatus needed is a fairly strong torch, preferably with a focusing spot, and a shield of red cellophane or celluloid (it need not be nearly as deep as a photographic darkroom lamp), though, of course, a more powerful and elaborate light, such as a car headlamp, makes it possible to watch from a greater distance. Owners of Land Rovers might well try fitting their headlamps with red shields and using them as observation posts, moving or stationary, though it would be as well to remember to remove them before venturing on the highway!

A point to note is that modern binoculars with bloomed optical surfaces, especially those with a large object glass (50 mm) give a very bright image in red torchlight and, with these, details of form and actions can be watched with remarkable ease and precision. Incidentally, this way of observing animals in the dark makes photography a very straightforward matter: photographic flashes, especially those which employ a discharge tube instead of a bulb, do not disturb the subjects too much, but it is an urgent matter to know the right moment to release the shutter. Here the red light is particularly valuable because an observer can use it to show him just the right moment to take the photograph.

Testing this method with a bait point sited in woodland cover, a bright red torch focused on the area around the bait and a camera and electronic flash apparatus set up in readiness resulted not only in many pictures, but also in a fascinating glimpse of the nocturnal ways in which a Wood Mouse lives. The efficiency with which it moved like a flash through the tangled herbs and bushes of the forest floor was clearly exhibited; furthermore, the personalities of each visiting Wood Mouse stood out clearly in behaviour as well as in form. This same method can also be used with Yellow-necked Mice, House Mice and Rats.

Our other common species of small rodents, the Bank Vole and the Short-tailed Vole, can also be watched by attracting them to a bait point, but, since they are nearly as active by day as by night, especially if the bait is placed near dense cover from which they can make quick, foraging sallies, a red light is not really necessary to watch them. However, there is some evidence (Sälzle, 1936) that Bank Voles are unusual among small rodents in that they can perceive colours, and, therefore, may be disturbed by the red light.

The less common Harvest Mouse and Dormouse present a contrast. Though both may build their nests above ground and are deft climbers, the Harvest Mouse is very active by day and can probably be watched at its nest by a patient observer. The Dormouse, however, is fairly strictly nocturnal and a red torch would undoubtedly be a great help in making observations.

Some naturalists have questioned the necessity of using a *red* light and cite instances where animals (Badgers, deer) have responded to an ordinary white light with indifference. This may be so but, until critical experiments have been made, I feel sure that the red light is safer and, for some species, it may be essential.

Shrews come in rather a different category as far as direct watching is concerned. As Crowcroft (1954) has shown, their activity extends almost equally throughout each 24 hours and there is little point in trying to study them at night, though they are undoubtedly red-blind. They are noisy animals and can be located easily by a practised ear: but even in daytime much patient watching and following is necessary to get even a glimpse in the thick ground litter which forms their usual habitat (I say 'usual' because I *have* seen a Common Shrew searching a hollow tree eight feet above the ground). Nevertheless, pertinacious and careful study will make the task less formidable and in Godfrey's work (1955) tracing the movements of Moles marked with radioactive rings, it was striking how often these animals were actually seen by somebody whose whole energies were devoted to the hunt.

Direct observations, therefore, even of such unpromising creatures as small mammals, is far from being unproductive and, associated with study in captivity, can add much to our knowledge of general behaviour and habits. Indirect study is just as important, if not so exciting to the naturalist.

One of the simplest ways of studying small mammals indirectly is by the use of live traps. In general these are admirable for introducing a naturalist to the different species and for bringing him to realize how abundant and widespread are our commoner kinds of mice, voles and shrews. But the method is not so satisfactory as watching for giving information about behaviour. It is far more important, indispensable even, for getting to grips with problems of distribution and population dynamics. Since the way of approach to these cardinal aspects of mammal ecology is fully discussed in chapters 4 and 5, no further mention need be made here of live trapping, nor, indeed, of other devices which involve the capture of the animals studied.

The scrutiny of traces on the other hand can tell us indirectly a great deal about behaviour as well as about distribution, and there is great scope for the exercise of ingenuity and field craft which is the first delight of a good naturalist.

Food stores and the remains of meals could easily constitute a whole field of investigation on their own. It is only necessary to suggest a few examples of the lines on which initiative and diligent investigation could be concentrated. The fruits of trees and shrubs form a highly desirable part of some small rodents' diets and methods of dealing with, say, hazel nuts probably differ between species. The scrupulous observer will detect and record these differences, thus opening the way to estimating the parts played by the various animals in demolishing each year's crop of nuts. There are a few scattered notes on this subject but, apart from obvious gross differences, for instance between the splitting of squirrels and the neat nibbling of mice, there is nothing very systematic or convincing. Needless to say, captive animals can again often give a key to field observations.

In spring especially the nibbling of young herbaceous shoots or of seedlings is widespread and it is conceivable that a good show of spring woodland flowers or forest regeneration may be directly connected with the abundance of mice and voles. The shredding of bluebell flower buds, for instance, which is commonly seen, is probably done by Wood Mice, but there is yet no certain evidence to prove this. Again, therefore, the field is wide open and carefully compiled results would have economic, as well as academic, value.

Distribution and foraging range can be inferred with some species, like Short-tailed Voles, Moles and rats, from studying runway systems and burrows. The way in which the runway is made and the level it occupies (e.g. the Short-tailed Vole at root level in grassland, Brown Rats and Water Voles on the surface of the grass) are often diagnostic, and faeces, deposited along the runway or at certain defined places, help to confirm identification (see under each species).

The persistent nature of runway systems webbing a home range is most valuable in enabling comprehensive studies to be made on the distribution and activity of some species. Such runway systems probably exist even through ground where they are hard

D

to detect, and many small mammals have an extensive system underground, like the Mole, as well as surface runways. Hewson (1948) has shown that the Orkney Vole does this. Claw marks and worn patches of bark show favourite trees and jumps of squirrels, and it is likely that Dormice and Harvest Mice, as well as Wood Mice and Bank Voles when they venture above the ground, all have their network of major and minor aerial roads.

Again traces in the form of droppings (see under separate species), scrapes, nibbled herbage, runways and (in the case of deer) trees frayed and marked with scent, and so on, may give information not only on presence and distribution of animals, but can often be marshalled in a rough quantitative way to follow trends in the numbers of animals. The Short-tailed Vole is notorious for the way in which its numbers oscillate from year to year and a way of gathering extensive information about its status over wide areas was devised by the Bureau of Animal Population. A wire frame, 2 sq yds in area, was dropped at successive points along a line which might be many hundred yards long and the presence or absence of traces recorded. An index to numbers of voles was provided in the percentage of points with positive results.

Similar checks can be devised for other small mammal species. Emlen *et al.* (1957) have recently described a method of deriving a population index from placing a grid of small rough-surfaced boards upon which small mammals apparently delight to deposit their droppings. Information about such population changes or trends is most valuable and may have important economic significance. The question is discussed further in chapter 5.

In gathering all these kinds of information it is essential to have field notes with very complete detail, supplemented, if possible, with sketches and plans. Such notes should be made on the spot or after the shortest possible lapse of time, at whatever inconvenience, otherwise the details become 'conglobated', as Dr Johnson remarked, and impossible to reconstruct.

After the abundant and widespread small mammals, the squirrels are probably the most easily encountered of British species, now that myxomatosis has produced a scarcity of rabbits. The present situation in Great Britain with the invading Grey Squirrel replacing, though at a diminishing rate, the native Red Squirrel, lends interest and importance in some areas to straightforward observations upon which species is present.

Monica Shorten (Mrs Vizoso) who has contributed notes upon which the following pages are based, has published much valuable general information about the biology of squirrels in her book (1954) and has given in this and (in more detail) in various papers an account of the spread of the Grey Squirrel in Great Britain (1946, 1953, 1957). The latest information is as follows: in England and Wales Grey Squirrels have not yet been recorded in Northumberland, Cumberland and the Isle of Wight; their presence is doubtful in Anglesey and Caernarvon, and they are rare yet in Norfolk, Suffolk, Durham, Cornwall, Westmorland and Lancashire; elsewhere they are in occupation, usually to the exclusion of Red Squirrels. In Scotland the Red Squirrel is still the dominant animal, and the Grey is confined to Dunbarton, Stirling, West and Mid Lothians, Fife, Kinross, Clackmannan and Perth. For Eire and Northern Ireland information upon the present status of the Grey Squirrel is badly wanted; in 1953 it had been reported from the following counties: Longford, Leitrim, Roscommon, Westmeath, Wicklow, Cavan, Down, Armagh, Tyrone and Fermanagh.

Thus careful identifications are badly needed in areas marginal to the present distribution.

Squirrels are not difficult animals to observe because they are diurnal in their activity and, being so arboreal, even their refuges, when they are alarmed, often leave them in full view. This is most true where they have not been persistently shot at and persecuted.

On the whole they seem to detect movement more surely than any other sign of danger, so that an observer who keeps motionless as much as possible and moves, when necessary, slowly and deliberately will not alarm a squirrel unduly. Colour discrimination is certainly poor, perhaps absent, so camouflage clothing is unnecessary. The way in which squirrels can locate and dig out food which has been buried several inches in moist earth or under snow might suggest an acute sense of smell, yet they do not seem to use this sense to detect danger and will enter traps that have recently been in contact with dogs, foxes, ferrets, weasels, stoats and man. This together with the fact that squirrels are most frequently observed in trees well above the scent of an observer means that no special note need be taken of wind direction. Early morning and evening are the times of greatest activity, though they can be seen out and about during all daylight hours. Similarly, they are active throughout the year and there is no true hibernation: inclement weather—heavy rain, mist and especially strong wind—seems more important in keeping them indoors than do low temperatures.

The type of country in which squirrels can be most surely found is in woodland, both coniferous and broadleaved. It is often stated that the Grey Squirrel prefers deciduous and the Red evergreen trees, but this is not entirely true. In winter woodland an immediate indication of squirrels' presence is given by dreys (see later): furthermore, the presence and quantity of their important food trees (oak, Scots pine, hazel, sweet chestnut and beech) will suggest the order of abundance that will be encountered. In open country, gardens, orchards and so on squirrels will only be found permanently if there is an assured supply of food: usually they are only visiting a transient crop.

If a naturalist wants to make intensive observations on the behaviour and ecology of squirrels, it is well worth his while to go into the history of control measures in any area he contemplates studying. Some estates pursue the Grey Squirrel with vigour and the population may be sparse and shy. On the other hand, if dreys are annually poled out of the trees, it will be easier to assess the strength of the population in the absence of a confusing mass of old dreys.

The mention of dreys brings us to the question of detecting the presence and deducing the habits of squirrels from signs and traces. Grey Squirrel dreys are usually more bulky and untidy than those of the Red Squirrel. The breeding dreys are spherical, well roofed over, warmly lined with grass, leaves and shredded bark and, in broadleaved woodland, often have green buds or leaves built into them. They are placed usually in a large fork of the main trunk in distinction from the thinner summer dreys which may be in quite slender branches. These latter are only used temporarily as resting platforms, whereas the big dreys are permanent year-round homes.

Examination of tree surfaces often reveals the presence of squirrel pathways. The smooth, alga-covered surface of sycamore boles, especially, show up the three parallel scratches made by the claws while the squirrel is climbing. On large trees with heavy limbs coming away from the trunk at an angle, there is often a deeply eroded mark just beneath the point where limb joins trunk.

This is presumably made when squirrels make an extra thrust with the back legs to take them round the overhang. Quite rough-barked trees may show bare brown patches where the under bark has been exposed.

Squirrel faeces are only infrequently found because usually they scatter while dropping to the ground. However, the upper surface of nearly horizontal limbs of trees may reveal faeces and, sometimes, the remains of meals.

The faeces vary much in size and appearance according to the food eaten, and there is no certain way of distinguishing which species has produced them. When catkins are being eaten, the droppings are bright yellow or yellow green, which makes them distinctive enough to be seen on the ground. When the food is pine seeds or unripe cones, the droppings are usually black and shiny, firm and shaped like a pea-nut. At other times, they are similar to those of a Brown Rat; or, again, they may be very small and black like those of mice. Insect fragments, pollen grains, small feathers and bits of woody tissue can often be found in droppings.

The remains of meals give an excellent clue to the food and movements of squirrels. Hard parts of seeds and fruits, like scaled pine cones, acorn and chestnut skins or hazel shells cannot very well be dated, but perishable food like buds and shoots, catkins, fungi, corn and fresh fruits indicate the recent presence of squirrels and will often direct attention to the part of the wood in which they are foraging at that particular season. The following tentative list indicates where squirrels may most profitably be sought throughout the year. Fresh observations could fill in the details of this list and discover whether the diet varies greatly between places.

G (= mainly ground feeding)   T (= tree feeding)

January	G	Nuts, acorns, seeds of previous autumn; fungi, bulbs, roots; some green shoots, buds and insects.
February	G	As above.
March	G	As above, but more buds and shoots.
April	GT	Beech catkins, young leaves and buds, insect larvae and pupae, some birds' eggs, sycamore and maple seeds.

May	G T	Oak catkins, green pine cones, wych elm fruits; spruce and chestnut catkins; beech, sycamore and spruce bark. Insects.
June	G T	Green spruce cones; beech, sycamore and spruce bark (other trees also); strawberries, cherries, wheat.
July	G T	Bark, cherries, wheat; spruce, larch and other cones.
August	T	Green acorns, hazel nuts and beech mast; ripe corn; apples, blackberries and other fruits; cones.
September	T	Ripening acorns, nuts, beech mast and other seeds.
October	T G	Acorns, sweet chestnuts, ground and tree fungi.
November	G	Remains of tree seeds; fungi.
December	G	As above.

During hot weather squirrels drink frequently and pools and water tanks may have well-defined runways leading to them. It is probable that their routes among the branches may be just as stereotyped and this is a point on which useful information could be collected.

Baiting at fixed points with acorns or whole maize can draw squirrels down for observation or for live trapping and marking (details of the procedure are given in a Forestry Commission leaflet (Anon. 1959)). It is also possible, since squirrels will sometimes make their nests in tree holes, to attract them into large nesting boxes. On an estate near Oxford nesting boxes designed for Tawny Owls (the construction is described in the British Trust for Ornithology, Field Guide no. 3, 1957) are frequently occupied by Grey Squirrels. Naturally when young squirrels first come out of the nest from late March to May and again from August to Sept they are much easier to watch while they are learning to climb and forage than the adults.

As with other animals, it is a great help to have a method of marking which distinguishes groups or individuals. Various dyes (see chapter 6) can be used on the tail hairs, but this does not show up very well against the sky or in poor light.

Finally, for those naturalists who have patience and do not mind being occasionally bitten or having their hair torn out, squirrels are fascinating and informative pets and will breed in captivity if they are given plenty of room. In the case of the Grey Squirrel, however, a licence from the Ministry of Agriculture is required for this because the law now regards it as a pest.

After the squirrels, rabbits and hares are the most widespread of our mammals which can be seen and studied by daylight. At least this was certainly true of the rabbit until myxomatosis so drastically reduced its numbers. The survivors have become warier and more nocturnal in their habits, but all accounts suggest that this state of affairs is unlikely to persist and that, with the establishment of less virulent strains of the disease, rabbit numbers will increase again, even if they do not reach their previous levels.

Rabbits are easiest to watch at and just around their warrens at dusk and dawn. The more open the terrain, the simpler it is to arrange to approach against the wind and to enter or climb up to an observation post without giving alarm. Nevertheless, on open ground, such as pastures, rabbits are more on the alert and can spot an intruder from a greater distance. Whether the rabbits, having once been alarmed and bolted into their burrows, will come out again and resume their activities before a patiently waiting observer, depends upon the time of year, the time of day and the weather.

From many hours of watching rabbits at a warren in an open grass field, I found that from spring to early autumn the rabbits would come out in numbers an hour or two before sunset and were usually above ground until a couple of hours after sunrise, though activity was less than in the evenings, especially if there was heavy dew. At one warren studied intensively, a proportion of the rabbits had been caught and marked and this made it possible to estimate that something like a quarter to a third of the warren population could usually be seen above ground at these times of day (Southern, 1940; Myers, 1957). More recent information from Australia on this subject has been published by Dunnet (1957). Naturally, activity is intensified in early spring when the breeding season starts and, in the following months, the crop of young rabbits makes observation easy both because they are far less wary than the adults and because, with the population at its yearly peak, they stimulate the aggressive behaviour of the adults.

During these dusk and dawn periods, there is usually only casual feeding, so that the rabbits have leisure to pursue sexual and territorial activities. How fascinating this phase of their behaviour can be may be judged from the account of a three-year study at the warren mentioned above (Southern, 1948).

Far less is known about the rabbit's activities during the night. Some evidence from examining stomach contents of rabbits, caught at different periods over the hours of darkness, suggests that feeding is intense during the time just after dark and again in the hours before dawn (Southern, 1942). It is probable that rabbits will travel directly to their feeding ground, which may be some distance from the warren. Rabbits, startled by dogs or headlamp beams from their feeding at night (both these are favourite poaching techniques) will travel at speed along their highway tracks, and it is when they make these faster and longer journeys that they can be most successfully tangled in snares or long-nets.

During the winter, feeding activity predominates and watching at a warren with a red light has revealed that some of the rabbits emerge only when it is quite dark and go straight off towards their feeding grounds. It seemed clear from these preliminary tests which I made, that the rabbits were quite unconscious of the red light, and careful stalking with a powerful torch would undoubtedly reveal much about their nocturnal behaviour.

Of course, a white light can show up feeding rabbits successfully, but their behaviour may be unnatural. When a strong beam is switched on suddenly they bolt or appear dazzled and hesitant in their movements. Under these conditions a well-trained dog may well pick a rabbit up, but little will be revealed about normal behaviour. However, Carrick (1957) in Australia found that rabbits were undisturbed by a constant illumination. This method may be useful if a rough count is needed of rabbits out feeding. Under some circumstances a focused pencil beam will pick up rabbits far beyond the distance at which they are visibly illuminated because of the intense eye-shine which they return to the beam. However, the intensity and colour of this varies greatly: no doubt this has much to do with the angle at which the beam strikes the eye, but this cannot be the whole story. More tests are needed to explore this matter, and to discover how far other species of our mammals can be detected in this way. Mr J. Taylor

Page informs me that a red light will evoke a glow from the eyes of deer. This is important because it means that some animals will not be conscious of the fact that they are betraying their presence. Rabbits' eyes also reflect red light in this way.

Turning from actual observation of rabbits to the detection of their traces, we may note that one of the oldest of country skills is the tracing of rabbit paths or pads which they use with incredible conservatism when travelling between their burrows and their feeding grounds. These are easy to detect when the traffic is heavy and when the grass is growing fast, but even when the grass is short the skilled eye will perceive just where each rabbit places hind and fore feet each time it travels along a particular pad. The main interest of tracing these pads is to map the area used for feeding around a rabbit colony; but the cultivation of the poacher's eye will also assist in catching rabbits alive for marking and releasing. This can be done by using snares with knots which arrest the tightening of the noose at a certain point and so hold the rabbit unharmed (see chapter 6).

Once a number of rabbits are marked so that individuals can be recognized, a great field is opened for observing behaviour, activity rhythms and so on. The marking of big numbers will give vital information about the size and composition of populations and also on range of movements. Work on these lines has shown that the Rabbit is usually an unadventurous animal and will only exceptionally range more than 2–300 yards from its warren (see figures in Southern, 1940 and Phillips, 1955).

Information about simple presence or absence of rabbits and about rough categories of density can be obtained from general traces of their activities—droppings, scrapes, nibbled herbage and burrowings apart from such signs as altered composition of vegetation and so on. This last subject alone is of great ecological interest and by studying works such as those of Farrow (1925) and Phillips (1953) naturalists may be encouraged to continue this line of research.

When we turn to the Brown Hare, we can quickly see that there is even greater scope for discovery than with the Rabbit. There is a good deal of random observation about habits collected in B.-H.&H. and much traditional country lore, but hardly any systematic research has been done. A broad study of the species has recently been made in Denmark, but so far the only details published have been about the population fluctuations (Andersen, 1957). Most of these are derived from the analysis of game-bag records, and some preliminary information from the same kind of source for the British Isles was published by Middleton (1934). It is worth noting that changes and fluctuations in numbers of game animals can be traced by such armchair methods, but there may be considerable errors involved, as pointed out by Andersen, and such an approach is best used to obtain extensive data where intensive work on a smaller area by personal observation has already been done.

Some point is given to this by the experience of Dr Norman Moore of the Nature Conservancy. The Mammal Society was founded in 1954, just before myxomatosis began to spread in England, and it was thought timely to try and institute a survey of Brown Hares to determine whether the expected reduction of rabbits would cause them to increase. Dr Moore has organized this survey and collected the replies to the questionnaire issued. The results have been extremely difficult to analyse and Dr Moore believes that estimates of the number of hares in a district based on sight counts are of little value unless an observer practically knows all the animals by name! Hares are remarkably clever at avoiding observation and so a rise in their numbers is not recorded by this method until they have reached a very high density. Nevertheless, in some areas it was clear that hares had increased.

All of which brings us back to the strict necessity of careful and painstaking field observation, and with Brown Hares the field is wide open for any naturalist to elaborate his own techniques and approaches. Some rough guide can be obtained from what has already been said about rabbits, though the absence of burrowing and colonial habits naturally makes the area of observations more diffuse. It is possible that more help may be obtained from the methods of study already worked out for the Mountain Hare, although the closed nature of the countryside inhabited by the Brown Hare brings observation down to a more piecemeal scale. Under the circumstances it is probably best to consider next the methods of studying Mountain Hares in Scotland (Hewson, 1961; Flux, unpubl. thesis, 1961).

Direct observation with field glasses or telescope is perfectly feasible, but the daily movements of individual animals may be considerable, so, even on the open grouse moors where the hares are common, it is as well to choose a corrie or a hillside for observation. On flat ground the observer is constantly being unsighted by the hares disappearing over slight undulations.

Marking with ear tags and coloured collars (see chapter 6), of course, helps the observer to follow the movements and behaviour of single hares with confidence, but increasing familiarity with the ground and its inhabitants will enable him to make highly probable identifications. Again, the cardinal point of advice to the field naturalist—know your animal—comes to the fore. There are, too, several factors which help these identifications beyond constantly repeated patterns; mutant forms of low frequency in the population (albinos, melanics, yellows and so on) may pinpoint an individual hare more efficiently than a numbered marking tag or collar; and during the change into and out of the white winter pelage animals may be recognized over limited periods by their particular patterning of dark and light fur.

But, as with all the species so far mentioned, the most helpful feature of their natural history to the observer is the constancy with which each hare adheres to its resting places (forms and—in the case of the Mountain Hare—burrows) and to its pathways which lead from the resting place to the feeding grounds. Naturally in such open country, where the climate is often rigorous, feeding areas and daily routine may vary according to exposure but, by and large, once a hare has settled in to a home range it will spend the rest of its life mainly within an area about half a mile across.

Most of the daylight hours are spent in cover, often at a higher level than the feeding grounds, and the outward journey in the evening and the return in the early morning may be observed in reasonably good light. These hours, too, are the times when hares are generally most active and details of their general behaviour can be studied. As with rabbits, the details of their night activities are hardly known at all and it would be worth investigating the possible use of a powerful beam of red light to watch these after darkness has fallen, especially at areas which are known to be regular feeding grounds.

The Mountain Hare is an example of the way in which (as previously suggested) extensive information on distribution and fluctuations can be obtained from game bag records. Such information from most of its range in Scotland has already been reviewed by Hewson (1954). Clearly also, if it is possible to arrange to examine the results of a day's shooting, much of value can be recorded about age classes, moult sequence, breeding season, litter rates and so on.

When we turn to the carnivores, we may think it strange that more attention has not been given to the systematic study of British species. They are a successful and widespread group and yet the only sterling piece of work so far produced in this country is Ernest Neal's book *The Badger* (1958). We even miss the help of B.-H.&H. because they had to cease publication before reaching the section on carnivores. The literature that does exist is diffuse, often unreliable and generally mixed up with partisan viewpoints. It is all the more urgent that sound systematic natural history observations should be made on foxes, otters, stoats and weasels, following the excellent lead that Neal has given on the Badger. The only attempt, apart from this, at sustained research has been the inquiry into the natural history of the Otter carried out by Miss Marie Stephens and recently published by the Universities' Federation for Animal Welfare (1957). The investigation was financed for two years only and most of the results are, therefore, tentative and preliminary. Identification of food from stomach contents and faeces shows some points of interest, but the author was faced with the task of working out right from the beginning keys to the tiny fish bones, fur and feathers contained. This needs more elaboration and the collection of material was restricted by the shortness of the time. The same applies to the data on size, breeding condition and so on, since relatively few bodies had accumulated. Most interesting are the accounts of the distribution of traces (footprints, faeces, trackways, lying-up places, slides into the water and so on) found along a stretch of Welsh stream, but again the time for field work was very limited. As to the organization and condensation of the literature on the Otter, Miss Stephens has struggled hard with an intractable miscellany of observation, dogma and anecdote, which is a fair representation of the state of our knowledge about carnivores (Badgers always excepted).

However, to return to methods of watching. Some of the larger species localize themselves conveniently by having what we might call collectively dens ('earths' for foxes, 'sets' for badgers, 'holts' for otters), though only Badgers will use them consistently throughout the year. A hide, a convenient crotch of a tree, or even a background against which to stand motionless together with a red or a dim white torch will supply a patient observer with much information about general habits, litter size and food. Provided that the observer watches the wind direction and approaches his watching station accordingly, he may watch Badgers most of the year (the exceptions being the colder winter nights when they may stay below ground), Foxes during spring and early summer (especially if alternative earths are known to which the family may move) and Otters nobody really knows when. The occupation of holts seems to have as little consistency as the breeding season of the Otter. We need to do much more concentrated watching of Otters before we even begin to understand the 'rules of the game', let alone start collecting solid information. The same must apply to our rarer larger carnivores, which frequent dens at least during the breeding season, Wild Cat, Marten and Polecat.

Watchers should, however, realize that den studies are somewhat specialized. For one thing individual animals or pairs may have their own peculiar habits and it is as well to aim at watching as many animals as possible for purposes of comparison. Secondly, watching of this kind is most rewarding when there are small young in the den (when they grow older, the family tends to move off more quickly on the forage) and at this time habits are specialized. A biased picture of food especially might be obtained at this restricted season. Scott's careful study of the Red Fox in Iowa (1943) gives information which bears out this point.

The recognition of occupied dens needs careful study. With an animal like the Fox, which lives in its own den during the rearing of its family, a reasonable census can be carried out in this way. A previous paper by Scott (1941a) shows the result of comparing occupied den counts with an index derived from the proportion of squares on a gridded area containing 'sign' (i.e. footprints, dung, etc.). The den counts gave a density of about 1 pair per sq mile. With Badgers a set may be a ramifying underground citadel of vast size and it is not easy to determine the numbers occupying each one, without a team of watchers covering adjacent sets for several nights, as was arranged by Neal (1958).

Apart from watching at dens, direct observation of carnivores can often be done by careful stalking. Wind direction and noise must be attended to carefully, but, otherwise, as their visual discrimination is poor, one can often move up quite close to foraging animals. This is easier with Badgers than with Foxes (indeed Scott (1943) states that tracking is more rewarding in learning about Foxes than stalking). For one thing they are much noisier and an observer can watch his chance to move up only when the sound of his approach will be drowned. Of course, a red torch is a great help in this game.

Indirect information about the habits and movements of our carnivores can be derived by the practised eye (and sometimes nose) from what are collectively known as 'traces', i.e. footprints, dung, trackways, hairs, remains of meals and so on. Wherever snow is a regular feature of the winter, this kind of information can be remarkably complete, for the tale of a whole night's doings can be read in a few hours. In the south of England, however, such chances are few and far between and the task is accordingly more laborious. For anybody wishing to develop his abilities at this kind of woodcraft, the readiest source of instruction is probably the local gamekeeper. Hardly anything of a systematic nature has been written in this country, but it is worth consulting the work done in N. America by, e.g. Scott (1941a, 1943).

Traces will reveal better than any other evidence the range hunted over by a single animal or pair and I still believe there are great possibilities in the idea of marking individuals by the removal of toes (see chapter 6) so that their footprints can be distinguished, even if this means preparing surfaces at strategic points to take clear impressions. This might work very well with Otters. Would-be users of this method are advised to adopt the maxim 'first catch your Fox', but again the technique of digging out Foxes and Badgers is still fairly well known to country folk.

Adult animals settled in their home ranges will, of course, give the most consistent and valuable results. Young and unmated ones may wander fairly widely. Of 236 three-quarter grown Red Foxes dug out, tagged and released in N. America away from home, 17 records were returned and the mean distance travelled was 30 miles (Errington & Berry, 1937).

A word may be said here to those observers who have keen noses. The Fox's custom of marking the home territory with strongly smelling urine may be a useful clue to its movements. Freshly made marks can be detected quite easily, but it would be interesting to know how long the smell persists in different weather conditions. The habit is most indulged during the breeding season, and Scott (1943) has a record of a dog fox who 'badged' his territory in this way 14 times in about 20 minutes.

There is plenty of scope for testing the sensitivity of the human nose to other methods used by other carnivores.

Both watching and tracking will reveal much about the methods which our carnivores use to catch their prey and, at the same time, what kind of prey they prefer. Most of our species may be seen about in daytime, especially during the early morning: indeed, it seems probable that many of them are only secondarily nocturnal because they are persecuted by man. Evidence for this may be seen in the increased confidence and boldness with which, e.g. Foxes, move about during the day on areas where they are little disturbed. The Badger is perhaps the most completely nocturnal but, even so, during the long summer days they may be out even before sunset. Actual observations on food and feeding habits can be checked against examination of the remains of meals left outside dens and of the contents of faeces. When a series of bodies can be obtained, the stomachs also supply useful evidence. Excellent examples of systematic work on these lines are Scott (1943) on the Fox in the United States and Andersen (1954) on the Badger in Denmark. Each source of information checks the other: watching and tracking may not give sufficiently systematic results to form a general picture, from which seasonal and yearly trends can be perceived, but can show up some items which may vanish in the faeces or stomach.

Stoats and weasels are probably the least known of our carnivores. They may wander widely if their food varies in availability. Hamilton (1933) gives some interesting evidence for the Stoat in New York State, where the species is trapped for its fur and local fluctuations are easily followed. He also notes an instance where the trail of one animal was traced for four miles in the snow.

Results, showing similar fluctuations in this country, are given in the Annual Report of the I.C.I. Game Research Station at Fordingbridge, Hants (Anon. 1960). Stoats changed more strikingly than Weasels. These changes are partly, but not entirely, due to myxomatosis.

Some knowledge of movements seems an essential preliminary to studying the natural history of these animals. Large numbers are still killed in this country every year by gamekeepers and a system of trapping and marking would yield valuable results. The tradition of vermin trapping, practised widely on estates where game is preserved, could readily be adapted to catch Stoats and Weasels alive. Wire cage traps with drop doors at either end could replace the gin in the traditional tunnel trap (see chapter 6) and the catch could be handled in a wire-netting sleeve, such as Shorten & Courtier (1955) have described for Grey Squirrels. J.D.Lockie (unpubl.) has recently made a promising start on the capture and study of Stoats and Weasels by using the type of wire cage trap sold for catching alive rats and squirrels.

It seems probable that quite a large proportion of a population could be trapped and marked in this way. Hawley & Newby (1957) have recently published some interesting results on the American Marten (*Martes americana*). They were able to catch practically all of the animals present on a large study area and they also found a sharp division between resident and transient, wandering animals. More than half of the catch were wanderers.

Finally, with animals which are considered as vermin, like many of our carnivores, it should be possible to examine quite large series of bodies, which will give valuable data on growth, age and sex ratios, breeding season, moult and so on. Much has already been done in this way. Basic studies on reproductive physiology are mentioned in chapter 5: valuable information on weights and moult (especially on the assumption of white winter pelage by the Stoat) can be found in Flintoff (1935 a & b) and on weights of Wild Cats in Kirk & Wagstaffe (1943). Mention should also be made of a valuable method of ageing carnivores from the baculum (penis bone) which has not yet been applied to British populations. Details of the method as applied to the Otter (*Lutra canadensis*) can be found in Friley (1949) and in Hooper & Ostenson (1949): the Long-tailed Weasel (*Mustela frenata*) is similarly treated in Wright (1947).

Such work may seem rather a far cry from natural history observation, but it does tell us much about the growth of individuals and about the growth and balance of natural populations. The question is considered further in chapter 5.

When we turn to the other group of carnivores, the pinnipedes or seals, we find that, with the other marine group of mammals, the whales, they constitute a rather special case for the field observer. They spend much of the year at sea and are then mainly inaccessible for watching. The Grey Seal (*Halichoerus grypus*) has increased greatly in numbers round our coasts during the last few decades and, since it breeds colonially and attends its pups on dry land for some weeks, interesting observations can be carried out with binoculars, particularly on the early stages of the formation of a breeding colony. They are also accessible ashore in large numbers during the spring, when they haul out during the moult. Even when the majority are at sea, fishing, considerable numbers may be seen either in the vicinity of breeding grounds (e.g. Farne Islands) or even far removed from any breeding area (e.g. West Hoyle Bank, Cheshire). Little is known about this phase of their activity. A scheme for marking the young animals has been in operation for some years and the results to date have been summarized by Hewer (1957). Studies on the Common Seal (*Phoca vitulina*), which is less bound to definite breeding localities than the Grey Seal and, in any case, does not stay ashore during the breeding season, are much more difficult. Any naturalist who wishes to pursue such studies would be well advised to consult Venables & Venables (1955, 1957) who are the only people to have carried out major field observations on this difficult animal.

The Cetacea are even more difficult to study systematically. The smaller whales and dolphins can often be seen close inshore around our coasts and can be watched from cliff-tops or from boats. They tend to come inshore to feed on a rising tide and may frequent the same areas for some while, giving the chance of continued observation. They can also be observed when, as they sometimes do, they ascend rivers.

The last two groups left to consider are both rather specialized. The bats contain more species than any other group of British mammals except the Cetacea and their study in the field needs concentrated attention. The deer are few in species and the study of their natural history is bedevilled by enthusiasms about their status as beasts of the chase, or (to put the opposite view) as vermin. It is hardly necessary to go deeply here into the methods of studying either group in the field because this very aspect is dealt with in the first two Field Guides issued by the Mammal Society. The first of these, *A Field Guide to British Deer*, compiled and edited by F.J.Taylor Page (1957), is already available: the second which will deal with British bats on the same lines is being prepared for publication by Michael Blackmore.

E

Nevertheless, the following condensed notes, prepared by these two authors may be useful in stimulating naturalists to take an interest in these groups.

During the day one must search for bats in their roosts in buildings, quarries, caves and trees. Such searching is laborious until a naturalist has cultivated an 'eye' for the right places. Although bats will use any part of a building that is dark, e.g. attics, lofts and cellars, they avoid draughts and are seldom found among timbers that have been treated with chemicals such as creosote. Many vespertilionid species show a special preference for the space between joists and ridge-tiles. Deep cracks in masonry are also commonly used.

Bats will sleep either singly or in a compact mass. Large colonies betray their presence after long occupation by the piles of excrement that form underneath the dens. The musky smell of the dung, which has a high nitre content, is an unmistakable sign that bats are present even when the occupants themselves are out of sight. In warm weather colonies sleep lightly and are restless during daytime and often draw attention by their high-pitched squeaks while jostling for the most comfortable positions.

Caves, cellars and quarries are used mainly for hibernation. Horseshoe bats (Rhinolophidae) are usually found there between Oct and April, hanging from walls or roof. Most of the vespertilionid species also use caves in winter but generally prefer to crawl into crevices instead of sleeping in exposed situations. Vespertilionidae are seldom found in caves during summer and, although Rhinolophidae often desert them in April, some colonies use caves for parturition. These 'nursing' colonies usually consist of adult and immature non-breeding females with, occasionally, a small percentage of one-year-old males.

Noctules, Leisler's Bats and species of *Myotis* are typical tree-dwellers in summer. They frequent hollow trunks and small cavities, especially woodpeckers' holes, about forty feet above ground. Some colonies of Noctules move from one tree to another at frequent intervals. All species except Rhinolophidae will use tree-cavities during summer but the Barbastelle is more likely to be found behind pieces of loose bark in dry weather.

It is not easy to watch low-flying bats on the wing at dusk owing to their erratic flight among trees and bushes. This handicap can be offset to some extent by the fact that some species, especially

Pipistrelle and Whiskered Bats, will hunt along a regular beat. The observer should choose a vantage-point with an uninterrupted view of the western sky when possible, so as to take full advantage of the afterglow of sunset. A moon is also helpful when watching bats late at night. They can be seen best along the edge of woods, in lanes with low hedges, and over streams and ponds that are not overhung with tall bushes and trees, though the observer must watch for changes of beat in variable weather. Wind, rain, moonlight and thunder all have their effects.

Specimens can be obtained on the wing with a large butterfly-net mounted on a strong six-foot bamboo pole. This method requires much practice, but, if a bat is missed at the first stroke of the net, it should be whirled vigorously and continuously in the path of the animal's flight because many species (except Rhinolophidae) will usually circle round a moving object and be caught by a subsequent stroke.

Mist nets may also be used for catching bats. Lord Cranbrook has recently had considerable success at catching by this method Noctules which had congregated to feed on crickets at a rubbish dump. These bats can often be brought down into the nets by a pebble thrown below them which they mistake for an insect (see further details in chapter 6).

One method of attracting bats is by using mercury vapour lamps, or car headlights. This works best in wooded areas and Natterer's, Whiskered, Long-eared and Bechstein's Bats can be lured near enough to be caught.

Most species take their prey to a resting-place where it is dismembered and eaten. Porches and outhouses are often used for this purpose and the remains of insects (moths' wings and elytra of beetles) accumulate below the resting-places. When these temporary perches are known it is possible to watch bats feeding if a dim light is used. An electric torch with a piece of coloured tissue paper pasted over the glass is useful for observing bats in these conditions.

Other signs by which the presence of bats can be detected are the stain made by droppings under a tree hole, and the squeaks that proceed out of such holes in summer time. In a building the presence of cobwebs is a useful indication that no bats are inhabiting it. In caves the humidity is important. If it is high (c. 88 per cent R.H.) then Horseshoe Bats may be sought and they are easy to detect because they roost in the open and do not, like vesper-tilionids, crawl into crevices.

The traditional lore of stalking Red Deer on the mountainous 'forests' of Scotland is too intricate a matter to go into here. It is far the best thing to enlist the help and guidance of an experienced stalker. The amateur naturalist who plays a lone and inexperienced hand will see far less than he would under expert tuition and he may make himself unpopular with the owners and staff of the forests. Anybody who really prefers to learn the job by himself should at least give careful attention first to Darling's *A Herd of Red Deer* (1937).

With woodland deer the matter is rather different. For one thing there are many areas, especially those devoted to forestry, where they are considered more or less 'vermin' and their disturbance is not necessarily looked upon as a social solecism: secondly, deer have spread during the last 30 years into much country which is not primarily forest. It is, indeed, remarkable how successfully a large animal like the Fallow Deer can stay out of sight in areas with relatively small patches of woodland. There is plenty of scope for the naturalist to train himself in this kind of woodcraft.

The two most abundant species in woodland are the Fallow and Roe Deer, though in some places Red Deer, Sika and Muntjac may also be encountered. Two very important things are (i) to know the area to be studied very thoroughly and (ii) to appreciate the keenness and limitation of the senses of each species. All have acute senses of smell and hearing, but the Roe Deer has the sharpest ears of all. Sight is only moderately keen, except in the Roe Deer, while in the Muntjac it is definitely poor.

The general diurnal cycle of activity should be carefully noted. On the whole, dawn and dusk are the most active periods, though it may be that by the use of red-light stalking and observation, we may modify our ideas about the importance of nocturnal activity. Daily movements, e.g. from lair to feeding place and (in the case of Red Deer) to wallow, tend to be stereotyped and follow set paths, unless the animals have been badly alarmed. Here an intimate knowledge of the terrain is indispensable for knowing the best places to intercept such a movement or to come unobserved upon the feeding area under the prevailing wind conditions.

Interception and stalking in this way are far more rewarding than trying to follow the trails of deer into dense cover.

It is always best to work singly, avoiding noise or the use of a torch (unless it is covered with a red filter). If hides are constructed, it is wise to clear a path or paths for silent approach and one should always remember that quiet movement is needed not only to prevent the deer being disturbed, but also to avoid, as far as possible, other creatures indicating one's presence. Once deer are in sight, precautions should be redoubled and no attempt made to move closer except when all the deer have their heads down. In any case it is not advisable to try and get nearer than about 50 yards. With good binoculars (say 7 × 50) all necessary detail should be visible from this distance. Finally, withdrawal should be carried out as carefully as approach. Alarming deer *may* not have untoward results, but, if they become too nervous, they may well move away to new ground.

The Field Guide already mentioned gives many more hints about stalking, about the construction and siting of hides, and about the detection of deer from traces.

In conclusion I would emphasize that, although this chapter has been concerned with a few general principles and a lot of practical hints about field work on mammals, the most important equipment must always be provided by the observer himself. This consists of an infinite zest to be out in the field with eyes and ears wide open and attention concentrated to detect ways and means of circumventing the animal to be studied and so coming to closer terms with it. Whether or not this curiosity about the ways of animals leads to more systematic and scientific work is relatively unimportant from a personal point of view. The scientific naturalist likes to think that his approach is a more constructive one, but it necessarily entails much tedious work indoors—sifting literature, giving quantitative expression to his results and so on. This may well mean that he has even less time than the amateur naturalist to be enjoying the use of his eyes and ears out of doors.

CHAPTER 3

Breeding

L.HARRISON MATTHEWS

The main purpose in life for any animal is to breed so that more similar animals are produced; secondary purposes are to eat enough to reach sexual maturity and to avoid being eaten by other creatures, starving, or dying of disease or exposure, until the main purpose is accomplished.

As animals are not immortal it is essential for the survival of the species that its individuals shall reproduce successfully and that each pair shall leave at least one successor of each sex to replace it. The natural hazards of life are such that in most animals large numbers of young must be produced in order to reach this end; in many invertebrates each pair produces thousands of young but in mammals where one or both of the parents exercise some parental care the number produced is less. Even among the mammals many species, especially the smaller ones, produce several litters of up to half a dozen or more young in each breeding season. The mortality rate before reaching sexual maturity is high in such species.

The basic problem of breeding is to get the egg cell produced in the female fertilized by the sperm cell produced in the male and to provide for the protection and nourishment of the embryo produced by fertilization—the fusion of the two cells into one—until the young new animal is capable of independent existence.

It might well be asked why this apparently cumbersome method of sexual reproduction is desirable, seeing that some animals (but no mammals) and many plants are able to reproduce asexually. The advantage of sexual reproduction is that it enables the *genes* or 'units of inheritance' to be recombined continually. The constant shuffling of the 'gene pool' of the species acts in two opposite directions. Under the influence of natural selection it tends to keep the characters of a species stable by preventing the segregation of genes and by the elimination of unsuccessful combinations of genes, but under certain conditions it equally allows the evolution of new forms by the preservation or segregation of new combinations of genes or *mutant* genes—genes that have altered either 'spontaneously' or under the influence of some external cause.

In all animals the egg cells are produced in the *ovaries* which in mammals are small compact organs lying near the kidneys. Each is a solid mass of cells, some of which supply nourishment to the egg cells. The egg cells are in the minority and in their young stages they lie near the surface of the ovary, each surrounded by a thin envelope of slightly different cells. Only a few of these primitive egg cells mature at one time; within their envelopes they sink into the inner part of the ovary and increase in size. While this happens the cells of the envelope increase greatly in number so that it no longer fits the egg cell tightly but is many times greater in diameter. Some of the envelope cells surround the egg cell, some line the cavity, some extend as strands between the two layers, and the intervening space is filled with fluid. By the time the egg cell is mature this fluid-filled *follicle* is so large that it bulges from the surface of the ovary. When the egg cell is ready to be fertilized the bulging follicle bursts, and the egg cell is washed into the *uterine* (or *Fallopian*) *tube*, a narrow canal of which the funnel-shaped end partly wraps the ovary. In this tube it meets the *sperm* cells received from the male and is fertilized by fusing with one of them. The composite cell soon divides into two, the two into four, and so on, and the development of the new animal has begun.

The embryo thus formed passes into a much larger tube, the *uterus*, which has a thick spongy lining (*endometrium*) richly supplied with glands and blood vessels. It becomes implanted in this lining; its outer layer forms an envelope (*chorion*) and the inner cells form the beginning of the body of the future animal. As soon as the heart and blood vessels are formed, part of the gut (*yolk-sac*) and of the bladder (*allantois*) grow outward, carrying their blood vessels with them, and fuse with part of the original outer envelope thus bringing the blood vessels into very close proximity with the glands and blood vessels of the lining of the uterus. A thin layer separates the circulations of the mother and the young, now called the *foetus*, so that nourishment and oxygen can pass from mother to foetus and waste matter and carbon dioxide in the opposite direction. There is, however, no direct connection between the blood streams of the mother and the foetus and the exchange of nutrients and so on takes place by diffusion through the intervening membrane. Concurrently with the establishment of these outgrowths the belly wall of the embryo grows outwards in the form of folds that arch over the back and fuse to produce a closed bag, the *amnion*, completely enclosing it. The amnion and allantois become filled with fluid so that the foetus floats in a 'bag of waters'. When the foetus reaches full term the uterus contracts, the bag of waters bursts and the foetus is forced out through the *vagina*, the tube connecting the uterus to the outside.

Long before the time of birth the yolk-sac to a greater or lesser extent and the allantois have become modified to form a cord of tissue (*umbilical cord* or *navel-string*) through which the blood vessels run between the foetus and the *placenta*, a thickened pad derived partly from the portion of the yolk-sac and allantois in contact with the lining of the uterus and partly from the lining itself. The placenta is a structure of great complexity and differs widely in its details in different species. In some mammals the membranes separating the blood of mother and foetus are comparatively thick as in the ungulates, the whales, and others, but in some it is extremely thin as in many rodents. Furthermore, the opposing surfaces are generally increased in area by being drawn out into finger-like processes or *villi* that interlock to make a very close contact. In some types of placenta, as in man, the villi of the maternal part of the placenta break down so that the villi of the foetal part dip into the spaces left and are bathed directly in the maternal blood which nevertheless does not penetrate into them.

In most mammals the foetal part of the placenta is formed chiefly from the allantois, the yolk-sac forming part of it only in its early stages of development, but in some, as in the squirrels, the yolk-sac forms an important part of it throughout foetal life. In the marsupials, the pouched mammals of Australia and southern America, the yolk-sac forms the main part of the short-lived placenta and the allantois participates in its formation in only a few species. The marsupials are consequently often spoken of as 'non-placental' mammals in distinction from the eutherian or 'placental' mammals.

At birth the umbilical cord is broken or bitten through by the mother, and the young animal draws its first breath. Shortly afterwards the placenta separates from the wall of the uterus and is expelled by muscular contractions as the *afterbirth*. The mother dries the babies and cleans off the remains of the envelopes by licking the babies thoroughly, and in most species she then eats the afterbirth. The short end of the umbilical cord left attached to the baby shrivels and falls off after a few days leaving a permanent scar, the *umbilicus* or *navel*.

In mammals there are two ovaries, one on each side of the body, two narrow uterine tubes, and two uteri which join each other to a greater or lesser extent at their outer ends where they are connected to the vagina, a single tube (except in the egg-laying monotremes and the marsupials) in the mid-line leading to the external opening. In only a few mammals, notably in the order Primates which includes the monkeys, apes and man, are the two uteri so completely joined that they form a single organ.

In the male the sperm cells that fertilize the egg cells are produced in the testes, the equivalents of the ovaries, and at first, like them, lying near the kidneys. But unlike the ovaries the testes do not retain their original position; they migrate to the hind end of the abdominal cavity where they pass through its wall and lie outside in a sac, the *scrotum*. In a few mammals such as the elephant this descent of the testes and formation of a hernia or rupture does not occur. On the other hand in some rodents and bats the descent is only seasonal and temporary so that the testes are withdrawn into the abdomen after the breeding season is over, though they never return completely to their original positions near the kidneys.

Although the testes are solid bodies they consist of numerous long but very narrow tubes tightly coiled up in a tough covering; the interstices between the coiled tubes are filled with specialized *interstitial cells* (see below). The narrow tubes are lined with cells some of which give rise to the sperm, and others act as nurse cells for supplying nourishment to them. The sperm, which are highly modified cells that carry a head of nuclear material and a long thread-like tail, are produced by numerous successive divisions of the original sperm mother-cells. When ripe they pass down the tubules and are stored in a single long tube of larger diameter, the *epididymis*, which is coiled up and closely wraps one side and the two ends of the testis. When fertilization is to take place the penis of the male enters the vagina of the female at copulation. The sperm pass from the epididymis of each side through a long narrow tube, the *vas deferens*, to the base of the bladder where they are diluted with the secretions from the accessory glands such as the *seminal vesicles* and the *prostate*. The secretions provide not only the medium in which the sperm float but also contain substances that nourish and stimulate them and, in some species, cause the fluid to set into a jelly when received by the female. The combined mass travels on into the male's *urethra* (the tube through which the urine is expelled from the bladder) and is deposited in the upper part of the vagina of the female. Thence, by lashing their tails, the sperm swim through the uterus to the uterine tubes where they meet and fertilize the egg cells.

In most mammals breeding does not occur at all times of the year but is concentrated into a well-defined breeding season; during the rest of the year the animals are functionally non-sexual. As the breeding season approaches the ovaries of the females show signs of activity; some of the follicles increase in size and become filled with fluid which contains a hormone, the *oestrogenic hormone* or *oestrone*, and the animal enters the state of *pro-oestrus*. The hormone circulates in the blood and has a specific effect upon the reproductive tract causing a general enlargement and a growth of glands in the uterus, and stimulating the activity of the lining cells. It also has a psychological effect which when fully built up causes the female to be receptive to the male—at other times she will repel him. When this occurs she is said to be 'on heat', or in the state of *oestrus*, and the follicles in her ovaries are fully ripe and ready to burst.

In some species the follicles burst spontaneously but in others they burst only in response to copulation. In both cases, as soon as the egg cells are washed out of the follicles into the funnels of the uterine tubes, the lining cells left behind in the follicle immediately start growing and soon fill its cavity with a solid mass of cells. At the same time they change their character, become glandular, and secrete another hormone, *progesterone*, into the blood. The cells are yellowish in colour so that the transformed follicle is now called the 'yellow body' or *corpus luteum*. On reaching the uterus the progesterone causes the glands to secrete and produces a change in its lining, with the formation of a specialized kind of cell, so that it is prepared to receive the embryos as soon as they enter it after their journey through the uterine tubes which they entered as egg cells. The changes produced by progesterone can happen only after the uterus has been prepared or primed by the previous action of the oestrogenic hormone.

Oestrus lasts for a comparatively short time and finishes when the animal becomes pregnant through the implantation of the embryos among the cells of the uterus which are modified by the action of progesterone. Progesterone has another action; it prevents the ripening of other follicles and the production of oestrogenic hormone, and thus prevents the onset of another oestrus while the animal is pregnant. The life of the corpora lutea is limited; they may cease functioning at about the time of the birth of the young, or even before, or they may persist for some time during suckling. When their function has been performed they cease producing progesterone, shrink in size and are eventually absorbed, though the last traces sometimes persist for a considerable time so that successive batches of differing age can often be recognized in the ovary.

At or a little before the birth of the young the mammary glands, which have increased greatly in size during pregnancy, start secreting. The first secretion differs from the milk that is given during most of the suckling period, and in some species it contains substances that confer an immunity to certain infections upon the young; in other species these substances are received by way of the placenta from the mother before birth.

Although a number of egg cells may be released from the ovary at each oestrus it does not follow that they will all produce embryos, still less living young. At every stage in their development there is often some mortality; when embryos die they are resorbed—they degenerate and their remains are taken back into the blood stream of the mother. The cause of the death and resorption of the embryos is not fully understood; sometimes it appears to be brought about by malnutrition of the mother in unusually adverse climatic conditions during the breeding season, but it may be induced by more subtle causes, for it has recently been found that in domestic mice resorption can be brought about by subjecting the pregnant female to the scent alone—not the actual presence—of a strange male.

In those mammals that breed only once every year the reproductive tract of the female returns to inactivity when the young are weaned, and this state of *anoestrus* persists until the next breeding season. But in many mammals, especially the smaller ones with a short gestation period, each breeding season contains a number of *oestrous cycles* in quick succession. Sometimes there is a short period of anoestrus between each cycle, but more commonly oestrus recurs almost at once after the birth of the young and hence is known as a *post-partum oestrus*. It comes on when the new batch of follicles in the ovary ripens, usually within twenty-four hours of the birth. The first litter, consequently, has to be weaned by the time the second litter is born, and there may be three or even four litters consecutively. Many small mammals have a natural life span of about eighteen months; the majority breed only in the season after their birth, though animals of early litters may breed in the later summer of their birth-year and again in the next breeding season.

There are some peculiar special cases. In the seals, the Roe Deer and many of the mustelids such as the Badger and Stoat (but not the Weasel) the embryo formed after fertilization in the uterine tube does not become implanted in the lining of the uterus on entering that organ. The *blastocyst*, as it is called at this stage, remains loose and unattached in the cavity of the uterus and development is halted. It is not until many weeks or months later, when activity and growth are resumed, that the blastocyst becomes embedded in the lining of the uterus. This *delayed implantation* gives an apparent gestation period longer than the period necessary for foetal growth. In the seals the delayed implantation follows a post-partum oestrus. In some bats, on the other hand, the sperm received from the male in the autumn are stored in the vagina or uterus from some months during hibernation, and the egg cells are not released from the ovary and fertilized until the animal resumes permanent activity the following spring. Delayed implantation and *delayed fertilization* must presumably have some selective advantage for the species in making a compromise between the most convenient season for the sexes to meet and the most propitious season for rearing the young.

The events of the oestrous cycle are closely associated with the hormones produced in the ovary, and similarly male sexual activity is mediated by the hormones derived from the testis and especially the interstitial cells that lie between the coils of the tubules. The male hormone, *testosterone*, controls the growth of the male sexual tract and stimulates the accessory glands into activity. It also induces the development of the secondary sexual characters such as the mane and antlers of the stag, and the sexual behaviour or 'rut' which is the functional equivalent of oestrus. In the males of some mammals, as in deer and seals, the seasonal rhythm of activity is well marked, but in others, as in some rodents and carnivores, it is absent and the males are potent at all times whether the females are in oestrus or not.

The production of the sex hormones in the ovary and testis is itself stimulated by other hormones that are secreted by the front lobe of the *pituitary gland*, a small gland situated at the base of the brain. The anterior pituitary hormones are numerous and those that stimulate the production of sex hormones are known as the *gonadotropic* hormones (often less correctly spelled *gonadotrophic*). These hormones are of different kinds: one stimulates the development of the follicles of the ovary or the tubes and the interstitial cells of the testis, another controls the formation of the *corpus luteum* from the burst follicle, and another stimulates the production of milk. Many other hormones are produced in the pituitary but they do not act directly upon the reproductive structures.

The production of the gonadotropic hormones in the anterior pituitary is stimulated by many factors. In some mammals the length of day or seasonal change in day length is sufficient stimulation; in others activity is promoted by stimuli received through the senses of sight, hearing or smell. The hormones thus produced in the pituitary stimulate the secretion of the sex hormones, which not only bring on oestrus and rut but induce sexual behaviour such as display and courtship. These activities react on the sense organs and provide further stimuli for the pituitary, the whole system forming a self-reinforcing cycle leading to successful breeding.

This account of the phenomena of breeding in mammals is no more than a general outline, and the mammals play an infinity of variations on the basic theme. Even the comparatively few species that make up the mammalian fauna of the British Isles show a great diversity of patterns in their breeding biology as the following table demonstrates.

TABLE I

Types of Sexual Cycle shown by British Mammals

Insectivora				
Shrews and Hedgehog	Polyoestrous	Polytocous	Post-partum oestrus	Male cycle
Mole	Monoestrous	Polytocous	No post-partum oestrus	Male cycle
Chiroptera	Monoestrous	Monotocous	No post-partum oestrus Delayed fertilization	Male cycle
Lagomorpha	Polyoestrous	Polytocous	Post-partum oestrus in rabbit ? no post-partum oestrus in hares	No male cycle in rabbit ? male cycle in hares
Rodentia				
Rats, mice	Polyoestrous	Polytocous	Post-partum oestrus	No male cycle in *Rattus, Mus* Male cycle in *Apodemus*
Voles	Polyoestrous	Polytocous	Post-partum oestrus	Male cycle
Squirrels	? polyoestrous	Polytocous	Probably a post-partum oestrus	Male cycle with short infertile period
Carnivora				
Mustelidae				
Badger, Stoat, Marten	Monoestrous	Polytocous	No post-partum oestrus Delayed implantation	? no male cycle in Badger Male cycle in others
Weasel, Polecat	Polyoestrous	Polytocous	? post-partum oestrus No delayed implantation	? no male cycle
Otter	? polyoestrous	Polytocous	? post-partum oestrus No delayed implantation	? no male cycle
Fox	Monoestrous	Polytocous	No post-partum oestrus	? no male cycle
Wild cat	Polyoestrous	Polytocous	No post-partum oestrus	? no male cycle
Seals	Monoestrous	Monotocous	Post-partum oestrus Delayed implantation	Male cycle

Artiodactyla				
Deer—Red & Fallow	Monoestrous	Monotocous	No post-partum oestrus	Male cycle
Roe	Monoestrous	Polytocous	No post-partum oestrus Delayed implantation	Male cycle
Cetacea				
Whales, dolphins	Polyoestrous until pregnant	Monotocous	No post-partum oestrus	Male cycle in some; no male cycle in others

Polyoestrous = more than one oestrous cycle in each breeding season.
Monoestrous = only one oestrous cycle in each breeding season.
Polytocous = more than one young at each birth.
Monotocous = only one young at each birth.

Note.—Some species are monoestrous because the female almost invariably becomes pregnant at her first oestrous cycle of the breeding season. If for any reason she fails to become pregnant oestrus recurs at short intervals until she does: she is then polyoestrous.

The table includes only those animals about which more or less definite information is available. The omissions and queries show how much remains to be learnt in spite of the wide researches that have been made on the reproduction of animals. There is a vast literature on the subject, and those who wish to study it further should consult Bullough (1951), Darlington (1953), Frazer (1959), Parkes (1956–60) and Waddington (1939).

CHAPTER 4

Distribution, Range and Habitat

H.N.SOUTHERN AND IAN LINN

Even for birds, which are conspicuous and well-studied, we are far from knowing the detailed distribution patterns of British species. For mammals, especially the smaller ones, we are often ignorant of even the limits of their geographical ranges. The ideal way of recording and displaying the distribution of an animal would be by means of a contour map on which the contours represented density in the way that the contours of a conventional map represent altitude. Unfortunately, even for our best-known mammals, we are nowhere near being able to produce such a map to cover the British Isles. With information so meagre that the boundaries of their ranges are sometimes in doubt, we are reduced to filing every record and waiting until sufficient have accumulated for us to sketch in the main outlines of distribution. Reliable distribution maps, even though, at first, they must be much simpler than our ideal map, are urgently needed to reveal possible relationships between species—to show, for example, how one species may replace another geographically, physiographically or by habitat. Over a period of years it will be possible to see from such maps whether a species is expanding, receding or remaining more or less stationary; and perhaps also, from the pattern of change, to detect clues to its causes.

It is urgent, therefore, that information about distribution should be gathered and stored. For this, encouragement and guidance in collecting, verifying, filing and finally digesting and publishing such data are needed. It is one of the objects of the Mammal Society to accomplish this basic task. It is a task which amateur naturalists, because of their considerable numbers scattered through the country, are ideally situated to perform but the difficulties are great with such self-effacing animals as mammals. We hope that the advice given in this book will both

F

save records from oblivion and also stimulate their active pursuit. The unsatisfactory state of our present knowledge can be judged from the paragraphs on distribution in Part 2; some of this information is over 50 years old, having been summarized from the *History of British Mammals* by Barrett-Hamilton and Hinton.

The simplest method of collecting information about distribution is to accumulate for spot localities records of 'presence or absence'. Obviously 'absence' is more laborious to establish than 'presence' and, in any graphic representation, areas where an animal is known to be missing should be carefully distinguished from other areas where no investigation has yet been made.

A broad and approximate picture of geographical ranges, like that given in the distribution maps of Van den Brink (1955) can, of course, be sketched in from quite general information and from museum collections. Some assumptions have to be made about continuity between gaps and difficulties arise wherever the land becomes at all finely divided but we can at least see approximately how far certain species replace or overlap one another.

An advance on this stage is to black in conventional units of land (e.g. counties, parishes, National Grid squares) where a species is known to be present. The picture so given is strictly in accordance with the facts but, of course, where the facts are few the result is so generalized as to have little value. To fill in a whole county on the evidence of a single record may, in fact, amount to distortion. On the other hand, there is little to be said for producing counterfeit precision by such a method as varying depth of shading on subjective grounds, as appears to have been done, e.g. by Sandars (1937). The elaboration of the method should be scaled to the quantity and value of the records available. One of the most careful essays on these lines for British mammals is the mapping, carried out by Shorten (1946) and later by Lloyd (1962), of Grey and Red Squirrels on a 10 km grid (Fig. 3). The smallest National Grid squares shown on the 1 in. Ordnance Survey maps are 1 km across but the 10 km square is small enough to minimize the distortion that arises from an entire square being filled in from a single record, and is also easy to work with when localities are defined by the National Grid map reference. Maps like this are probably the best way of depicting the distribution in the British Isles of any of our mammals. Even for the few which are thought to be ubiquitous, e.g. Wood Mouse, Pygmy Shrew, details of

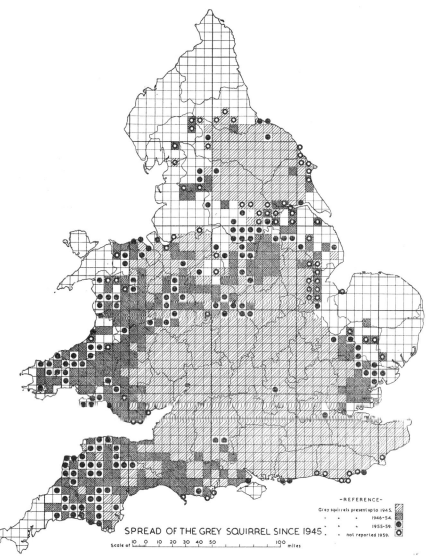

-REFERENCE-

Grey squirrels present up to 1945.
"   "   "   1946-54.
"   "   "   1955-59.
"   "   not reported 1959.

SPREAD OF THE GREY SQUIRREL SINCE 1945.

Scale of 10 0 10 20 30 40 50 100 miles

FIG. 3. Distribution of Grey Squirrel (*Sciurus carolinensis*) showing extension of range in the British Isles between 1946 and 1959 (from Lloyd, 1962). By permission of the Controller of H.M. Stationery Office. An example of the use of the 10 km square National Grid for depicting distribution.

distribution become important in some areas, e.g. in our western islands, some of which may never have been colonized, or in the Highlands, where steep contours make for radical changes of habitat in a short distance.

A basic distribution record should, therefore, comprise the date, a note on the habitat in which the animal was seen or otherwise detected (see below) and some evidence or authority to support the identification as well as some precise method of fixing the locality. For all species a note should be kept and copies sent to the local Natural History Society recorder and to the Scientific Secretary of the Mammal Society for filing and eventual publication.

Periodic surveys of such distribution records will enable a student to determine quickly how elaborate a method of graphic portrayal is justified and where the investigation of prominent gaps needs stimulating. A start could be made now, perhaps sponsored by the Mammal Society, on constructing reliable distribution maps for many British mammals, on the lines of the Badger survey organized by Mr T.J.Pickvance.

The various methods of obtaining these records can be classified roughly as follows: (1) sight or sound records, especially for larger mammals, (2) trace records—footprints, droppings, nests, burrows and so on and (3) obtaining actual specimens (or identifiable parts of specimens) by trapping, by searching in places where capture is possible or by finding casualties or remains. Methods 2 and 3 are most useful with shy, small or nocturnal species. Indirect ways of obtaining records can be devised with ingenuity and the following are suggestions of what can be attempted. Species of deer can be located and distinguished from their footprints; rabbits and hares can be detected and distinguished by their droppings; the presence of some predators can be established from the remains of their kills (e.g. Foxes will bury prey that they do not eat at once, Otters leave fish with a single bite taken out of them); small mammal species can be identified in the pellets regurgitated by birds of prey (fortunately the teeth and many of the bones are specifically diagnostic, see p. 144), or recorded from the captures carried home and displayed by cats; and finally such concentrated habitat units as corn ricks (for small rodents) and hollow trees or caves (for bats) can be investigated. A good example of the value of attending the threshing of ricks is

Southwick's (1956) work which established a geographically limited resurgence of Harvest Mice in the middle Thames area. Continuous recordings in the same localities are valuable for tracing such fluctuations in numbers. By a similar method Rowe (1958) detected an increase of this species over the years 1955 to 1957 on a Hampshire farm.

Specimens collected for record purposes can fulfil a valuable secondary purpose as museum material. Single specimens and small local series add up, with the other material in a collection, to a basic picture of distribution which is objective because the specimens remain permanently available for examination. Many of the smaller mammals are so abundant (embarrassingly so at times, e.g. when Yellow-necked Mice raid apple stores) that valuable series of study skins from different local populations could be obtained during the routine protection of property.

A tool for studying (among other things) the distribution of small rodents and insectivores, which has recently been perfected by the Bureau of Animal Population at Oxford, is the Longworth live trap, whose construction and use are described in chapter 6. This has the advantage over the breakback trap in that the animal can be released unharmed and that unwanted animals like birds rarely get into them. With this trap it is possible to determine quickly what species of small mammals are present in any locality, and to gain some idea of their abundance relative to each other and to type of ground, from season to season and year to year.

However, the moment we try to measure *differences* in abundance from place to place, we enter into a new and more complicated field of investigation. It has been suggested earlier that the ideal way of depicting an animal's distribution would be by a contour map of densities. It is doubtful whether this could ever be done satisfactorily except in rare instances and over small areas. Useful approximations are possible, however, which demonstrate quite adequately the broad trends in abundance over the British range of a species. Ornithologists have already produced useful distribution maps for easily counted species, such as the Heron and the Great Crested Grebe, using the vice-counties as the basic units of area and classifying them into rough density categories, shown graphically by different conventions of shading. Vice-counties are not, however, all the same size, so that it is probably better to use some form of square as the unit, based on the National Grid, as is done in plant distribution maps, e.g. the recent Atlas of the British Flora, edited by Perring & Walters (1962), and as was done by Shorten (1946, 1954a) and by Lloyd (1962) for squirrels. Even if it is not possible to make numerical estimates of the abundance of a species in different places, trends may be indicated by subjective estimates (e.g. simple categories like 'rare', 'common' and 'plague numbers') but, if this is done, the greatest care must be exercised in equating the judgments of different observers. When changes in abundance over periods of time are being studied, subjective estimates are less risky because they can be made in answer to the query 'Is the species this year more numerous, less numerous or the same as last year?' This method has been used for tracing the fluctuations in abundance of Arctic mammals by Elton and others (see account in Elton, 1942).

The discernment of these broad trends in density introduces us to the self-evident fact that most animals are distributed *patchily* within their geographical range. *Theoretically*, distributions can take three forms. (1) Random, as if a handful of animals had been thrown down on the ground, as corn used to be scattered from the hand of the sower. Random distribution is rather rare among animals. (2) Uniform. A distribution spaced evenly, like a grid, is also rare but can occur where man has created an artificially even habitat like a plantation of trees. A tendency towards evenness can arise from strict territorial habits in an animal, e.g. in a colony of Gannets or in a herd of fur seals, or from natural nesting uniformities in the environment, e.g. in a forest where mature trees are spaced out evenly by competition. (3) Patchy or clumped. Just as a uniform distribution is a departure from randomness in one direction, so a patchy or clumped distribution departs from randomness in the other direction. The term contagious distribution is now much used by ecologists, but it seems to express no more than the simpler term, patchy.

This last kind of distribution is the general rule among animals, so it may seem a waste of time to have detailed the other two theoretical possibilities. The fact is, however, that the degree of patchiness shown in an animal's distribution is often best measured statistically by the amount of its departure from randomness. The usual tests for this are given in standard statistical text-books. But, when we are studying patchy distribution in mammals, most of us need something much simpler, in fact a yardstick to apply to samples of populations, which will enable us to say that an animal is twice (or 5 times, or 10 times) as numerous in one place as it is in another.

Patchiness, or clumped distribution, in animals arises from many causes which can be classed in two main categories, those connected with the type and pattern of the habitat and those connected with the behaviour of the animals concerned.

Environmental factors which cause patchiness differ with the scale of patchiness that is being studied. The habitat of an animal is the part of the environment to which its way of life is adapted and in which it finds everything that is necessary for that way of life. We can think of a habitat from the very broadest sense, e.g. the boreal conifer forest, or temperate deciduous forest, right down to the very narrowest sense, e.g. a dead log in a woodland glade. At every stage it is the habitat and its distribution which primarily influences the patchiness of animals.

This point is best clarified by examples. The major life zones (or vegetation types) of the world are governed by climate, the effects of which are graded by latitude and altitude. Moorland and tundra occur above the tree line, which is quite high in the British Isles (though it comes down to sea-level in northern Scandinavia) and the Mountain Hare is confined to this habitat. Similarly, squirrels are confined to the forest zones and many large ungulates to steppe and savanna. All this may seem blindingly obvious but, until we have distinguished these broadest possible habitat effects, we shall not be able to see so clearly the importance of habitat differences on a smaller scale. Thus, the result of the Grey Squirrel's invasion of this country suggests that the Red Squirrel is best adapted to conifer woodlands; yet it does well enough in Europe in deciduous forest, from which the Grey Squirrel is missing.

On a smaller scale, habitats are governed by geology and soil, rainfall, physiography, exposure and so on. Thus we come to expect oak woods on clay soils, beech on chalk, heather on the exposed side of a hill and trees on the protected side, grassland on well-drained flats and bog on ill-drained ones. These differences are clearly of the first importance to animals and will account for the major patchiness of their distribution within their geographical range. Thus one would naturally seek the Brown

Hare in open grassland or arable country, the Otter along the marshes and bogs of river systems, the Short-tailed Vole in scrub and grassland and the Dormouse in deciduous woodland. Again, a naturalist knows these things intuitively and measuring the patchiness of any of these animals is largely a matter of measuring the distribution pattern of their available habitats. Even so, careful study may reveal things that at first were not so obvious.

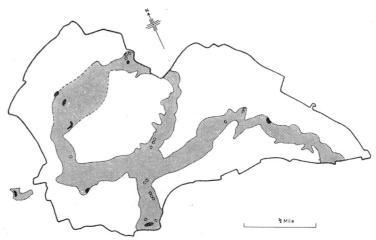

FIG. 4. Distribution of Badger (*Meles meles*) sets in Wytham Estate near Oxford. The stippled areas indicate the bands of Calcareous Grit Sand. The black patches show large sets and the open circles single holes.

An interesting example is the distribution of Badgers in Wytham Woods near Oxford (Fig. 4). The woods cover a hill with Oxford Clay on the lower slopes and Corallian limestone capping roughly the upper half. Between these two formations there is a belt of Calcareous Grit sand, following the contours most of the way round the hill and, in some places, forming a steep scarp. There are eight large Badger sets in the woods and all of them, as the figure shows, are located on this sand belt.

This distribution illustrates several factors, both environmental and behavioural. In the first place woodland with its cover is a preferred habitat of Badgers. Again, the slope of the hill means that the ground is well-drained. The lower-lying, open country surrounding Wytham Woods has few Badgers, while the density on the hill, although not known accurately, must be accounted high (the area is only 1,000 acres in extent).

Secondly, the geological formation controls the disposition of the Badger sets. Sand is both well-drained and easy to burrow into and, where it is exposed on a steep slope, the excavated material can be pushed downhill causing far less trouble than if the ground was flat. Furthermore, a burrow that penetrates into a sloping face soon becomes so deep below the surface that it is exceedingly difficult to dig out. This may not be so important today as it was in previous years, when badger-digging was a widespread pastime. From such fastnesses the Badgers can forage over the whole of the woodland and even beyond its boundaries.

Two further effects may be noted upon the distribution of the Badger in Wytham Woods, both due to behaviour. First, the sets are mostly spaced out, presumably because each group prefers to keep neighbours at arm's length. Secondly, the distribution of individual animals is clumped because they prefer to live in family, or at any rate, small social groups. The Badgers of Wytham, therefore, illustrate well four of the principles which govern the distribution of animals.

Further down the size scale, habitats, sub-habitats and even micro-habitats (there is no settled terminology) can be distinguished. An oak woodland will be divisible, at ground level, into barer patches with only a covering of dog's mercury in summer, areas of blackthorn or of bramble, dense stands of bracken and so on; vertically, it is divisible into a field layer of herbs and grasses, a shrub layer with hawthorn, elder, guelder-rose, spindle and others and a canopy layer composed of the crowns of the larger trees. Similar subdivisions can be distinguished in all the other major habitats, such as moorland, grassland, fens, rivers and lakes. The smallest subdivisions of habitats—such fragments of the environment as dead logs, the undersides of leaves, birds' nests, fungi and so on—are usually of little importance to mammals, although they obviously have a wide influence on the patchy distribution of insects and other invertebrates. But the larger subdivisions are extremely important for the distribution of most of our mammals and their effects have not yet been thoroughly studied. What may be attempted can best be illustrated by an example.

A standard line of live traps (the method is discussed in the next chapter) can give valuable information on the habitat preferences of different species of small mammals. It has been pointed out, especially for birds (see e.g. Lack, 1944) that the more closely two species living in the same area are related, the more they tend to occupy different habitats; ecological replacement presumably reduces competition just as geographical replacement does. Trap-line catches from different habitats (Table 2) show results consistent with this principle and they are expressed in a standard way so that the work of different people at different times can be strictly compared. Note that the expression 'trap-nights' indicates the number of traps used multiplied by the number of nights during which they were set.

TABLE 2

Catches of Small Mammals in Different Habitats
(288 *trap-nights, East Bergholt, Suffolk, September 1951)

	Wood strip and tall hedgerow	Low, scrubby hedgerow	Grassy banks and open, grass fields
Wood Mouse	22	21	5
Yellow-necked Mouse	5	0	0
Harvest Mouse	1	1	4
Bank Vole	14	2	0
Short-tailed Vole	4	9	22

* Trap-nights are the product of the number of traps and the number of nights during which they were set. Thus, 288 trap-nights may indicate that 288 traps were set for one night, or that 144 traps were set for two nights and so on.

From records of habitat preference accumulated in this way it should be possible to obtain a clearer picture of the pattern and perhaps the causes, of patchy distribution at varying times and places, under different circumstances. Table 3 is an attempt to bring together some of the data we already possess to point the way towards what could be achieved in this line of investigation with small mammals. Broadly speaking, it looks as if closely related species tend, when not geographically separated, to diverge in their habitat preferences. No doubt quantitative methods will be devised in due course to enable this kind of problem to be studied in other groups of British mammals.

TABLE 3

Geographical and Habitat Distribution of Small Mammals in the British Isles

	S.E. England	Rest of England	Scotland	Isles	Ireland	Wood-land	Scrub	Fields	Ricks	Heaths	Water	Domestic
Common Shrew	X	X	X	X		X	X	/		/		/
Pygmy Shrew	X	X	X	X	X	/	X	X		X		
Water Shrew	X	X	X	X	X	/	/				X	
Wood Mouse	X	X	X	X	X	X	X	X		X		
Yellow-necked Mouse	X	/				X						
House Mouse	X	/	X	X	X		/	X	X			X
Harvest Mouse	X	/				X	X	X	X		*	
Bank Vole	X	X	X	/		X	X	/		/		
Short-tailed Vole	X	X	X	X		/	/	X		X		

X = main habitat; / = subsidiary habitat; * = reed-beds.

Table 3 suggests a further interesting line of thought. It might be that in Ireland, poor in mammal species (only 3 of the 9 listed in the table occur there), each one might occupy a wider range of habitats than it does in England. Conversely in Europe, with twice as many mammal species, greater habitat specialization might be the rule. Investigations with standard trap-lines would answer these queries.

From all this discussion about the habitat it will be clear that, in any field study of mammals or collection of specimens, careful notes and descriptions of the environment should be made. It is a great help that practical classification schemes for habitats have already been published by Elton & Miller (1954) on a structural basis (though their full analysis has not yet been published) and by Yapp (1955) on a mixture of structural and botanical features.

Lastly, we have to consider departures from random distribution which occur on a very small scale geographically. Thus, when we have accounted for patchiness caused by different types of country and habitat, we may still find inequalities in a patch of ground that appears homogeneous. In a grass field, for instance, distribution of Short-tailed Voles may still be clumped because of their organization in family groups or because different population units are out of phase in the fluctuations of their numbers.

In broad-scale distribution surveys these small inequalities can usually be neglected; densities determined for sample areas in a grass field may have values that indicate non-random distribution of the species within the field but a figure for average density over the whole field will be near enough to the truth for many purposes.

Finer details of distribution are more likely to be interesting to people making an intensive study of the behaviour, ecology or genetics of a single species. Such studies must always be based on sound and concentrated natural history observation and they are, therefore, outstandingly the concern of the field naturalist, amateur or professional.

One of the first needs, in approaching such problems, is to discover how animals live in relation to their own species. Many birds will vigorously defend quite large territories from the trespassing of strangers and their intolerance will push their distribution pattern away from the clumped or random towards uniformity. Mammals, especially small rodents, have a much narrower field of spatial awareness and could not possibly defend such large areas. Field observations, combined with laboratory experiments, have shown that the area they normally cover in the course of their day-to-day activities is not a territory in the sense in which we speak of a bird's territory; thus the term 'home range' has come into use. The home range of a mammal is an intimately known area in which it fulfils its life cycle and which it may share with a number of its species.

Some mammals, of course, especially those like the Lynx or the Arctic Fox, both of which depend on one or two species of prey which fluctuate violently, can hardly be said to have a home range during part of their lives. When food is scarce, they have to adopt a nomadic existence. Others, e.g. social ungulates and some carnivores, travel over a wide circuit, settling only for a comparatively short time and then moving on. Yet others, like the Caribou and many seals and whales, perform long migrations and only live a settled life at each end of their journeys.

For most species of British mammals, however, the home range in which they spend most of their days is an integral part of the organization of their lives and affects the small-scale detail of their distribution. Thus, there will be a focal point, a nest or a refuge, which will be defended with as much determination as a bird's territory, an inner zone shared amicably with members of the same family group and peripheral areas shared with comparative strangers. Encounters with strangers near the nest will result in battles and, the nearer to the nest the encounter occurs, the more bloodless will the victory be. The sense of ownership, conferred by an intimate knowledge of the terrain, is a powerful aid in evicting trespassers.

Obviously the more overlap there is in home ranges, the more battles there will be so that, beyond a certain point, reproduction may be interfered with and there will be an automatic check on population increase. In some species high densities may be reached very rapidly because of the coherence and tolerance existing between members of family groups. Fierceness in encounter is literally graded according to 'familiarity' (see e.g. Crowcroft's work on House Mice, 1955).

This kind of knowledge explains certain aspects of the small-scale patchiness of the distribution of mammals. At a low average density this patchiness may result from the coherence of family groups (corn-rick populations often show this at an early stage of their growth); or it may reflect the uneven nature of the distribution of cover in the major habitat. Crowding produces a more evenly spread population with available habitats fully occupied. In an English oak woodland with ground vegetation of dog's mercury interspersed with clumps of bracken and bramble Bank Voles will be confined during the winter sparseness of population to the bracken and brambles but, after the breeding season, they will spread to the more open ground. Wood Mice, on the other hand, are much more evenly spread throughout the year, with perhaps a tendency to prefer the areas of dog's mercury.

These finer types of clumped distribution can be studied by the live-trapping methods described earlier but naturally attention must be concentrated on much smaller areas. A system of individual marking either by numbered metal leg-rings, or by ear-punching and toe-clipping, can be combined profitably with live-trapping (see chapter 6).

In this chapter the intention has been to show (a) how badly we still need general distribution records for most of our mammals, (b) that distributions by habitat can be profitably studied by a method such as the trap-line and (c) that for finer details of distribution we must concentrate our energies on small areas and accumulate more precise numerical data. This line of thought carries us on to the consideration of population studies in the next chapter.

CHAPTER 5

Population Studies

H.N. SOUTHERN AND IAN LINN

Both to the ecologist and to the systematist a population means, fundamentally, an aggregation of animals of one species which is to some degree isolated from its neighbours spatially and, therefore, reproductively. This isolation may be almost complete as on islands or incomplete where the barriers are zones separating areas of the same habitat. Populations may also be marked off by different degrees of isolation. We can speak of the British population of Wood Mice when we are contrasting it with other populations outside the British Isles; we can also speak of the Wood Mouse population of an oak wood because the surrounding fields, which are less suitable, impede the free movement of the mice over to another oak wood.

To those interested in evolutionary studies—systematists and geneticists—the importance of a population is that it usually differs in genetic composition (though not always visibly) from neighbouring populations. Trinomial nomenclature was introduced in an attempt to describe in crisp terms the geographical pattern of variation (in size or colour or any other character) *within* a species (see chapter 7). With birds and mammals such variation follows broad patterns because the species, ranging so widely, encounter a similarly broad pattern of environments, each of which exerts its own selective influence. Nevertheless, it is now realized that the dividing lines can be so blurred and graduated that it is not always possible to make distinct categories of subspecies. Therefore, most modern Handbooks have reverted to the old binomial system (which, with a few exceptions, is followed here) with a section indicating the main trends of variation within each species. Thus we should say of the Bank Vole that it increases in size from south to north in the British Isles with a slight jump between the Scottish Lowlands and Highlands and a larger jump between the mainland and the island forms (see p. 276).

At the same time genetics has taught us that, at a much lower level, all populations, even if they extend over a few square miles only, have their own peculiar hereditary make-up, providing they are sufficiently isolated from their neighbours. This kind of variability, which occurs in both space and time, can be due either to different pressures of natural selection in different environments or simply to isolated population units varying at random in different directions.

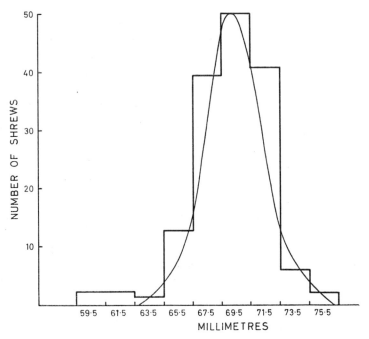

Fig. 5. Distribution of body lengths (nose to anus) of immature Common Shrews (*Sorex araneus*) collected in Wytham Woods near Oxford between June and December 1950. Data from unpublished thesis of W.P.Crowcroft (1954b). The histogram gives the data and a normal curve is superimposed.

The characters which show such regional differences are also variable at any one place. Thus, measurements of body length, even when confined to a single size-class of an animal, will vary between certain limits and will cluster around the mean value in a well-defined and consistent way. The pattern of this distribution around the mean is called a normal distribution and if measurements are plotted graphically as histograms, they conform approximately (the more the measurements, the nearer the approximation) to what is called a normal curve. Fig. 5 plots the distribution of body lengths in a number of Common Shrews, all belonging to one age-class. Each column represents the number

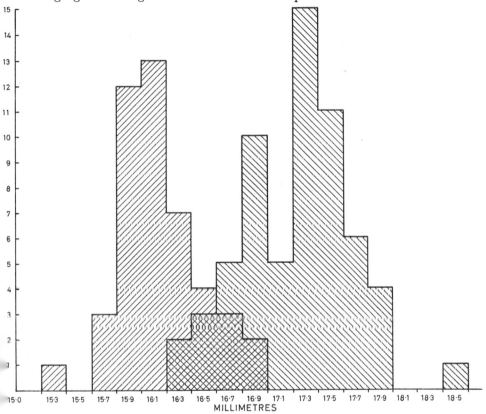

FIG. 6. Distribution of hind foot lengths of Bank Voles (*Clethriono-mys glareolus*) from two localities in Scotland. Data supplied by Dr G.Corbet. ▨ Monikie, Angus; ▧ Sunart, Argyll.

out of the total falling into a certain size-class, these being determined arbitrarily, e.g. intervals of 2 mm were chosen for this illustration. We are indebted to Dr W.P.Crowcroft for allowing us to use these data. It will be seen that the histogram takes roughly the shape of the normal curve which is superimposed on it.

Now, let us compare samples from two populations separated

G

geographically. Fig. 6 constructed from data kindly made available by Dr G.Corbet, shows measurements of hind foot length for Bank Voles collected at two localities in Scotland. Each distribution follows the shape of a normal curve but the two curves do not coincide. There is a real difference between the mean hind foot lengths of the Bank Voles at the two localities. But, since there is an area where the two curves overlap, some specimens cannot be assigned to one or the other population from these measurements. Thus it is important that systematists should have reasonably long series of specimens from each component population before they can determine adequately the pattern of variation within the species.

Figs. 5 and 6 illustrate the important point that any samples from a single population will contain a certain amount of random variation (just as a collection of men and women will show variation in height, weight, colour of hair and so on). Therefore, if two separate populations are to be compared to decide whether their mean measurements are truly different, some statistical assessment must be made to distinguish between random variation and valid regional differences. Methods for this can be found in any of the standard statistical text-books.

The immediate practical point of all this is that if information is published about animals that have been caught and measured, it should be in such a form that anybody interested in analysing the information more thoroughly or in comparing it with other people's information can apply standard statistical tests. The simplest way of achieving this is to publish all the individual measurements made, but this is obviously cumbersome and wasteful of space for anything but a small series. The best way is to give the average, or *mean*, of all the measurements together with the *standard error*, a statistic which need not be defined precisely here (again, any standard text-book will do this). Briefly it is a measure of the spread of the individual measurements round the mean. With these figures should also be given the *number of measurements* upon which the mean is based.

An alternative is to give the mean, the number of observations and the range (i.e. the highest and lowest recorded), as has been done in Part 2 of this book.

Before we move on to the ecologist's view of populations, we must notice one other remarkable aspect of intra-specific variation

—the phenomenon of polymorphism. Here the variation is usually discontinuous, in fact the most obvious expression of it is a dimorphism with two contrasting and clear-cut phases which interbreed without producing intermediate types. An example from British mammals is the Water Vole, which has a normal, dark-brown form distributed all over England, Wales and Scotland and a black form which occurs rarely in England and Lowland Scotland (excepting two places in the Fens of Cambridgeshire and Norfolk where it was known to be common at the turn of the last century), and is about as abundant as the normal form in the Highlands.

These patterns of dimorphic distribution sometimes coincide with climatic variation and they may represent a balance of naturally selective factors in the environment keeping the frequency of the phases more or less constant, or a stage in the elimination of one form by the other. In any event, the phenomenon provides most valuable opportunities for measuring the progress of 'micro-evolution', because a map of colour-phase ratios, obtained from straightforward counts of different populations, will show, when repeated after a lapse of time, whether change is taking place. Furthermore, the effect of different degrees of isolation between sub-populations in promoting or preventing variation in phase ratio could be readily detected by the same method of counting samples of each sub-population. There are other British species of mammals which offer similar chances to the field naturalist to study evolution in action.

Populations are characterized, therefore, by slightly variable constellations of hereditary factors, but they have other traits which interest more particularly the ecologist. He needs to know primarily what are the density and distribution of a species over a given area, and he must also consider the rates at which animals enter and leave the population by birth, death and movement. The basic problems of population dynamics are all encompassed in these simple terms, despite the frightening cloud of statistics and parameters with which the biomathematicians have invested them. If we are considering the effect of a population of animals upon another which lives with it and is eaten by it, it is vitally important to know what we can call most vividly the 'turnover' of a population. There may be at the beginning of the breeding season 100 animals to an acre in each of two successive years but the point of urgent significance for another animal which eats it is whether it reaches a peak of 200 after the breeding season *or one of 2,000*. It is just as necessary to know how fast a river flows, as it is to know its width and depth.

The natural history of populations, or demography, is worked out most thoroughly for man but, in spite of this, mankind shows only a slow aptitude to learn how to control his rapidly rising numbers. There are many complexities in this study of the vital statistics of populations, and there are many conventional methods of treating population data, involving such things as life tables, age distributions, intrinsic rates of increase and so on (see e.g. the relevant chapters in Allee *et al.*, 1949, Odum, 1953 and, in simpler terms, for rodents, Davis, 1956), but it all comes down to the simple proposition that, if an animal population remains approximately *stationary* in numbers from one year to the next (and by and large this is true for the majority of our species), then deaths during the year must cancel the births. It follows also that, other things being equal, the longer an animal lives, the slower is the turnover of its population. Furthermore, for each specific length of life and rate of turnover, there will be a corresponding 'stationary age distribution' taking the form of a pyramid (Fig. 7A) and, if deviations from this are detected, one can say that the population is no longer stationary, but rising or falling in numbers (Fig. 7B & C).

In the previous paragraphs we have considered the 'income and expenditure' of a population under the heads of births and deaths. Obviously immigration and emigration must be added under these heads. Although in a resident population with the well-known propensity of animals to 'stay put', movement will contribute far less to the balance than births and deaths, and, in any case, will usually cancel out between different populations, this kind of dispersal is of immense long-term importance in effecting the colonization of new habitats and in shuffling around hereditary factors.

These aspects of population dynamics are important not only to the ecologist but also to the systematist who needs this knowledge to tell him how much material is present in each generation for natural selection to act upon; and how fast genes will diffuse across the boundaries between populations.

Naturally, these relatively simple propositions about the

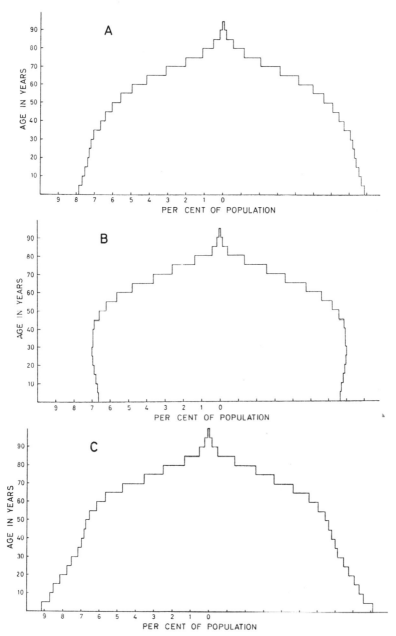

Fig. 7. Age distribution of white males (*Homo sapiens*) in U.S.A. in 1930 (after Dublin & Lotka, 1936). (*a*) Stationary population, (*b*) with rate of *decrease* of 0.005 per head per year and (*c*) with rate of *increase* of 0.005 per head per year.

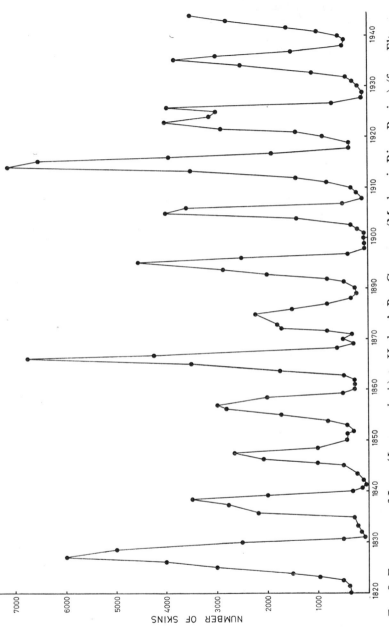

Fig. 8. Fur returns of Lynx (*Lynx canadensis*) to Hudson's Bay Company (Mackenzie River Region) (from Elton & Nicholson, 1942).

processes which regulate populations are so difficult to discern in the field that, at times, one is inclined to doubt their validity. The redress of the naturalist's viewpoint quickly curbs optimism. For one thing there will be oscillations around any point of equilibrium: sometimes these will even be regular and cyclical as typified by some Arctic mammals, e.g. lemmings and Snowshoe Hares with their dependent predator (how dependent can be seen from Fig. 8) the Lynx. Sometimes they may be so subject to violent environmental fluctuations operating both in time and space, that the result is bewildering. Finally to the plodding field observer such puzzling results may be further overlaid by the imperfections of his techniques. The rest of this chapter, therefore, will deal with the methods that have been devised for obtaining population data from the wild, and the many types of bias and error that creep in.

We shall concentrate attention on populations (i.e. of single species) rather than on communities since the former is the type of study which is the easiest for naturalists interested in vertebrates. Two basic sets of figures are needed, as mentioned above, to describe the 'turnover' in an animal population. The first should give information about the numbers of an animal present on a given area at convenient points in its life cycle. Counts or estimates of this kind are really the basic theme of this chapter because they are fundamental and must be achieved in some way (depending on the natural history of the animal studied and on the ingenuity of the observer) before any further investigation can be made into the second necessary set of figures—the income and expenditure account of a population. For animals which have an annual breeding season, it is convenient to assess the numbers at the beginning of the breeding season each year, since this forms the most satisfactory 'standard' low level to which a population returns each year, and therefore comparisons can be made from year to year and place to place.

I shall return to this central question of estimating numbers later. Now we must consider briefly the further stages necessary if a picture of the population turnover is to be elaborated. Firstly, a rough assessment of the annual ups and downs of a population can be made by simple repetition of the census. It is a great advance to know the range over which numbers fluctuate between the pre-breeding low point and the post-breeding high point. In this way we can discover that a mouse population will increase each year between fourfold and tenfold; whereas a deer population will not even double itself.

However, simply discovering the maximum population during the year does not tell us what is the total 'income' because some animals will be dying while others are being born. Note here that, if a population is more or less stationary in numbers from year to year, we can confine our attention to *either* the total entering the population each year *or* the total dying, because these must be equal. Possessing either of these figures *and* a pre-breeding census, we can then get a rough idea of the population turnover and the mean expectation of life. Now that the term 'mean expectation of life' has been introduced, mention should be made of the life table which is a comprehensive and detailed method used by demographers to express the distribution of mortality in a population. Table 4 gives an example from laboratory stocks of Short-tailed Voles (Leslie and Ranson, 1940). The second column (l_x) gives the basic data, the number of animals surviving from an original cohort of 1,000 young animals (the actual figures may be more or less, but are usually scaled to 1,000 in a standard life table) at successive periods throughout their lives. The third column (d_x) gives the numbers dying in each interval of time and this is expressed as a rate or percentage in the fourth column (q_x). In the last column (e_x) is given the total number of weeks left to live by each class of survivors, divided by the number of survivors. This useful figure is known as the mean expectation of life and is valuable in comparing the turnover of different populations. As an example from Table 4, the number of survivors at 11 weeks is 802 and the total number of weeks left for them to live is (681 + 530 + 378 and so on) × 8 (since the intervals are 8-weekly). Since deaths are spread over each interval, half the weeks lived between weeks 11 and 19 are added (802 × 4) and half of those lived between weeks 91 and 99 are taken away (1 × 4). The result shows that each animal alive at 11 weeks may expect a further 25.3 weeks of life.

In the field, the accumulation of life-table data usually proceeds by marking animals and observing the rate at which they disappear from the population in subsequent trappings (with safeguards adequate to measure or exclude emigration). It is not, of course, necessary for all animals of a cohort to be marked at the same time. The life histories of each individual can be scaled to a common starting point. In this way the massive amount of ringing done by ornithologists can be used to construct life tables; a comparative account of the expectations of life of various species is given in Lack (1954).

TABLE 4

Life Table for Laboratory Stock of Short-tailed Voles
(*Microtus agrestis*)
(from Leslie & Ranson, 1940)

Age in weeks	Survivors from initial total of 1,000 (l_x)	No. dying in interval (d_x)	Mortality rate per cent (q_x)	Further expectation of life in weeks (e_x)
0	1,000	135	13.5	29.7
2	865	0	0	32.2
3	865	64	7.4	31.2
11	802	121	15.1	25.3
19	681	151	22.2	21.1
27	530	152	28.7	18.0
35	378	131	34.6	15.6
43	247	99	40.1	13.8
51	148	67	45.1	12.3
59	81	40	49.7	11.1
67	41	22	53.9	10.1
75	19	11	57.7	9.2
83	8	5	61.3	8.4
91	3	2	64.4	7.3
99	1	1	67.3	5.3

Note.—The standard interval used is 8 weeks, but the figures for the first few weeks have been based on smaller intervals, as convenient.

The method of following through the lives of marked animals can be very time-consuming, if the species is long-lived. A 'cross-section' method, however, can be used, if the age of an animal can be determined. Counting the rings on fish scales is a classical technique but mammals are not so obliging. Nevertheless, wearing down of teeth, growth of their roots (e.g. in Bank Voles) and other ingenious methods of determining age are being elaborated and a useful summary of these methods may be found in Mosby (1960).

Having in this way arrived at an age-distribution at a point in time, one can then deduce an approximate life table by assuming that each age-class represents the average number that will survive from the previous age-class. Naturally this cannot be pressed too far, especially if the population and the age distribution are fluctuating.

Table 4 shows that, even in the laboratory, the Short-tailed Vole's expectation of life rises during the first three weeks after birth (most animals have a vulnerable stage when they are young and inexperienced) and then steadily declines throughout the rest of their lives. This is the usual pattern with mammals. On the other hand, with some other animals (notably some birds) the expectation of life, after an initial fall, due to the dangers of immaturity, remains at the same value through the rest of their lives. This makes it simple to arrive at a rough figure for expectation of life during maturity because records of survival time can be used without taking account of age.

Turning to population income, it is often possible to arrive at a figure for mammals by collecting embryo and litter rates. Undesirable species especially, like rats and rabbits, can be examined in large quantities and from the mean number of embryos and the percentage of females pregnant at stated intervals throughout the breeding season, the basic income can be determined. Valuable information of this kind has been collected for the Brown Rat by Leslie, Venables & Venables (1952), for the House Mouse by Laurie (1946), and for the Rabbit by Rogers Brambell (1948): less comprehensive studies exist for other species.

These embryo and litter rates give a maximum figure for population income indicating that an equal number of animals must die before the next breeding season if the population remains stationary. But mortality is never evenly spread: a heavy death rate falls on young animals (sometimes even before they are born (see Brambell on rabbits, 1942) and, indeed, some individuals may fail entirely to breed), so it is usually more to the point to have a figure for annual reproductive increase determined at a time when the young are weaned, or are on the way to independence. This can be done much more easily for birds, especially for game birds, by counting the numbers of grown-up young in family parties and repeated counts can trace the course of this juvenile mortality up to the point where the shooting season starts and an assessment of the proportion of young birds in what can now be called the overwintering population can be made from game bags.

With conspicuous mammals like Red Deer a skilled observer can collect this kind of information by straightforward stalking and counting. With other species that are shot in large numbers, like hares and squirrels, or can be otherwise obtained in substantial numbers, like small mammals, it is often possible to devise some method of separating the generations. Watson & Tyndale-Biscoe (1953) have successfully applied such a method to the rabbit, V.P.W. Lowe (unpubl.) and Crowcroft (1956) have achieved similar results for the Bank Vole and the Common Shrew respectively by studying the teeth.

Methods such as these for measuring the annual income of animal populations are outstandingly valuable when economic interests are involved. With sporting birds and mammals, where the crop to be removed and devoted to man's use (in effect, rescued from subsequent *natural* winter mortality) must be judged with care, such information is of paramount importance. With so-called vermin it is equally urgent to know a population's income, otherwise much energy and money may be spent merely in keeping the population 'happy' and producing the same well-balanced result as with game populations. Anyone who has studied figures of returns from tail-money and similar bounty schemes will know that the usual result is the establishment of a cropping system which benefits the animal cropped far more than it does man's interests (except the few people who claim the tail-money).

Now we have discussed approaches to determining in the field the income and expenditure of populations, we can return to the basic business of measuring numbers and density.

Clearly the most direct way of knowing the numbers of an animal on a given area is to count them by eye or ear. Equally clearly this is rarely feasible: deer and hares, perhaps, and limited populations of communally roosting bats can be so enumerated but the observer must know his animal's habits intimately, so that he does not leave part of the population uncounted. The breeding season provides special difficulties because females and young may become more secretive then.

If the destruction of the population to be counted does not matter, then some way of capturing the complete population can be adopted. This can be done with rats and mice in corn-ricks (see Venables & Leslie 1942; Southern & Laurie, 1946) and with rabbits in a warren. With rabbits a laborious system of gassing a warren and digging it out has been adopted several times (see Thompson & Worden, 1956) but this is using a sledge hammer to crack a filbert.

Break-back traps used on a large scale for catching House Mice can produce useful figures because the numbers caught from day to day follow a curve which starts high, drops fairly steeply and then flattens out. This tail of the curve presumably represents the dribble of colonists seeping into the vacuum and can be left out of account. Typical sequences are given in Chitty & Southern (1954).

A 'trap-out' method which avoids killing the catch can occasionally be used. An area, which is isolated either by different surrounding habitats (such as a grass field in the middle of plantations) or by a sunk wire-netting fence (though this means toil) can be trapped with live traps and the daily catch kept, for subsequent release, in cages. The breeding season should be avoided for obvious reasons. This method does not allow for the possibility that a fraction of the population may be untrappable. Leslie, Chitty & Chitty (1953) have shown that such trap-shy individuals occur in populations of Short-tailed Voles, though E. Shillito (unpubl. thesis, 1960) has examined the problem experimentally and suggested ways of minimizing the bias. When netting enclosures are used, there is also the danger of reinvasion by juveniles, unless the trapping-out operation is done swiftly. An elaboration of this 'trapping-out' method converts it into a way of estimating the total population. Hayne (1949) showed that, if certain conditions were fulfilled, trapping could cease when enough catches had been made to determine the rate at which each successive catch was reduced. Thus plotting the total caught each time against the accumulated total for all previous trappings will give a line which slants downwards and, if this line is produced down to the abscissa, the point where it meets it will give an estimate of the population. The method has been more rigorously examined by Zippin (1958).

This same method is also applicable to areas which are not isolated, in which case the catch is not removed but marked and released, so that they can be distinguished in later catches. This avoids creating a vacuum into which new animals will flow. There are two obvious sources of error here: a high density of traps is necessary and the marked animals, becoming habituated, will get in first and exclude unmarked ones; secondly, unless the area trapped is large (of the order of 100 acres), results along the margin, where the traps hold both incoming and outgoing foragers, will err on the high side. A correction is often used, which adds to the area trapped a surrounding corridor half as wide as the diameter of the animal's home range. It is not difficult to see that a considerable error may creep in here if only because the size of the home range may vary between sexes and seasons. On the whole, if such a method of trapping-out is to be used, it is safer to work a large tract in which the relation of margin to contained area is relatively small. This will also minimize errors which arise from clumped distribution of the animals studied.

An alternative method of determining the number of animals in a given area is, instead of counting all or most of them, to count a fraction (a 'sample') and relate this somehow to the total. Thus, if we need a measurement of population density extending over 1,500 acres, we can, with adequate statistical safeguards, choose 15 one-acre patches at random, work out a figure for each of these and multiply the average population by 100. There is an extensive literature now on the principles of sampling, and any naturalist embarking on such a method will do well to make sure either that he has digested these principles himself or that he has one of the growing population of biological statisticians at his right hand. If we are to make these inferences about total populations in this way, it is essential to make sure that the samples withdrawn from them are really representative of the whole or, if they are not, that certain safeguards are taken in interpreting the results. Thus a systematist will need to be certain that some varieties do not occur in his samples in too high or too low a proportion and the ecologist must similarly verify that some classes, like pregnant females, are not avoiding his traps. The samples, in other words, must be *random* samples. The statistician is helpless here, and only the naturalist who knows the habits of his animal thoroughly is in a position to say whether he is getting a true picture from his samples. If the results of sampling a number of sub-areas within the whole fall in with certain defined distributions, which are set forth in standard text-books, then there is a *prima facie* case for concluding that these are truly representative of the whole area, and therefore that the distribution is 'homogeneous'. But, to take a crude example, only the man working in the field can say whether there is a lake in the middle of the area and habitats vary in far subtler ways than this.

This sampling of sub-areas means that each sub-area must be subjected to a count or estimate of numbers like that discussed in sections above, and suffers from the drawbacks detailed there. Another method of sampling is to withdraw a number of animals at random from the *whole* area to be studied, mark them (methods of marking animals are described in chapter 6) so that they can be recognized individually or collectively at a later date, and then return them to the population. Then, as soon as the marked animals can be presumed to have mixed with the unmarked ones again, a second sample is withdrawn and the ratio of marked to unmarked animals noted. It is clear that, if 100 animals were marked and released on the first occasion and these appear in the later samples in the proportion of 1 marked : 9 unmarked, then the total population will have been about 1,000.

This proportional method of arriving at an estimate of the whole population is sometimes known as the Lincoln 'Index', because its first use is generally ascribed to Lincoln (1930) who applied it to wildfowl in the U.S.A. It is said, however, that the mathematician, Laplace, employed the method for estimating the population of Paris. Since the numbers of monks in the city was known, he simply counted the proportion of monks to non-monks in a number of samples and so arrived at an estimate of the total number of citizens. A more descriptive term is the 'capture-recapture' method, though with some of the larger mammals, like deer and rabbits, the 'recapturing' may be done through a telescope.

The capture-recapture method is laborious and should be done on as big a sample as possible, otherwise the resulting figure is subject to a large error. Nevertheless, with most mammals no other method is anything like as efficient. Furthermore, by extending the markings and recapturings over a whole chain of trappings, it is possible to assess the 'income and expenditure' between each operation. This ingenious method has been applied to Short-tailed and Bank Voles with great care by Leslie & D. & H. Chitty (1951, 1952 and 1953).

Theoretically, the simplest way to obtain a population estimate by the capture-recapture method is to catch, mark and release a number of animals and then immediately to catch another sample and determine the ratio of marked to unmarked animals. This might be called an instantaneous method and can be applied to some kinds of animals, particularly invertebrates, e.g. grasshoppers, of which large numbers can be caught in a short time.

With mammals this is rarely possible because the initial capturing and marking and also the recapturing are time-consuming. There is another reason: trapping makes mammals aware of the benefit of free meals and for a while marked animals may become trap addicts and will return to the traps in relatively

TABLE 5
Hypothetical Example of Capture-Recapture Results

Trapping	1	2	3	4	5	6	7
	100	10	10	5	5	5	5
		90	9	5	5	5	5
			81	4	4	4	4
				86	5	5	5
					81	4	4
						77	8
							69
Total sample	100	100	100	100	100	100	100
Estimated population	1,000	1,000	1,000	1,000	2,000	2,000	1,000

greater numbers than unmarked animals, thus introducing a serious error into the population estimate. It is better, therefore, to carry out the recapturing about a month after the first capturing and marking, when interest in the traps has faded. Nevertheless, it must be remembered that the estimate obtained will refer to the time of the first capturing and marking because the subsequent recapturing is giving information about the situation created when the marked mice were first introduced (i.e. it measures the marked : unmarked ratio established then).

Table 5 presents an extremely simplified version of a series of trappings to illustrate how population income and expenditure are detected by the capture-recapture method. Suppose that we are studying a population of 1,000 mice (though, of course, we do not know the total to begin with) in a confined area from which they cannot escape and into which other mice cannot penetrate. We shall put down live traps for one night each month and carry on doing this for seven months. Let us also suppose that over the first three trappings, there are no births or deaths in the population—it is not only stationary, but static. In fact, we find that, in conducting this work in the field, it is a great help in interpreting results, if a start is made in the non-breeding season, when mice are not being added to the population.

At the first trapping we catch 100 mice out of the 1,000 present, mark them and release them to mingle with the yet unmarked part of the population. At the second trapping we again catch 100 mice. (The sample size at all trappings throughout the series is standardized at 100 for simplicity: in the field naturally the numbers vary and when the population declines, we have to be content with a smaller sample, or increase the trapping effort.) Of these 100 mice, 10 will be ones that were marked and released on the previous occasion, this being the same proportion as the original 100 marked mice bore to the total of 1,000. By simple proportion one discovers that the original population at the time of first trapping was 1,000, viz.

$$\text{Marked mice released at trapping 1 (100)} \times \frac{\text{total sample caught at trapping 2 (100)}}{\text{marked mice in sample (10)}} = 1,000$$

Again, in the field, the numbers will not work out so precisely. If 10 per cent of the population are marked, we shall expect to find, in a sample of 100, any number of marked ones between, say, 7 and 13 because chance enters into the operation. The precision of the example is for the sake of simplifying a complex matter.

At every subsequent trapping we may expect to find in a sample of 100, 10 mice marked on the first occasion because the proportion of marked to unmarked mice remains the same, *providing that no births have occurred*. A death rate will make no difference to this proportion because we must assume that marked and unmarked mice die in the proportions in which they are present in the population. We should, therefore, be able to run an eye along the first rank of figures in the example, representing the recaptures at each subsequent trapping of mice marked at the first trapping, and find that, out of a sample of 100, 10 marked mice turn up consistently. But, in fact, at trapping 4 we suddenly find that there are only 5 marked mice instead of 10. This can only mean that the proportion of mice marked at trapping 1 has changed from 1 in 10 to 1 in 20. In fact, the population has been doubled in the interval between trappings 3 and 4 and another 1,000 newcomers have suddenly arrived. This would be a somewhat staggering birth rate anywhere but in our simplified example! Note that, while population estimates are for points in time, the dilution factor (or here simply the 'birth rate') is referable to the intervals between trappings. Thus, although it is normal to estimate the population at the time of trapping 3 from animals marked and released then and recovered in period 4, the estimate (2,000) has to be modified in the light of the dilution which occurs (i.e. it must be reduced to 1,000). We can also see that the effect of dilution cannot be measured except against a background of stability (it is the difference between the frequency of recaptures at trapping 3 and at trapping 4, emphasized in the table by the left-hand shaded rectangle, which gives the clue to the increase that has taken place). A series of three trappings is the least in which this effect can be demonstrated.

Whereas we can detect population *increase* by inspecting the subsequent recaptures from a single batch of released mice, we have to detect *decrease* by comparing the fates of adjacent batches of releases. The relevant comparison is indicated in the table by the right-hand, shaded rectangle. Somewhat similar batches of marked mice were released into the population at periods 5 and 6 (81 and 77): yet of the first, some 5 per cent were recovered at the next trapping, of the second about 10 per cent. This must mean that the second batch represented twice as large a proportion of the population it was taken from and restored to than the first; in other words, the population had declined by a half in the interval.

The important point about the capture-recapture method of measuring population turnover is that, if births and deaths are occurring simultaneously, as they so frequently do, the totals of each can be assessed separately. This would be impossible from simply inspecting the estimated totals of the population at each trapping unless each of the population changes were isolated, as they have been for the sake of simplicity in the diagram.

Even if this method were free from bias introduced by the animal's behaviour (see below), it would be laborious for the

H

amateur to use unless plenty of help was at hand. During one study of a woodland population of mice and voles which lasted four years, some 10,000 animals were marked (H.N.Southern, unpubl.). The need for such a large total arises partly because the larger the area studied (in the instance given above it was *c.* 250 acres), the smaller is the error from animals moving across the margin. With everything in its favour, the method can give results which are accurate to about ±10 per cent.

However, there are many drawbacks to the method on the biological as distinct from the statistical side, and some of these will vary from species to species. Some animals will scratch off the tabs or markers; some are distributed in such a clumped way that their estimated densities over an area may be practically meaningless; some may be much more mobile at one period of their life cycle than at another; finally, and most important, animals, being individuals, will not all react to trapping methods in the same way. Some may avoid traps: others, especially after experience, may seek them. Thus it may not be possible to capture, or, even worse, to recapture a random sample of the population. For example, if marked mice come into traps more readily than unmarked ones, it is easy to see that serious under-estimates will be the result. Experimental examinations of this trap bias have recently been carried out for the Short-tailed Vole by E. Shillito (unpubl. thesis, 1960), and for the House Mouse by Crowcroft & Jeffers (1961).

Here again there is no substitute for intensive observation of an animal's domestic habits in the field. Only the naturalist can detect, let alone measure, such sources of error in population estimates.

Even with this assurance that natural history work is fundamental to any kind of population study, many who are not full-time professional ecologists may feel that population studies of this complexity are beyond their resources and that they should confine their attention to elucidating as much of general life history information as they can. This is, of course, infinitely rewarding to the individual because it satisfies his *naturalis curiositas,* but there must come a point where most inquiring minds will need some quantitative data to test the thoughts that arise in them.

It is fortunate, therefore, that naturalists are used to working with figures that are rough and approximate. Physicists and mathematicians are inclined to look down upon the biological sciences for this reason, but there is no sense in refusing to accept the limitations of one's subject matter. Animals, especially birds and mammals, are individual creatures and do not behave like molecules, though for some purposes it is helpful to suppose that they do so and to see what deductions follow from such a supposition.

But for many purposes it would be a waste of energy to introduce massive quantitative data to establish some broad tendency. If one needs to know merely whether a population of animals reaches a peak of numbers twenty times as great as the springtime 'low' or only twice as great; if it is important whether an animal spreads out into second-class habitats during its yearly peak and retreats at other seasons; then it may be sufficient to devise an *index of density*. This need not even be an enumeration of animals themselves, but simply of some trace or evidence of their presence. Droppings, remains of meals, footprints, runways, etc., can all be given some appropriate quantitative expression whether by presence or absence in squares or strips in the area studied or by broadly categorizing their densities, as was suggested for the wider mapping of distribution in the last chapter.

The most important thing to remember about an index of density is that its chief use is for comparison, and any attempt to convert such an index into absolute numbers of animals on a given area will run up against great difficulties. In any case, for many purposes, it would be an absurd elaboration to strive for complete population figures. For comparing numbers and/or activity between seasons, years, times of day, sex and age-classes, localities, habitats and so on the only essential is that the method of obtaining an index should be standard and universally applicable.

A simple example of this kind of index is provided by work done by the Bureau of Animal Population at Oxford before the last war (see details in Elton, 1942) to trace the cyclical changes in abundance of the Short-tailed Vole on young forestry plantations and sheep walks in the Lowlands of Scotland. The method was to carry a wire frame, to drop it at stated intervals and to count the number of fresh dung pellets enclosed. Apart from their intrinsic simplicity, such rough methods can often be applied most valuably to give extensive information about a problem which is being studied intensively on a much smaller area.

With small mammals a convenient way of achieving an index to density is the standard trap-line. Analogous methods could be devised for other mammals, but so far the main work on these lines has been concentrated on small mammals. Break-back traps have often been used for this purpose but, since the perfecting of the Longworth live trap, it is no longer necessary to kill the catch. In the last chapter examples were given of comparing the frequencies of small mammal species in different habitats; in the same way numbers of single species, or relative numbers of several species, can be compared from place to place, season to season and so on.

No rigid standard procedure can be laid down, but the following suggestions were proposed for testing and criticism at a recent meeting of the Mammal Society. (1) A trap-line should consist of at least five, preferably ten trap points, placed five yards apart in grassland (where the more densely distributed Short-tailed Vole is likely to form the main catch) and ten yards apart in woodland and other non-grassland habitats. (2) Five traps should be placed at each trap point, ensuring such a density of traps that the number of animals excluded shall be small. As a rule of thumb, if over 80 per cent of the traps are full, more should be used. (3) Longworth live traps should be used and they should be set on the morning of one day and examined and collected on the following morning. (4) When the population is at its lowest, i.e. roughly from Dec to June inclusive, the traps may be 'prebaited' (placed with bait inside and the doors pinned up) for 48 hours before setting in order to familiarize the animals with them and so increase the catch. However, the value of this is debatable and it may be argued that it frustrates comparisons. (5) Bait should be whole oats. (6) A trap-line should not be run through more than one habitat.

The intention behind these recommendations is to make the procedure as simple and quick as possible. If the traps are set for only 24 hours, this will avoid drawing in animals from a distance or familiarizing predators, e.g. Weasels, with their positions. The main drawback is that Longworth traps are costly and rather bulky, but there is scope here for individuals and societies to co-operate. In any event, 50 or at least 25 traps are needed to provide adequate figures for making comparisons between one line and another and the production of a lighter and less expensive trap would help greatly. Naturally the more traps used, the more valuable will be the results because more detailed analysis of the catch, e.g. by age, sex and so on, can be attempted, but it is not advisable to try and increase the catch by leaving the traps set for more than 24 hours. This immediately produces complications; if the catch is marked and released, they become 'trap-addicted' (see earlier) and we have known Bank Voles, after 4 to 5 days of continuous trapping, to return to a trap the moment it had been reset. If the catch is removed to be returned to the area when trapping has finished, then the catch may be biased by the entrance of new animals into the area to fill the gaps.

If a line is to be retrapped at its identical sites to provide information about changing numbers from week to week or month to month, again the problem of trap-addiction arises. This is most serious during the winter when the population consists of the same animals, all growing wiser and wiser about the possibilities of free meals. To some extent this can be avoided by prebaiting (see above) which aims to make all the animals within range of the traps equally familar with them, but this does not overcome the difficulty of a troublesome residue of animals which refuses to enter the traps even after long tempting.

It is probably a safe rule never to trap at the same localities unless 3 to 4 weeks intervene between trappings. An alternative is to carry out the repeat trapping 100 yards away from the first line, but there must be good reason to suppose that the populations are similar in each place.

A word is needed about the snags of using live traps set in a line or a grid for measuring range of movement. It is tempting to assume that a frequency distribution of the number of trap positions through which an animal moves before recapture will map the home range. Indeed, such information can be obtained in this way, but only on very broad and approximate lines because the very fact of being caught in a trap prevents an animal from foraging over the area it would otherwise have covered. A statistician once pointed out to us that figures of this kind really constitute a very elaborate and laborious way of estimating the distance between the traps!

Without doubt the best method of finding out about an animal's movements is to catch it, mark it with a radio-active ring and follow it with a Geiger-Müller counter (*Photograph 21*). This has many limitations (e.g. only 1 animal can be studied at a time) and should only be used by those who are acquainted with its hazards to health, but for animals that live below the surface of low vegetation it can be most valuable. The results obtained on Short-tailed Voles and Moles by Godfrey (1954, 1955) should be consulted.

The above discussion on the density index has been focused on the trap-line for small mammals but, for each group, naturalists will usually be able to devise some appropriate index. Often the number of animals seen in a stated time can be valuable, e.g. squirrels in woodland, but again only the careful observer will know what are comparable times of diurnal or seasonal activity. For people who travel frequently over certain railway lines or roads, transect counts of animals seen or enumeration of those run over can yield information comparing densities at different times and seasons. An interesting study on these lines has been carried out on the Hedgehog in New Zealand by Brockie (1960).

Perhaps many people will be deterred from attempting this kind of quantitative work by the snags that have been mentioned, but it must be insisted that to carry out or oversee such work a first requirement is skill as a naturalist. A little trouble in mastering elementary sampling principles will open wide fields of investigation into many population problems that are, as yet, practically untouched, while preserving the chief joy of the naturalist which is to be out in the field with his animals.

CHAPTER 6

Technical Aids to the Study of British Mammals

Compiled by
H.N.SOUTHERN

With a special section by
G.CORBET

The purpose of this chapter is not so much to suggest ideas about the techniques of studying mammals (chapter 2 is devoted to this) as to give information about the practical application of the techniques, in particular where special kinds of apparatus can be obtained (and how they can be devised) and what is their approximate cost.

Obviously, there is no end to the things that could be included and the material for this chapter has had to be selected. The selection will not cover everybody's wants and it will be a great help for the future if readers will indicate what they consider to be major omissions as well as point out inaccuracies.

Where specialized materials are concerned, we have tried to cite manufacturers who can supply them. Again, there will be many gaps and we shall be grateful for further information. In some instances we have gone into details about the handling and use of some types of apparatus but, when an easily obtained reference deals with the matter adequately we have thought it sufficient to cite this.

Since British mammals are mostly self-effacing, their study has often to be conducted through the medium of traps; 'catch-alive' traps (or 'live' traps for short) are more popular than 'dead' traps nowadays but, since the latter are often convenient to use for eliminating pests or for collecting series of study specimens, we shall describe them here.

First, to deal with traps for small mammals (voles, mice and shrews), we can neglect the unusual types (though browsing

97

through the patent specifications of traps can afford endless entertainment), and concentrate on break-backs or snap traps.

All of these operate on the principle of a spring loaded wire-loop which, on release, flings over and pins the catch to a base board. Death is usually exceedingly swift, but it is possible for a mouse to be caught by the tail or by a leg. The older types of break-back, of which there were many kinds that could be bought at the local ironmonger for a few pence, usually have a wooden base plate ($3\frac{1}{2} \times 2 \times \frac{1}{4}$ or $\frac{1}{2}$ in.) and a wire arm which holds down the spring loop by being engaged under the catch of a treadle. The treadle may be quite small, consisting of a wooden tongue or a wire prong or it may be a platform, as in the Little Nipper, half as big as the base plate. The former type tends to jam if the mouse eats at the bait with an upward motion. This cannot arise in the Nipper because a mouse has to tread on the platform to reach out to the bait. However, all traps of this type are difficult to set delicately.

There are now at least two types of trap which are made of metal and are set with one simple motion, the Klik and the Selfset. They cost 1s. 4d. and 1s. 10d. compared with 5d. to 10d. for the wooden ones, but are efficient, easy to set and do not warp in wet weather. The efficiency of all these traps has been compared recently in a publication by Phillips & East (1961) which should be consulted.

The small size of these break-back traps means that a mouse is sometimes caught right across the skull, making it useless as a museum specimen. This can be mininized by using the Museum Special trap with a wider loop, but, of course, correspondingly more bulky to carry about in quantity since it measures 5×3 in. The Museum Special is one of the many products of the Animal Trap Co of America (address Lititz, Penn.) and its cost is about 2s. 9d.

For success with break-back traps there are a few simple rules to be observed. In the field, let the traps be set only during the hours of darkness, otherwise birds may be caught. Even during the night they may catch the wrong animals and Foxes, cats or Stoats may be condemned to go around with a trap hanging on to a paw. If it is possible, therefore, set the traps under a cover. They should always be placed cross-wise to the path of the animal, either in a run-way or against an object which will be skirted, so that an animal may be caught from whichever direction it approaches. A certain number of losses will fall to raiding pre-dators but there is no point in presenting them with the trap as well, so it is advisable to push in stakes and fasten the traps to them with stout string. Prebaiting can be done to increase the catch, though much of this will be mopped up by Pheasants, squirrels and small birds.

The bait used must vary with the type of trigger. On a short wooden trigger pea-nut butter or cheese can be used; on a wire prong cheese or bread; and on a platform porridge oats or flour can be scattered. Finally, with traps set in runways, e.g. for Short-tailed Voles, bait may not be necessary.

A rather specialized type of trap for a small mammal is a mole trap. Needless to say, none of the standard small traps would catch a Mole, but the usual scissor-type which is set in the Mole's run is fairly familiar and can be bought at ironmongers for $c.$ 3s. 6d. (Young's of Misterton, Somerset, sell them at 30s. per dozen). Godfrey & Crowcroft (1960) have given a clear account of the different types of mole traps and how they should be used.

When we come to consider *live* traps for small mammals we shall confine ourselves mainly to describing the use of the Long-worth Trap which, although expensive, has established itself as the most dependable live trap obtainable in this country. A previous description has been given in Chitty & Kempson (1949) and, more particularly with regard to shrews, in Crowcroft (1957), but, in view of the persistent barrage of questions about live trap-ping, the procedure with Longworth traps will be dealt with rather fully here.

The principles and construction of the trap were evolved at the Bureau of Animal Population, Oxford, by D.H. Chitty and D.A. Kempson, and it is manufactured by the Longworth Scientific Instrument Co, Radley Road, Abingdon, Berks, from whom it may be obtained for the price of 25s. *Photograph 1* shows the appearance of the trap: it is made in two parts, the tunnel or trap proper containing the door which is released by a simple prop moved by treadle action; and the nest-box, which clips firmly to the trap and contains bedding and food, so that trapped animals will be warm and fed during their enforced stay.

If only a few Longworth traps are being used, their carriage presents no difficulties because the trap fits neatly into the nest-box, which measures only $5\frac{1}{2} \times 3\frac{1}{4} \times 2\frac{1}{2}$ in., and the whole thing, being made of aluminium, weighs only 210 g (*c.* 7 oz). However, when 50 or more traps are being used, it is a different matter. For carrying anything up to 70 or 80 a sheet aluminium box fastened to an Everest frame answers well, but for distributing traps a hand-carrier is more suitable. A light model made from strip aluminium and retaining the contents (28 traps) with a coil spring curtain rail is illustrated in *Photograph 2.* These numbers of traps may sound excessive but it is often better to use a large number of traps set for 24 hours visited evening and morning, or only morning, than a smaller number left set for several days or a week. If traps are left down, much energy is spent dealing with an accumulating army of 'regulars' and, not infrequently, a Weasel will learn where mice and voles are being attracted or a squirrel will pull the traps apart for the bait.

Longworth traps should be placed as far as possible in cover where mice and voles will be foraging and sited with an eye to natural guide lines, such as fallen branches, ditches, and tree roots, which direct their traffic (*Photograph 3*). Where people are likely to pass by, it is better to disguise the traps well anyway, even to the extent of dulling their brightness with a spray of khaki paint. It is possible, too, that this will make them less alarming to voles and mice (E. Shillito, unpubl. thesis, 1960). The better they are hidden, the more efficient should be the marking system because nothing is more frustrating than a long search for the one elusive trap. In private ground the more arresting the marker, the better: strips of scarlet and white celluloid are excellent. Where human predation may occur, conspicuous markers may be placed at a constant distance and bearing from the traps, or unobtrusive indications used like broken twigs. Naturally it helps to place the traps on a line or grid with standard separations. Whether pre-baiting is done or not depends upon the probable abundance of mice and upon the time which the trapper has to spare. The Longworth trap has a small catch on the side of the tunnel near the entrance which can be pressed forward so as to lock the door against the roof. In later models this is replaced by a length of spring wire which can be similarly engaged under the door. Animals can now pass over and tread on the release wire as much as they like without dropping the door and can be accustomed to come and take bait freely before the traps are actually set for catching.

There are several points to be watched to ensure efficient setting. If the trap has already been down for prebaiting for 24 or 48 hours, it should be returned, when set, to the same position. The method of fastening trap to nest-box allows the latter to be tilted at a slight angle to the base line of the trap. Condensed moisture and urine will then drain out, rain is prevented from driving in and so the nest material keeps relatively dry.

A fresh supply of food is usually needed when the traps are set. Whole oats are the best all-purpose bait (supplemented with apple or carrot when the weather is hot or when Short-tailed Voles are likely to form the main catch), but may wedge the trap mechanism, which should always be tested immediately before leaving a trap set. Oats should be placed at the end of the nest-box and covered with nest material, otherwise they may dribble below the treadle and wedge it when the trap is placed horizontally on the ground. About a tablespoon of oats is sufficient for 24 hours' occupation of the trap.

Nest material in quantity is best obtained in the form of a bale of meadow hay. With a small number of traps, dry bracken or grass collected in the field gives sufficient insulation. Again it is best not to put too much nest material in the box (a twist of hay that can be held in a clenched fist is enough) because it makes the extraction of the catch more difficult and, if it is dry when inserted, it will expand as it becomes moister and again the treadle may become wedged.

New traps should be tested carefully before they are used. A few minutes with a file and a pair of pliers ensuring that the mechanism works smoothly may increase the catch out of proportion to the time spent.

Handling of the catch can be carried out at all levels of adeptness. For some trappers it may be sufficient to break apart trap and nest-box, eject the animal and identify it as it runs away. Most people will not be satisfied with this for long, and will want to learn how to handle the catch for noting various biological data. A way of learning withouts tears is to open the trap inside a large bag of polythene or net, so that the animal can be worked into a corner and secured.

There are two ways of holding a mouse or vole so that it cannot bite. One is by the loose skin at the nape; the other is by the tail, but this needs qualification. In some species, e.g. the Wood Mouse and the Dormouse, the skin sheathing the tail ruptures easily and strips off like a sheath, exposing the vertebrae to view. They should, therefore, only be grasped by the *base* of the tail. The House Mouse, on the other hand, has a very tough tail and can be handled by it with confidence. Laboratory stocks of mice are moved about normally by this method. Yet a warning is needed here: a wild animal is far from docile and usually agile enough to twist round, climb up its own tail and put in a shrewd bite before the holder knows what is happening.

It is always safer to regard 'tailing' as a temporary measure either for moving an animal around or putting it in a position where it can be grasped. In any case it is wise to keep an animal held by the tail swinging gently because the slight centrifugal force will distract it from biting.

The next cardinal point in handling mice and voles is more difficult to believe. Unless an animal is *grasped* it will not bite. Thus, when a mouse is extracted from a nest-box by its tail, it is best to put it immediately on your knee and cover it over with the other hand. Completely held in the hollow of the hand, but nowhere gripped, the mouse will remain quiet while the first hand, having let go the tail, works up the back to grasp the nape.

Much of the routine examination, sexing, determination of breeding condition and so on, can be done while the mouse is held by the nape, but sometimes it is useful to curl the fingers underneath it, so that it can be lifted clear of the observer's knee and held firmly for examining the hind parts (*Photograph 4*). This makes the fitting of rings or the palpation of embryos much easier.

Now we can go back to the problem of how to remove a mouse from a nest-box without having recourse to a polythene bag. The trap and nest-box are disconnected and broken apart, with the fingers of one hand covering the trap aperture, those of the other hand the nest-box aperture. A quick glimpse through the fingers will show whether the mouse is in the trap. Usually it is safely in the nest-box, having made itself a comfortable nest from hay, but, if not, it can be blown from the trap back into the box, if the two are loosely reconnected. Recalcitrant animals can often be persuaded back with a whiff of tobacco smoke.

A mouse is removed from the nest-box in the following way. Four fingers of the left hand are slid into the box below the covering fingers of the right hand. As soon as the mouse is located, a fold of skin can be grasped between the first and second fingers and the mouse pulled gently towards the surface. It will struggle to get back into the hay and, in doing so, usually presents its hind quarters to view first, so that it is a relatively simple matter to pick it out by the tail.

Throughout this description the captured animal has been referred to as a 'mouse' for simplicity, but the term must be understood as covering voles and shrews as well. For Moles Godfrey & Crowcroft (1960) suggest a similar method except that the animal is finally grasped around the body behind the front legs. For those just learning to handle the catch it is much better to practise on voles, which are generally more docile than mice and do not move so convulsively. If traps are set in the morning, a catch of only voles can be taken from them by the evening, especially during the summer. It is rare for Wood Mice to enter the traps during the day.

Finally, a word is needed about the maintenance of Longworth traps. It is important that routine oiling of hinges and spring anchor plate should be carried out periodically. The fact that the floor of the trap is hinged means that the whole thing can be opened widely for cleaning. This makes the job so easy that a routine cleaning of traps can be done in the field while they are being taken up for packing in the carriers. It is most convenient to keep aside the hay from the nest-box for wiping out the trap.

Mice and, more particularly, voles will nag at the traps and will sometimes bite quite large holes in the aluminium after a night's undisturbed application. The most vulnerable parts of the trap are the door and the walls around the door prop. The Longworth Co. supply extra doors at a small cost which can be fitted quite quickly, and these can be made of heavy galvanized iron or monel metal, both resistant to gnawing. On the other hand, if the doors are made of harder metal, the mice will go elsewhere to gnaw and damage to the body of the trap is more difficult and expensive to repair than are doors. It is probably more sensible to stick to aluminium doors and keep a stock to replace those that are damaged.

One advantage of the Longworth trap over other box traps is that the spring against which the release treadle has to be pressed can be set at various tensions. Thus the trip mechanism can be adjusted to respond to weights as light as 1.5 g and this is more than sufficient to catch the smallest Pygmy Shrew. If shrews are not wanted, then setting the tension at the other extreme, which means that nothing happens until about 8 g weight is applied, will pass most of them. If shrews especially are wanted, a bent strip of metal with a small hole in it (described in Crowcroft, 1957) can be inserted which will exclude all but the smallest rodents.

A specialized use of the Longworth trap (used normally with nest-box) is as a cover in which to place a break-back trap. This is a useful method of catching mice and voles for the examination of stomach contents. With break-backs or Longworths alone bait has to be used and stomach contents will consist largely of this. If Longworths are set without bait, stomach contents may be well digested by the time the catch comes to be examined. A spell of prebaiting with Longworths, then trapping without bait and with break-back traps set in the nest-box solves the problem.

There are other types of live trap for small mammals which can be obtained from outside the country. One of the best known is the Sherman trap which is made in the United States. Like most small mammal traps except the Longworth, it consists of a simple tunnel with no nest-box and a technique would need to be evolved for extracting the catch by hand. A similar type of trap used in France can be constructed in the workshop and Davis (1961) has recently published a description of it. In addition, the ingenious person will be able to design simple traps for catching small mammals alive and an efficient one is described in Davis (1956).

When we turn to the catching of medium-sized mammals (rats, squirrels, rabbits, etc.), we find that techniques are still at an experimental stage and there is no single trap that can be recommended for the purpose.

To consider first traps which kill outright; for rats and Water Voles, the larger version of a break-back trap with a base-plate measuring $7 \times 3\frac{1}{2}$ in. (bought at most ironmongers for about 2s., or the Selfset variety about 5s.) is useful. The same advice applies as was given about the smaller types except that it is even more painful to fumble the setting; hence the Selfset may be preferred!

Until 1959 the universal trap used for killing (or perhaps 'catching for killing' would be more accurate) medium-sized mammals was the gin trap. Since its prohibition, a number of traps have been tested and recommended, most of them for use only in burrows or artificial tunnels. The following ones are the most important: the Imbra trap, made by the Tetra Engineering Co, 1/3 Redhill Street, London NW1, and sold at 15s. each; the Juby trap, sold by Messrs Gilbertson & Page, Hertford, at 12s. 9d. each; the Fenn trap (the cheapest and perhaps the simplest; can also be set in the open on, e.g. rat runways) made and supplied by Mr A.Fenn, F.H.T. Works, High Street, Astwood Bank, Redditch, Worcs, at 7s. 6d.; and the Fuller trap (a box trap designed for catching and killing squirrels only) made and supplied by Fuller Industries, Marepost, Pondtail Road, Horsham, Sussex, at 18s. 6d. each.

All these traps and their operation are described in the Forestry Commission leaflet called *Traps for Grey Squirrels* (Anon., 1959) which was written by Monica Shorten and F.A.Courtier.

Live traps for medium-sized mammals again are a rather mixed lot with none of them outstanding. In the first place, there are a number of rat traps on the market which can be bought at the local ironmongers or from firms like Young's, Misterton, Crewkerne, Somerset. They make two types of mesh or wire traps at 14s. 6d. each and larger models costing from £2 to £5 10s. These either have a push-through, non-return entrance or a bait or platform trigger which drops a door. Usually they have only a single entrance and are too bulky to be set in a burrow or tunnel.

To these may be added two very similar traps, which were primarily designed for squirrels and whose use is described in the Forestry Commission leaflet cited above. One is the Legg Single-catch Trap, patented and marketed by Fuller Industries (address above) for 22s. 6d.; the other is the Young Trap, which can be bought from Messrs. Nash & Morgan, Whitecroft, nr. Lydney, Glos, for 15s. completely assembled, for less if the purchaser assembles it himself.

Although these traps were originally designed for rats and squirrels, they have been used with some success for Water Voles, Stoats, Weasels and Hedgehogs.

A good deal of attention has been paid to the trapping of squirrels, especially the Grey Squirrel and, as well as the types of trap mentioned above, there is also a larger, permanently baited Legg Trap, which will accumulate squirrels. There are two sizes, one selling at 35s., the other at 45s., and both are marketed by

Fuller Industries. Again a full description of its use is given in the Forestry Commission leaflet already cited.

The other general pattern of live trap for medium-sized mammals arises from the tradition of vermin trapping, which is used on most estates where game is reared. At strategic places over the estate, permanent trapping points are maintained consisting of tunnels sited on the main traffic routes of animals. Various kinds of trap are made with a door at each end, so that, when set, they offer a clear way through. These have never been very popular in the British Isles and, at the moment, no firms are making them. So types like the Havahart and Kindhart have to be bought from the U.S.A. and are correspondingly expensive. The smallest model of Havahart made by the Allcock Manufacturing Co, Ossining, New York, measures $3 \times 3 \times 10$ in. and costs just less than £1.

Tunnel traps, however, are becoming more popular to operate at such places and, though they have only a single door, they have a wire grille or glass at the opposite end to simulate a way through and can be set in pairs, one pointing in each direction. Their construction is simple, consisting of a square section wooden tunnel with a platform release, operating the door, and they can be made by any handy person. The design came originally from Germany (the Boisguelin trap) and such traps can be bought at 10s. 6d. each from the Cotswold Game Farm Ltd, Stroud, Glos, and, if operated on a large scale, combined with marking, should begin to yield some facts about our little-known small carnivore populations. Useful instructions about setting these traps may be found in I.C.I. Game Services Advisory Booklet no. 17, *Enemies of Game: Some Control Methods for Ground Predators*. We should not forget, however, that wastage will be high from the sharp teeth of squirrels or rats.

The use of traps placed up trees is probably more profitable abroad than it is in England, yet some interesting information might be obtained about whether species other than squirrels use these forest highways. An ingenious method, whereby a trap can be lifted up to a branch with a pole and anchored with a length of wire and a tobacco tin filled with concrete is described by Harrison (1960).

The handling of these larger species when caught demands more thought and practice than do the small species. If dead specimens are required, it is sufficient to fasten a sack over the trap entrance and drive the animal into this; here it can simply be chloroformed.

Where it is necessary for the catch to be examined alive, weighed and marked, a cone of small mesh ($\frac{1}{2}$ in.) wire netting in which the animal can be immobilized is far the best for rats, squirrels, Stoats and so on. If the examination is prolonged, it is advisable to use ether for ease of handling and for preventing unnecessary stress and struggling. For larger animals such an anaesthetic is essential. Information about anaesthetics and their application can be found in Croft (1957).

Finally, there are some miscellaneous methods of catching mammals alive which need to be mentioned.

The simplest possible type of trap is the pitfall, consisting of a tin or a jar sunk in the ground flush with the surface. These need to be at least 4 to 6 in. across and about 1 ft deep and they are quite efficient at catching shrews. Voles, especially young ones, will also blunder in, but Wood Mice can easily jump out again unless elaborate precautions are taken against this.

Two things should be remembered about pitfalls. They must be examined frequently, preferably every two hours, not only because shrews die very quickly but because a heavy shower of rain may make the bottom of the trap messy and dangerous. When they cannot be tended regularly they should be removed or put out of action.

The second thing is that one or two pitfalls will quickly catch most of the catchable animals in that area, so either they need shifting or a grid of traps should be prepared.

Probably the Rabbit has more traditional techniques associated with catching it than any other British mammal. Long nets, purse-nets and ferrets, dazzling with lamps were all used, as well as the notorious gin trap, when Rabbits were numerous. A useful summary of such methods was prepared by Major C.W.Hume and published by UFAW (*Instructions for Dealing with Rabbits*, UFAW, 7a Lamb's Conduit Passage, London WC1) to make known the alternatives to gin trapping. This can be used as a general guide and a catalogue of apparatus is issued by many firms (e.g. Young's, Misterton, Crewkerne, Somerset): the best guide of all, however, is the local rabbit catcher or gamekeeper.

The use of a strong spot-light was originally combined with a greyhound for picking up a dazzled and immobilized Rabbit.

I

More recently it has been found that, on suitable ground, a Land Rover equipped with a spot-light can approach near enough to a Rabbit for it to be caught by somebody approaching it on foot with a 2 ft diam. net on the end of a 6 ft pole.

Two other methods have been developed for catching Rabbits alive during studies involving marking and releasing. One employs 'smeuses' or metal tunnels with a swinging door hinged from the top which can easily be pushed up by a Rabbit passing through. These can be introduced into any wire-netting fence, or can be built into a wall. Rabbits quickly get used to pushing through them and, when they are to be trapped, a stout pin can be passed through holes in the smeuse down behind the door, so that it only opens in one direction. A box or wire cage trap can be fastened to the smeuse to collect the Rabbits which pass through it (*Photograph 5*). The use of these smeuses is described by Southern (1940).

A second method is to set in the runways wire snares which have a knot preventing them from drawing tight and strangling the Rabbit. Such snares can be bought (e.g. from Young's of Misterton, Somerset, at 26s. per gross), but it is a simple matter to knot a plain snare 5½ in. from the eye and secure the knot with a dab of solder. Again, the best way of learning to set snares, which is a task with plenty of room for the exercise of skill and judgment, is to go out with a rabbit catcher. Drawbacks to this method are that Rabbits struggle more in snares than in box or wire-netting traps and they are vulnerable to predators.

Another group of mammals, much studied now by capturing and marking, is bats. Apart from the species which congregate in caves and in the roofs of buildings, where some of them can be captured by hand or with nets set over the exit holes, the possibility of catching them in flight is being increasingly explored. For handling larger species it is always advisable to wear protective gloves. In America one or two reports have been published testifying to the success of a screen of fine vertical wires hung where bats are feeding (Rausch, 1946; Constantine, 1958). Mist nets of very fine thread, which are now extensively used to catch birds, should be almost as successful for bats, if they are organized so that the bats' sonar is 'switched off' or only 'ticking over'. The Earl of Cranbrook has kindly supplied this account of the technique as used for catching Noctules.

'Mist nets of fine terylene thread, ¾ in. knot to knot, set between two poles and across the wind, will catch bats flying low on, e.g. cricket-infested municipal rubbish tips, smoking farm dung-hills, ponds, rivers, etc. or indeed Pipistrelles almost anywhere. Bats must be removed immediately so the nets must not be left unattended and the whole net must be within immediate reach. The size of net used depends on the size of the team of bat catchers: using a 4-panelled net, 22 ft × 9 ft is suitable for two men, a 2-panelled net, 22 ft × 4 ft 6 in. for one man in these circumstances.

'With a team of 3 or more, poles and net can be held horizontally by two and swept up as bats fly over it. A high-flying bat can be brought down by a pebble lobbed into the air in its path so as to fall into the net, which is swept up to catch the bat as it swoops to the pebble.'

Though it is very desirable that as much experience as possible should be gathered and passed on about the use of this new tool, the method has its drawbacks, chief of which is the speed with which bats will inextricably tangle themselves, if not removed from the net swiftly. Incidentally, Noctules entangled in this way rapidly suffer from shock and go into a coma, from which they may have to be nursed back laboriously to normal activity. Conversely, when hibernating bats are being handled, they should not be wakened too much but rapidly returned to their perches. British-made mist nets are on sale in this country at the moment (Young's, Misterton, Crewkerne, Somerset, advertise them), but some control is exercised by the British Trust for Ornithology over the distribution of the finer imported nets of Japanese make. It is probable that some formula will soon be found for controlling the sale of all mist nets, so that they are only used by capable hands or under capable supervision.

Trapping methods for large mammals have not yet been developed extensively in this country and would mainly be needed for studying deer. Nevertheless, some experiments with nets and large traps are being carried out. The fawns of all species can be found and marked by using an appropriate stalking technique but this can only be achieved during the short period after their birth when they are left crouching in their forms. However, given enough energy and woodcraft, this method can yield useful results and is being used in Red Deer investigations in Scotland.

Cages or enclosure traps have hardly been used at all in the British Isles but there is a considerable literature (see, for example, Mosby (1960)) about these methods as applied in the United States. Nearer home, Andersen (1962) has described the very successful technique which he has been using in Denmark for Roe Deer.

But perhaps the most interesting recent development in dealing with large mammals is the use of drugs described as immobilizing and tranquillizing. These were developed mainly for veterinary use but were quickly extended for the capturing and marking of large mammals in the U.S.A. Now they are being used increasingly and enthusiastically on African 'big game'. The injection of the drug is achieved by a special, carbon-dioxide powered gun which, with suitable modifications, can be made effective up to a distance of 75 yards. The one which is most used is the Cap-Chur Gun made by the Palmer Chemical and Equipment Co, Atlanta, Georgia.

Many drugs have been tried and new ones keep appearing. Latterly the best results have been obtained with succinylcholine chloride and one marketed under the name of flaxedil. These act by temporarily blocking transmission between the motor neurones and the skeletal muscle. Their use is described by Buechner, Hartshoorn & Lock (1960 a & b) and Talbot & Talbot (1962), though for many species the best drug and optimum dose still require investigation. It is unlikely that such drugs will be safe for routine use until many more tests have been made.

DEALING WITH THE CATCH

Broadly speaking, the purposes for which individuals or series of animals are caught fall into two classes according to whether the animals are needed alive or dead.

For the field naturalist interested in distribution, ecology and behaviour, the examination, marking and releasing of the catch constitute the usual procedure. Marking is dealt with in a later section and this section will deal first with the handling of live animals.

The preservation of dead specimens is often necessary for reference during specific field investigations as well as for broad taxonomic and comparative anatomy studies. Dr Gordon Corbet has contributed the section dealing with the processing of material of this kind for a national collection.

We may note, incidentally, that, whether we study our material alive or preserved, more and more emphasis is now placed on quantitative information. The statement that 75 per cent of 128 animals examined were in breeding condition is much more convincing that the general remark that breeding reaches a peak in such and such a month. Similarly, broad conclusions about geographical trends in size and colour are best demonstrated from substantial series of skins giving a mean and its standard error at successive points along the direction of change.

Here then are the main purposes for which naturalists and professional zoologists wish to examine series of live or preserved animals.

(1) To provide an estimate of, or an index to, numbers of individuals and of species so that variation in time and place can be measured. Usually this demands live trapping, marking and releasing, though an index can be obtained by means of snap-trapping.

(2) To follow through the life cycle of one or more species. This means defining the breeding season, the succession of generations and the phases and strength of dispersion. Much of this can be pieced together without having to kill the catch but, for gathering precise details of age distribution (fusion of sutures and epiphyses, growth and wear of teeth, weight of eye lenses and so on), embryo rates and losses, progress of moult and development of young, dead specimens are necessary and histological detail (e.g. on gonad or endocrine cycles) may be needed.

(3) To study behaviour generally of individuals and populations. Live trapping, marking and releasing of individuals is essential for following behaviour traits, and for analysing social organization. It is often valuable to combine this with the killing and histological examination of specimens or groups of specimens so that their internal condition may comment on their behaviour and vice versa.

(4) Specimens, collected in quantity and by a prescribed routine, are needed for many practical and economic purposes. The transmission and epidemiology of some diseases can only be studied by examining samples of animals to discover how much they are acting as reservoirs for disease organisms and as vectors

of intermediate hosts, such as fleas. Both live or dead samples may be required, sometimes both.

(5) Specimens and series of specimens are needed for academic research on comparative anatomy, physiology, biochemistry, genetics and related spheres of zoological investigation; also for academic teaching, for general education and demonstration and for keeping in zoological gardens.

(6) Many of the above purposes need collections of dead specimens and tissues to be filed for reference. In addition there are the collections of local and national museums. These are primarily needed for providing basic identifications of species and for recording their morphological variability. Nomenclature and taxonomy which underlie all biological investigation are often regarded as essential services to be provided by the state. National collections in many countries have amassed the necessary data for modern systematic and evolutionary studies, and the standard of the research built upon these collections may depend upon initiative inside or outside the bodies that house and tend them.

Just as important, and possibly more important, in local collections is the intelligent display of material for the public. Normally this is confined to faunistic groupings based on taxidermic excellence but there is a future, for demonstrating evolutionary processes, in the use of series of preserved specimens.

Since so many and so diverse purposes underlie the collection of data from live and dead specimens, we shall confine ourselves to giving a general account of how to treat specimens to serve as many purposes as possible, together with a more specialized account by Dr Gordon Corbet of the methods of preserving, preparing and measuring specimens for a national collection. On the whole, mammals up to the size of a rabbit can be treated, dead or alive, in roughly the same way, and this account will concentrate on this size range with only short references to the more specialized and larger animals.

The following routine information is usually taken about a live specimen before it is released.

(1) Needless to say, it is vitally important to determine the species correctly. If the animal cannot be brought back alive or dead to where text-books are available, a very careful description should be written down. The subspecies should normally not be

specified. Any doubt about identification should be expressed in the field notes.

(2) Sex. From the external genital organs it is usually possible to determine sex. Even in immature animals the urinary papilla, sometimes strikingly similar in the sexes, e.g. in voles, is much further away from the anus in males than in females. Davis (1956) gives a useful diagram about this. Furthermore, the area of skin between the papilla and the anus is usually darkly pigmented in males. Immature shrews in their first winter cannot be sexed without killing and dissecting. In carnivores the penis bone, or baculum, of the male can be distinguished by touch.

(3) The localities of trap lines or trap grids should be exactly specified. Usually a National Grid reference to the 1 in. O.S. map is sufficient but, if trapping is to be repeated at the same sites, it is advisable to map them on the 6 in. or 25 in. O.S. map, as well as to mark them on the ground.

(4) Information about habitat is rarely recorded except in the vaguest possible way—woodland, moorland and so on. Habitat can be specified with more precision either by a botanical description or, more conveniently, by a code number derived from Elton & Miller's (1954) classification. The approximate altitude should also be noted.

(5) Reproductive condition. In live males this can usually only be specified by whether the testes are enlarged and descended into the scrotum (or can be manoeuvred gently into it). In the females of rodents and some other groups, the vaginal orifice only becomes open during the breeding season. In immature females there is no trace of an aperture: for a short time during pregnancy and during winter anoestrus the vagina becomes scarred over. Pregnancy is usually fairly obvious during the second half of gestation and Ranson (1941b) developed a technique for determining the number of embryos in voles by palpation. During active lactation the nipples are prominent and milk can be expressed from them; an area round each nipple remains hairless for some time, indicating that lactation has ceased recently. Bleeding from the vagina sometimes occurs at mid-pregnancy and after parturition the vagina remains expanded for a day or so.

(6) Age. In some species a distinctive juvenile pelage is found though the length of time for which this is retained is variable, and weight may be a more sure indicator of youth for a longer period.

The epiphyses of the limb bones may take some months to fuse to the bones and a nick at their margins may be felt with a finger nail (e.g. in rabbits and hares).

(7) Measurements. Length of head and body is a more sensitive indicator of age than weight but it is not easy to take on a live animal, unless it is anaesthetized. If this amount of trouble is taken, the standard measurements indicated by Dr Corbet in the following section can be made with small mammals. Head and body length can be measured by placing the live animal, held by

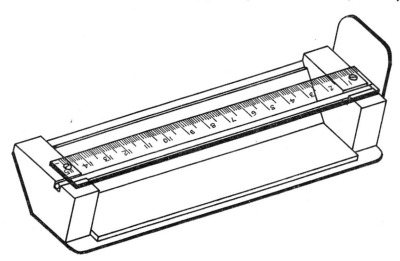

FIG. 9. Ruler for measuring body length (nose to anus) of live small mammals. The transparent plastic rule is mounted above two strips of mirror glass set at angles so that the scale can be read from below. The animal is held by the scruff in one hand and by the tail in the other, the nose is placed against the stop plate at the zero end of the scale and the body is gently, but swiftly, stretched out along the ruler.

the scruff and the base of the tail, upon a transparent ruler with a mirror fixed beneath it, about 1 in. away and tilted so the underside of the animal's body can be seen through the transparent ruler (Fig. 9). It needs some practice to stretch the body gently but firmly and read the distance from nose to anus via the mirror, but one person can become very consistent at this. It is not so satisfactory to compare measurements made by different people. Tail, hind foot and ear can be measured on the live animal more easily than head and body, either directly with a small celluloid ruler or with callipers.

(8) Weight. In the field spring balances are convenient because they are pocket size and reasonably accurate. Geo. Salter & Co Ltd, 31–35 High Holborn, London wc1, sell a variety of these balances, e.g. one type weighing up to 50 g×0.5 g, another weighing to 100 g×1 g and so on, at from 15s. to 30s. A more precise model which is about 2 ft long can be obtained through the British Trust for Ornithology, 2 King Edward Street, Oxford. There are two kinds, one weighing up to 45 g×0.1 g, the other up to 150 g×1 g and both cost 3 guineas each. Delivery takes about 6 weeks, since they are specially made. Small mammals can be conveniently weighed in fabric or polythene bags (deducting the weight of the bag) or, if the spring balance has a platform, this latter can be replaced by a wire cage of the same weight (*Photograph 6*).

(9) Sometimes, though not nearly so often as with birds, colours need objective specification. The colour atlases published by Ridgway (1912) or by Villalobos (1947) are useful for this purpose.

(10) Other items of information are slightly more specialized, though one which naturalists of leisure could very valuably include in their routine is the collection of ectoparasites, mainly fleas and lice. These can be collected from the live animal by blowing into its fur over a white sheet for the fleas and by searching with a paint-brush dipped in 70 per cent alcohol for lice. Some notes about fleas were given by Mr R.S.George in the *Bulletin of the Mammal Society* no. 15 (July, 1961, pp. 27–30) and naturalists were invited to communicate with him c/o The Mammal Society for further information. A general account of parasites is given in Rothschild & Clay (1952).

For other specialized procedures such as the collection of blood samples readers should consult Mosby (1960).

All the foregoing procedures apply to animals which are caught alive and are to be released during the course of field investigations. The preservation of dead material in the form of skins and skulls or as spirit specimens is discussed in the next section.

PRESERVATION AND MEASUREMENT OF MAMMALS
G.CORBET
Two principal methods of preservation are involved, 'dry' and 'wet'. Dry specimens, i.e. 'study skins' and skulls with or without the post-cranial skeletons, are used for taxonomic study, whilst wet preservation is necessary for studies of comparative anatomy, histology, etc. One group, the bats, forms an exception to this. With them, the form of the ears, nose and wing-membrane are important for identification and therefore a taxonomic collection of bats should always include some wet specimens in addition to dry skins and skulls.

DRY PRESERVATION
It is important that the minimum of time should elapse between death and skinning. Therefore specimens that are trapped alive should, if possible, be kept alive until the collector is ready to skin them. Killing is best done in a polythene bag with a few drops of chloroform. This also serves to kill ectoparasites which can then be collected from the pelage. In the absence of chloroform most small mammals can be killed quickly by steady pressure on the thorax. If the specimen is killed in trapping and if there will be a delay of more than, say, six hours in warm weather before it can be skinned, it can be temporarily preserved by injecting 5 per cent formalin into the abdominal cavity from a hypodermic syringe, or by carrying it in a widemouthed vacuum flask containing dry ice (solid carbon dioxide). But these precautions are usually unnecessary if excessive exposure to heat is avoided or if the animal can be skinned within twelve hours of death. When removing a dead animal from the trap it is wise to slip it quickly into a polythene bag to prevent fleas and other ectoparasites from leaving it. These can then be killed by adding a few drops of chloroform to the bag, and subsequently collected, if required, by rubbing the fur over a sheet of paper. The parasites should be collected in tubes of 70 per cent alcohol (one tube per host animal), and great care taken to avoid getting those from different individuals mixed up.

PREPARATION OF A STUDY SKIN
There are two current methods of preparing study skins, resulting in 'round' and 'flat' skins respectively (*Photograph 16*). The round

skin, in which the skin is filled to simulate the shape of the body, is the traditional method and most existing museum collections consist largely of round skins. Instructions for making round skins intended for the national collection may be obtained from the Mammal Section, British Museum (Natural History), Cromwell Road, London SW7, but flat skins are now usually preferred, particularly of British and European species. If a collection is being made for a particular museum the curator should first be asked about the methods of preservation preferred. The following instructions apply to specimens destined for the British Museum.

Flat skins are more easily prepared than round, and have many advantages when series of well-known species are being collected. A vole is an ideal subject on which to learn the technique. The following sequence shows the programme to be followed under ideal conditions. Items in square brackets can be left out without seriously decreasing the value of the specimen.

(1) Apparatus required: note-book; fine sawdust or magnesium carbonate powder; small scissors; scalpel or razor blade; forceps; bamboo splints (garden cane) or fine wire; fuse wire (5 and 10 amp); small tie-on labels; [borax powder; powdered arsenic or arsenical soap].

(2) The animal should be given a number, preferably using a single series irrespective of species, locality, date, etc., and the following measurements and observations should be made and entered in the notebook:

(a) Length of head and body (HB).

(b) Length of tail (T).

To obtain these make sure that the body is supple, then lay it on its back fully extended on a piece of paper, or better still on a soft wooden board. With a pencil, or by sticking in pins, mark the position of the tip of the nose, the tip of the tail (omitting the terminal hairs) and the base of the tail, the last by sliding the pencil or pin along the tail until it meets with resistance in the form of the pelvic girdle. Then measure between these marks or pins, to the nearest millimetre.

(c) Length of hind foot (HF), from the heel to the tip of the longest toe, excluding the claw. In small species this can usually be measured to the nearest 0.5 mm with dividers, or, with Vernier callipers, to 0.1 mm, and is then a very sensitive index of the overall size of the animal.

(d) Length of ear (E) from the notch to the tip, excluding the terminal hairs. (This is of little value in voles and shrews.)

(3) Select a piece of stiff, white card a little longer than the total length (nose to tip of tail) and *c.* 60 mm wide for voles and mice (45 mm for shrews, 100 mm for rats, etc.). Cut as shown in Fig. 10, the length of the shaped part being about 5 to 10 mm more than the length of the head and body, the width about a third of the length. For mice and shrews cut an appropriately pointed 'nose'.

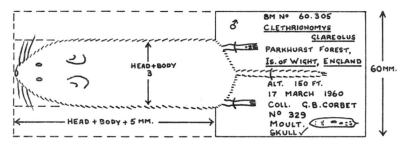

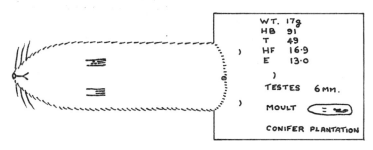

Fig. 10. Diagram of cabinet specimens of small mammals made up as flat skins according to Dr Corbet's specifications. The inscription of data lengthways means that they can be inspected without removal from cabinet drawers.

(4) Have ready fine sawdust or magnesium carbonate powder to absorb blood and to keep the hands clean while skinning.

(5) Start skinning by making an incision (with fine scissors) between the hind legs, from the back of one knee, behind the anus, to the other knee (*Photograph 7*). This is the only cut to be made in the skin.

(6) Loosen the skin around the incision, cutting through the rectum and urinogenital tract. Push one knee through the incision and cut through the muscle and bone (*Photograph 8*). Repeat with the other leg.

(7) Loosen the skin round the base of the tail. Grip the vertebrae with forceps and the skin at the extreme base of the tail with the fingers and pull to extract the vertebrae (*Photographs 9 & 10*).

(8) Peel the skin forwards, turning it inside out. Treat the fore legs as the hind (*Photograph 11*), cutting through the elbows, pull out the ears or cut through close to the skull, cut neatly inside the eyelids (a razor blade is useful here) (*Photograph 12*) and finally sever the skin from the body by cutting inside the lips (*Photograph 13*).

(9) Trim the flesh from the leg-bones and remove any remaining flesh, fat or glandular tissue (e.g. mammary gland) from the skin.

[(10) The inside of the skin may now show a pattern of black or grey markings, the dark areas being those where the pelage is about to moult. If this is the case the pattern should be sketched in the field note-book for dorsal and ventral sides (see Fig. 10).]

[(11) Rub powdered borax, or a mixture of powdered borax and arsenic, or a proprietary preservative soap, over the entire skin (*Photograph 14*). The function of the borax is to arrest decomposition of the skin during drying; of the arsenic to poison any insects or other pests which may eat the skin. The borax is therefore only really necessary (a) in very humid conditions and (b) with very large, thick skins. The use of arsenic is advisable if the specimens have to spend a long time in transit in packing cases etc., but otherwise is not necessary provided very careful precautions are taken to protect the collection of skins from insects and mites.]

(12) Into the tail insert a bamboo splint tapered to simulate the vertebrae, leaving about ½ in. projecting. Alternatively use a fine wire wound with cotton wool to the correct thickness.

(13) If the skin has become at all dry moisten it slightly, then holding the card and inverted skin nose to nose, roll the skin on to the card (*Photograph 15*). The fore legs may prove a slight obstacle but otherwise the skin should roll on without stretching. If it is too tight, cut a thin strip from the card and try again.

(14) Arrange the lips, eyes and ears symmetrically. Arrange the fore legs, one pointing forwards with the palm showing, the other

pointing backwards with the back showing. The forward one should be fastened down with a spot of rubber solution.

(15) Arrange the hind legs projecting backwards on the ventral side of the card, one turned each way. Fasten them to the card with short lengths of fuse-wire.

(16) Arrange the tail symmetrically, making sure that the skin is dorsal side uppermost for the whole length, and attach to the card with fuse-wire in such a way that the wire may be easily detached to examine the underside of the tail.

(17) Brush out the fur with a stiff brush (a nail brush is suitable).

(18) Write the collecting number on the card in pencil and leave it flat for a day or two until the skin of the legs has hardened (*Photograph 16*).

(19) Sever the head. Remove the eyes and immediately attach a label bearing the same number as the skin, threaded through the cheek-bone, or, in shrews, between the lower jaws and out through the mouth. If the skull is not to be cleaned immediately allow it to dry completely. If the animal is rat-sized or larger it will be necessary to remove the brain and some of the jaw muscles before drying.

(20) Examine the reproductive system. Confirm sex. In males, note at least the length of the testes; in females, whether or not there are visible foetuses and if so their number and approximate size. [If there are no foetuses, note whether the uterus is thin and pale or wide and vascular. The reproductive system may be preserved in 70 per cent alcohol, 5 per cent formalin or in Bouin's fixative for further study.]

[(21) Look for internal parasites in the stomach, intestine, liver, etc. These are best preserved in 5 per cent formalin, and their position should be carefully recorded. Detailed instructions for their collection can be found in a British Museum booklet (Anon., 1954).]

(22) As soon as possible copy all the measurements and other information on to the card in Indian ink as in Figs. 10 & 11. Keep the data close to the skin so that any excess card beyond the tail or beyond the labelling can be cut off.

LARGER SPECIES

The technique described above can be successfully employed for

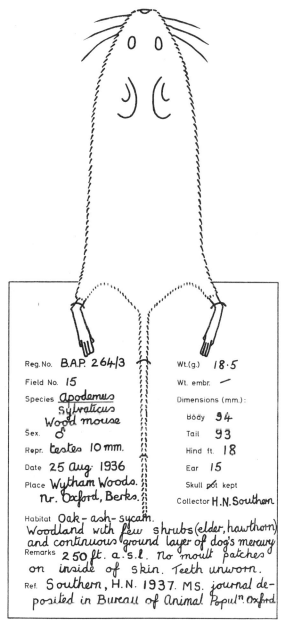

Reg. No. **B.A.P. 264/3** Wt. (g.) **18·5**

Field No. **15** Wt. embr. —

Species *Apodemus* Dimensions (mm.):
      Sylvaticus
      Wood mouse Body **94**
Sex. ♂ Tail **93**

Repr. **testes 10 mm.** Hind ft. **18**

Date **25 aug. 1936** Ear **15**

Place **Wytham Woods.** Skull not kept
  nr. Oxford, Berks. Collector **H.N. Southern**

Habitat **Oak - ash - sycam.**
Woodland with few shrubs (elder, hawthorn)
and continuous ground layer of dog's mercury
Remarks **250 ft. a.s.l. No moult patches**
on inside of skin. Teeth unworn.
Ref. **Southern, H.N. 1937. MS. journal de-**
posited in Bureau of Animal Populⁿ. Oxford

FIG. 11. Flat skin made up by the method used at the Bureau of Animal Population, Oxford. These are best protected by cellophane sleeves and stored in boxes.

species up to the size of rats and squirrels. For larger species, up to the size of a Fox or Badger, the following modifications can be employed: (a) skin by a ventral incision along the abdomen instead of between the hind legs; (b) skin beyond the ankle if the foot is fleshy, and wrap the leg-bones with cotton wool to fill out the skin; (c) the skin of the tail may have to be cut (ventrally) to extract the vertebrae; (d) use heavy cardboard (e.g. from packing boxes) cut to a shape which can be completely contained within the skin. Insert this through the abdominal slit before sewing it up; (e) the forelegs may be stitched to the body skin and the hind legs tied together on either side of the tail; (f) the data should be written on a large label tied to a hind leg.

With yet larger species, e.g. large deer, the skin should be cut from the throat to the tip of the tail and along the whole length of each leg so that it is quite flat when removed. It should be preserved with salt and dried to await 'soft dressing', an operation best left to a professional tanner.

CLEANING THE SKULL AND SKELETON
The method of skull cleaning usually employed in museums, using beetles, *Dermestes maculatus*, is not very convenient for small-scale operation and requires heated accommodation for the colony of beetles. The technique is described by Laurie & Hill (1951). If the skulls are destined for a museum that has these facilities, they can simply be dried, as mentioned above, and handed over for treatment. Advice on small-scale treatment of skulls and other bones is given on p. 128.

THE CARE OF SKINS AND SKULLS
Skins should be thoroughly air-dried before packing for transport or storing in a collection. Sealing in airtight polythene bags should be avoided at all costs, if the material is not absolutely dry. If skins must be packed for transport while still damp, they can be treated with a fungicide, e.g. Mystox LPLX, manufactured by Catomance Ltd, 94 Bridge Road East, Welwyn Garden City, Herts.

Carded skins can be kept in drawers or boxes rather like filing cards. In small collections they may be protected by cellophane paper sleeves sealed with polythene tape, but in large collections the boxes or drawers can be made reasonably airtight and the contents protected by crystals of paradichlorbenzene (the main constituent of most modern 'moth-balls').

After being cleaned and having had loose teeth stuck in with Cow Gum, skulls may be kept in pill-boxes or glass tubes and should have the collection number inscribed in Indian ink on the skull itself and on both mandibles.

WET PRESERVATION

The preservative preferred for permanent storage by most museums is 70 per cent alcohol, i.e. ethyl alcohol or industrial methylated spirit. Commercial blue methylated spirit is not suitable since it forms a precipitate on dilution. To avoid excessive hardening, the specimen should first be placed in 50 per cent spirit and transferred after a day to 70 per cent. But if it is placed directly into 70 per cent and the container is small, it may still have to be transferred to fresh spirit after a day or two since the spirit will have been diluted by the water contained in the animal. A cut should be made in the wall of the abdomen to admit the spirit or, alternatively, it may be injected by means of a hypodermic needle. The use of formalin as a preservative is discussed on p. 130.

MEASUREMENT OF SKULLS

The size and shape of the skull are among the most useful characters by which to classify mammals, mainly because variations in the mouth, eyes, ears, nose, brain, etc., all leave their mark on the skull in a form that can be measured much more precisely than the corresponding external structure. The degree of accuracy normally used for small skulls is 0.1 mm, for which a vernier calliper gauge is necessary.

The nomenclature of these skull-measurements can be very confusing to the inexperienced. This is partly due to the fact that skulls themselves are exceedingly complex structures, but the situation is not helped by the use, without definition, of names that are ambiguous: 'length of palate' and 'occipito-nasal length' are two examples. Thomas (1905) made a start on defining the measurements of length and below are described all the measurements usually employed in basic taxonomic work, and in particular those used by Miller (1912), where cranial measurements

K

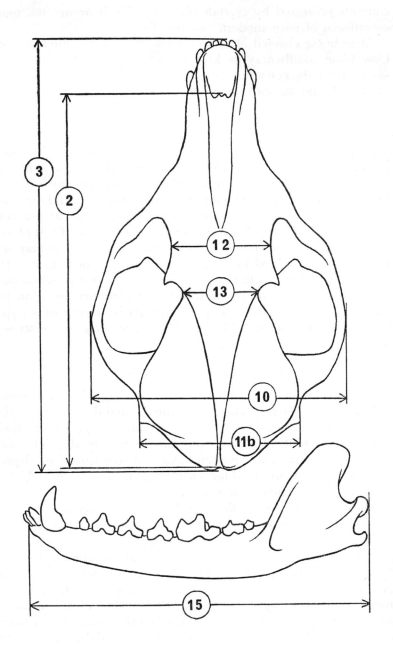

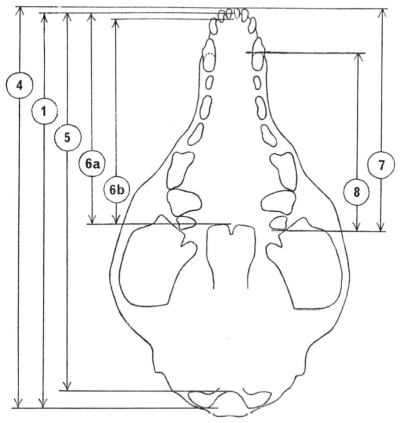

FIG. 12. Diagrams of Fox (*Vulpes vulpes*) skull from above and below and of lower jaw showing precise points at which standard measurements are taken. The numbers correspond with Dr Corbet's description of these measurements on pp. 126-8.

are given of most of the British mammal material in the British Museum (Natural History) in 1912. The measurements are numbered to correspond with Fig. 12.

(i) MEASUREMENTS OF LENGTH

By far the most frequently used skull-measurement is that of total length since it is the largest measure of an animal that can be taken on a rigid part, and is therefore useful as a precise index of the overall size of the animal. The five most commonly used measurements of length are listed below.

(1) Condylo-basal length. *The hindmost surfaces of the occipital condyles to the foremost points of the premaxillae, at, or close to, the mid-line (usually between the first incisors).* These are usually the most truly anterior points of the premaxillae, but in some rodents, e.g. *Apodemus*, the lateral lobes of the premaxillae, above the incisors, project even further forward, but these should not be used.

(2) Occipito-nasal length. *The mid-point of the supra-occipital crest to the foremost point of a nasal bone near the mid-line* (ignoring anterior projections of this bone away from the mid-line, as in the Fox, q.v.). This measurement has frequently been used without precise definition and is potentially ambiguous. In those groups in which the supra-occipital crest forms the hindmost projection of the skull (e.g. in lagomorphs and many carnivores) the above definition is always implied. But in those skulls in which the occipital condyles are posterior to the supra-occipital crest (e.g. in voles) the mid-point of the crest should still be used. This has not always been done and some American workers measure from the condyles. This measurement should not be made on immature animals.

(3) Greatest length. This is usually interpreted as *the greatest measurement that can be taken parallel to the long axis of the skull, including the teeth.* Following this course, if the hindmost points are not near the mid-line, the measurement should be taken from the mid-point of an imaginary line joining them. This is a most useful measurement since its interpretation does not require any knowledge of cranial nomenclature.

(4) Condylo-incisive length. *Hindmost surface of the occipital condyles to the foremost surfaces of the incisors.* This is frequently used for shrews and rodents.

(5) Basal length. *The mid-point of the lower margin of the foramen magnum to the foremost points of the premaxillae near the mid-line.* In early works this term was used for practically any ventral measure of skull-length, but it was precisely defined, with the above meaning, by Thomas (1905).

(ii) MEASUREMENTS OF PROPORTION
The following measurements, when associated with a measure of length, relate to the shape of the skull. Most of them have a precise meaning without further definition, but some have been (or could be) interpreted in more ways than one.

(6) Length of palate. As it stands this is ambiguous since it can be measured in two ways, each of which has a precise name: (a) 'palatal length' is that *from the foremost points of the premaxillae near the mid-line* (*i.e. the same point as used for condylo-basal length*) *to the foremost point on the hind margin of the palate;* (b) 'palatilar length' is that *from the hind margin of the alveoli of the first incisors to the rear of the palate as in* (a). The first is the more usual method, but the second is more easily taken in certain groups, e.g. lagomorphs and rodents.

(7) Length of upper tooth-row. This resembles the last in giving a measure of the anterior part of the skull. It is measured *from the anterior surface of the first incisor to the posterior surface of the last molar*.

(8) Length of maxillary tooth-row. *From the canine if present* (*or the first check-tooth if there is no canine*) *to the last molar inclusive*. This is best measured at the level of the alveoli or to include the cingula, if these are present (the cingulum is a projecting rim round the base of the tooth in most bats and insectivores).

(9) Length of diastema (in rodents and lagomorphs). *From the posterior margin of the alveolus of the last incisor to the anterior margin of the alveolus of the first cheek-tooth*. This measurement is omitted from Fig. 12.

(10) Zygomatic width. *Greatest width across the zygomatic arches* (*cheek-bones*). This is usually, but not always, the greatest width of the skull.

(11) Width of the posterior part of the skull. There are three principal forms of this measurement, the most suitable one varying according to the species concerned (usually being whichever represents the greatest width across this part of the skull). (a) Width of brain-case. *The greatest width across the sides of the brain-case discounting the root of the zygomatic arch and the various projections associated with the ear*. This can only be really accurate and self-explanatory when the lateral wall of the brain-case forms a rounded convexity independent of the auditory bones and of the root of the zygomatic arch, e.g. in shrews and moles. However, it is also commonly used for bats, hares and mice. (b) Mastoid width. *The greatest width between the mastoid projections*. These lie immediately behind the ear openings. This is used particularly for carnivores and bats but also for the Hedgehog and several rodents. (c) Occipital width. *The greatest width across the vertical ridges formed along the sutures of the squamosal and occipital bones*. These ridges start

just above and behind the ear openings. This is used particularly for voles and rats.

(12) Width of interorbital constriction. *The least width of the frontal bones at the interorbital constriction.* This should not be confused with the post-orbital constriction described below.

(13) Width of post-orbital constriction. *The least width of the frontal bones at the post-orbital constriction.* In many species, e.g. of rodents and insectivores, there is no post-orbital constriction (there being no post-orbital process dividing the true orbit from the more posterior temporal fossa).

(14) Depth of brain-case. *Greatest depth of the brain-case in the mid-line, at right angles to the floor, i.e. to the basi-occipital and basi-sphenoid bones.* This should not include the tympanic bullae. This measurement is omitted from Fig. 12.

(15) Length of mandible. *The foremost point of bone to the hindmost point of the articular process.* In certain species, e.g. the shrews, the first incisor is often included, but this fact should always be stated. In Miller's 'Catalogue' the measurements of the mandible are always exclusive of the incisors, even in shrews.

SOME GENERAL NOTES ON PRESERVATION

In the previous section Dr Corbet has dealt with the somewhat specialized techniques needed for producing specimens for a national collection of mammals. Clearly many amateur naturalists will wish for some rather simpler advice, ranging from how to clean a bone or skull rescued from a casually encountered corpse to the quickest method of preserving, in the most generally valuable way, tissues and animals of rarity and interest which may be collected in remote parts. The following notes are based on suggestions made by Dr K. Backhouse.

For cleaning skulls and bones in a small way nothing is better than the old technique of gently stewing until the flesh can be picked and scraped off. It is essential that the material to be cleaned should be put in cold water which is then slowly brought to simmer and thereafter kept simmering. Rapid heating or boiling will simply harden the flesh, as Mrs Beeton will verify. The process of suitably overcooking the flesh so that it comes easily away from the bones will take a variable time but, as a guide, a rat's skull needs 2 to 3 hours' simmering. The cleaning is best done with forceps and scrapers (dental scrapers or scalers can often be picked up cheaply from government surplus stores).

This part of the cleaning is straightforward as far as the removal of muscle goes, but young animals must be treated with great care. In skulls the sutures are not closed (sometimes far from closed) and the delicate and thin separate bones can easily fall apart by over-cooking or be damaged in handling. Similarly with the epiphyses of limb bones.

For cleaning a skeleton, it is a good plan to cook unit parts (e.g. limbs) in separate containers because this makes it easier to reassemble the separate bones correctly afterwards. Also it helps in orientating bones, if some of the ligaments are left in place.

It is far preferable to clean a skull or skeleton by stewing when it is fresh; otherwise the best procedure is to dissect off as much flesh as possible and to store it without any preservative so that the flesh simply rots away from the bones. Small specimens can be put inside a polythene bag and sealed tightly so that they do not dry and the smell cannot escape: larger specimens can be buried in the ground.

If it is undesirable to have rotting material around (e.g. in some expeditions or in some households) the best way is to allow it to dry, as Dr Corbet suggests for the museum procedure involving *Dermestes* beetles. When it comes to cleaning such material, prolonged soaking and boiling will do the trick in the long run but the result will never be so satisfactory as with freshly treated material.

Once skulls and bones have been cleaned, two processes remain—to remove the fat and to bleach the bones. The bleaching is done with hydrogen peroxide and dissolving the fat with a solvent such as alcohol, ether or carbon tetrachloride or with strong ammonia (0.88) diluted with an equal quantity of water. It does not matter which process comes first. One procedure is to place the material in the ammonia for 2 to 3 days and then remove to hydrogen peroxide (10 to 20 vols) to bleach for as long as necessary. Alternatively it can be bleached first and then removed, for dissolving the fat, first to alcohol, then to a mixture of alcohol and ether. In either case the bleaching should be sparing because, although the results of prolonged treatment look clean and satisfying, the excessive formation of bubbles may damage fine specimens, e.g. by allowing teeth to drop out or by loosening sutures and so on.

In a well-cleaned skull it may be difficult to prevent teeth from becoming loose and dropping out. These should be carefully gummed in, after the situation of each has been determined; the best medium for doing this is no longer the favourite glue but a photographic mountant called Cow Gum which holds firmly but never sets so hard that the teeth so treated cannot be removed for examination later. This gum is soluble in petrol or benzene.

Another cardinal point concerns the amateur naturalist and the zoologist who is not a museum systematist. Alcohol at a concentration of 70 per cent is, as Dr Corbet has indicated, the favourite medium for preserving museum specimens 'wet'. Its use is extremely simple. Nevertheless there is much to be said for the use of the other extremely simple liquid preservative—formalin.

Formalin is a solution in water of the gas formaldehyde and can, unlike alcohol, be bought by anybody over the counter of a chemist's shop in a concentrated solution of 40 per cent. It is used as a general preservative, diluted with water to a strength of 5 per cent. On journeys and expeditions, especially, it is economical to carry in the concentrated form and it causes no troubles with customs officials. Another practical point is that material fixed in formalin can be removed from the liquid at any time and sent through the post in a damp condition, if sealed in a polythene bag. The objection of Postal Services to carrying containers full of liquid is a reasonable one.

Perhaps the most important feature of formalin as a routine preservative is its excellence for general purposes. Not only can tissues and organs be stored indefinitely in it but, since it does not shrink tissues as alcohol does, much histological and histochemical work can be carried out on formalin-preserved material. This is particularly important in the study of breeding cycles. Finally there is the not unimportant point that formalin is less volatile than alcohol and so there is less danger of specimens accidentally being allowed to dry out. On the other hand, if specimens need close examination for some hours, the vapour arising from formalin is most irritating to eyes and nose, as any student will know from his first 'pickled' dogfish.

Lastly, there is this to be said against formalin as a long-term preservative, that the contained formaldehyde becomes gradually oxidized to formic acid, which will damage, especially, bones. Baker (1950) discusses this matter and suggests that, for all practical purposes, this danger can be avoided by keeping some powdered chalk at the bottom of each bottle of formalin.

There are many specialized purposes for which animals and their tissues have to be preserved, but there would be little point in detailing these. If material is being collected for specialist investigation, it is obviously necessary to seek the advice of the appropriate specialist. The broadest of these specializations is histology, and it is probably worth mentioning, as well as the book by Baker cited above, an inexpensive paper-back volume by Pantin (1946). Both these contain references to larger and more comprehensive handbooks.

MARKING APPARATUS AND TECHNIQUES

I attempt here a general account (perhaps rather prematurely) of methods for marking mammals. Readers should understand clearly that, for this purpose, mammals come in a very different category from birds. The use of a soft aluminium ring on the hard leg of a bird which does not grow is simple and should involve no discomfort to the bird: therefore, it is reasonable to allow people to ring birds with only a small amount of training.

Marking mammals satisfactorily is exceedingly difficult, not only because of their structure, but because their high degree of organization in the scale of living things makes them peculiarly susceptible to pain, both physical and psychological. Animal welfare societies are rightly watchful on behalf of wild animals as well as those in laboratories and pets. The naturalist who wants to mark mammals has, therefore, a clear duty to ask himself not only whether the marking is really necessary and can be carried out without violating his own conscience, but also whether it may contravene the law. Thus the notching of a mouse's ear for the purpose of identification may not come under the Vivisection Act but if it is done to make certain whether or not injury is sustained (i.e. can the method reasonably be used), it may well do so.

I cannot insist too strongly, therefore, that anybody with small experience proposing to mark mammals should first convince himself that real and substantial knowledge from a long-term, carefully planned investigation will result and, in the second place, should ask the Mammal Society's advice as to the legality, humanity and profitability of what he proposes to do. Haphazard marking on a vast scale with competitive numerical targets may be all right for birds but will not do for mammals. It is possible that this kind of marking is already developing to undesirable proportions in the case of bats and clearly unspecialized and unco-ordinated effort in this field is to be discouraged.

Readers are asked, therefore, to use the information imparted in this section against the background of the preceding paragraphs.

Marking methods for mammals vary considerably according to purpose and the degree of durability needed. There is a useful review in Mosby (1960), though this reference is difficult to obtain in England. Clipping of the fur may be quite sufficient if all that is wanted is to distinguish marked from unmarked animals for a week or so. If animals are retrapped and handled frequently a small numbered tag or ring will do, whereas if they are to be identified with field glasses from a distance a conspicuously numbered celluloid disc will be needed.

It is a safe rule never to use a more complicated method than the purpose needs. If it is not necessary to identify individual animals, then some group mark may be employed, such as differently coloured celluloid discs for different years or for different areas of marking. If the species to be marked does not gnaw the rings, e.g. Hedgehog, then softer rings, like bird rings, can be used (Herter, 1938), or soft silver rings, e.g. for shrews (Linn & Shillito, 1960). If a relatively small population is to be marked and studied (say 1,000 or less) then a combination of toe-clipping and ear notching will avoid the difficulties of using hard metal leg rings.

There are a number of serious objections to the use of rings. They have to be made of hard metal such as monel (an alloy made of two-thirds nickel and one third copper with traces of manganese and iron), or the sharp teeth of rodents will quickly gnaw them off. This means that the rings have to be clamped round the legs of mice and voles with special pliers (*Photograph 17*) and are extremely difficult to remove, if they are causing trouble. Chitty (1937) was the first to use this method successfully in England. It is essential that rings are made with jigs to ensure uniformity and correct shape. They are not generally on sale, though the firm of Lambournes (Birmingham) Ltd, 170–174 Great Hampton Row,

Birmingham 19, cater for some types of monel rings. Home-made rings of this kind can be produced and the best specifications for most British species of small mammals are discussed by Linn & Shillito (1960). But two things have to be considered: the rings must be fitted very carefully to achieve just the right amount of tightness (*Photograph 18*) and even when this is done, the animal is likely to go on growing. The trouble that is encountered only too frequently is that the ring becomes too tight (either because it was applied so or because it was applied too loosely and has slipped down and wedged on the joint) and occludes the blood supply of the leg. The result is a hideously swollen leg, which will finally (if the animal does not happen to be caught and the ring removed) mortify and drop off.

With great care and experience the casualty rate can be kept down to a few per cent, but, wherever even this amount of pain can be avoided, it is better to do so. Toe-clipping of small animals is relatively painless if a local anaesthetic or freezing agent, like ethyl chloride (put out by British Drug Houses under the name Chloroethane in 50 ml ampoules at 5s. 6d. each) is applied from a dropping bottle, and care is taken to remove only the distal phalanx of a digit (just clipping the nail is useless because it will soon grow again) and to do this swiftly and surely with a very sharp pair of dissecting scissors.

Ear notching of mice (it is not so successful for voles) is best done with a chicken toe punch which can be bought very cheaply at any poultry food dealers. It is wise to try a number on tissue paper and take the one which punches most cleanly and efficiently. Mice appear to take no notice of this but it is probably best to use a freezing agent here as well.

With Wood Mice five positions round the rim of each ear and 18 toes give a very large number of distinctive combinations and permutations. It is, of course, more laborious to read marks of this kind than to read the numbers on a ring, but the use of a simple code speeds things up. Thus RH3 can represent a clip on the third digit (counting from inside outwards) of the right hind limb.

Sometimes quite a simple mark is adequate if it needs to last a short time (1–3 weeks). With voles, cutting the brush on the end of the tail to make it square-ended distinguishes those which have been handled before. Clipping the fur in a more visible place will identify a marked animal coming to a trap or bait point to be photographed or watched and variations in the clipping will distinguish a small number of individuals.

Sufficient has been said above about numbered leg rings to make repetition unnecessary. All that need be added is the fact that a small cell soldered to a ring can be used to carry a chip of radioactive wire for tracing movements with a Geiger counter. Details are given in Linn & Shillito (1960) and in Godfrey (1954). Another method is to insert a small piece of gold wire beneath the skin (Kaye, 1961). It is hardly necessary to add that this method of tracing movements has its own special hazards and there are very strict regulations about obtaining radio-active materials.

The study, by marking, of bats has become popular in England during the last 20 years or so and some important facts have been discovered by the use of a special numbered ring slipped on to the forearm. However, the ringing of bats presents many problems and no wholly satisfactory ring has yet been devised. Experimental rings are being tested and anybody interested should get in touch with the Mammal Society.

Medium-sized mammals offer more scope for being marked. For one thing their ears are larger and tougher than those of small mammals and can take a tag or a disc pinned through them. One of the first uses of such a disc was by Krassovskii (1935) who marked Arctic foxes with them in Russia. Nowadays a wide variety of discs and tags is available and these, together with the tools for fixing them, can be obtained, e.g. from the National Band and Tag Co, Newport, Kentucky, U.S.A. Small tags such as are used for marking fish, are quite good for any medium-sized ear from rats up to rabbits but it is necessary to retrap the animals to read the numbers on the tags. Tattooing numbers on the inside of ears is a useful safeguard against loss of tags (*Photograph 20*). Tattooing forceps, such as those made by veterinary instrument makers for marking laboratory mice and rats (Lane-Petter, 1951) will do this job (e.g. Arnold & Sons, Veterinary Instruments Ltd, Standard Works, Lawrence Road, Tottenham, London N15). See also Thompson & Armour (1954).

For this reason a disc made of coloured celluloid or plastic with a pattern or number painted upon it and pinned through the ear with a monel or stainless steel pin (*Photograph 19*) (these can be supplied by Lambournes (see above) upon consultation) can yield identifications at a distance through a telescope or field glasses. Nevertheless, since these discs may pull out of the ear, a tag or a tattoo mark on the other ear allows an animal which has lost its disc to be identified when retrapped and also measures the rate of loss of different types of disc. The numbered disc was used successfully on rabbits before the war by Southern (1940) and improvements in the method were reported by Tyndale-Biscoe (1953). A cheaper alternative to tags are the chicken wing-tabs which can be pinned inside a rabbit-size ear and which can be obtained from any agricultural supply centre. Phillips (1955) used Startin chicken tabs, obtained from T.E.L.Startin, 106–114 Emily Street, Birmingham 12.

Again, complication should be avoided. If numbers tattooed inside the ear or toes clipped will give satisfactory information, then avoid ear tags and discs. But for these medium-sized mammal species toe-clipping is not so easy a matter as for small ones, and should only be undertaken by experts: for all these methods a freezing agent should be used but especially for toe clipping; the toe has first to be frozen with an ampoule of ethyl chloride and the last phalanx removed with a pair of bone forceps.

For temporary marking fur can be clipped or dyed, as was recommended for smaller species. Paint is not satisfactory, but many of the standard hair or fur dyes (such as Inecto Rapid Deep Black or I.C.I. Durafur Black R) will last up to 6 weeks if applied according to instructions. The former is a hair dye obtainable from most ladies' hairdressers. The other can be obtained via Imperial Chemical Industries Ltd, Dyestuffs Divn, P.O. Box 42, Hexagon House, Blackley, Manchester 9. It is stored in the form of flakes. The solution for use is made by dissolving the flakes in boiling water at the rate of 50 g per litre, allowing the solution to cool and then adding 10 to 20 ml per litre of 100 volumes hydrogen peroxide. This should be applied to the animal at once with a brush and it is advisable to use gloves for performing this operation.

More recently, since extruded plastic material has become available which keeps its bright colour and remains flexible, the use of collars with different colour patterns or numbers has been tried successfully on hares and rabbits, small carnivores and even on deer, but care must be taken that these shall snap easily if they get hitched on a branch. The design and use of such collars has been described by Downing & Marshall (1959). The visibility of such colour patterns can be improved by the use of Scotchlite tape applied to the plastic collars (Ealey & Dunnett, 1956), and the Safety Flag Co of America (P.O. Box 1005, Pantucket, R.I.) also supply exceptionally brilliant materials in the form of 'Day-Glo' nylon.

Finally we must deal briefly with marking methods for large mammals. The ears of deer can be treated in the same way as those of cattle, i.e. they can be punched or notched as a simple identification method, or they can have standard cattle ear-tags fixed to them. Coloured or numbered discs, however, enable identifications to be made from a distance. These can either be made in the workshop by each investigator according to his special needs or the firm of Lambournes (Birmingham) Ltd, already mentioned, can be consulted. The combination of a punched hole in the ear, a nickel-plated eyelet inserted from the back of this hole and through the disc, then pinched firm with pliers has been reduced to a simple and relatively cheap set of equipment by this firm. Also Dalton Supplies Ltd (Nettlebed, Henley-on-Thames, Oxfordshire) make an excellent plastic swivel tag. It is in two parts that punch together through the ear and eleven colours are available. Another method is to insert coloured polyvinyl chloride tape through a slit in the ear and seal it into a ring (Craighead & Stockstad, 1960). Readers are reminded again that a local anaesthetic should always be used.

For seals a number of slightly different marking techniques have been tried. One type of tag used on pups of the Grey Seal is described and illustrated by Hewer (1955) and a full account of marks that have been used on seals generally is given by Hickling (1962).

Some of these markers mentioned above are difficult to see at a distance and the use of plastic collars, especially on deer, whether enlivened with glowing Scotchlite tape or not, extends the range of identification far enough for the animals to be observed without being disturbed.

All these markers have a common disadvantage—they are liable to get pulled out and lost. Some permanent mark, such as a number tattooed on to the inside of the ear, is a great safeguard against the misinterpretation of recapture results.

Radio-active markers for small mammals have been mentioned on p. 134. An ingenious device which is suitable only for fairly large mammals and by expert hands is to attach a small transistor radio transmitter. This can even be inserted under the skin, so that the animal is hardly inconvenienced. Such a transmitter described by LeMunyan *et al.* (1959) measures only 7.5 × 4.0 × 1.4 cm, weighs 122.5 g and can be picked up at a distance of 18–25 yards. This model was used on Woodchucks.

Finally, we should not forget that, with the larger mammals, it is much more feasible to get to know individual animals by studying carefully their appearance and behaviour. This may make it possible to dispense with capturing and marking or it may mean that quite a small-scale marking investigation will confirm the identifications made from appearance. Some of the smaller mammals, also, have individual variations by which they can be recognized, e.g. the pattern of the pale belly in the Weasel (see Linn, 1962).

OBSERVATION

The keen naturalist will evolve his own private repertoire of dodges and wrinkles to enable him to watch his animals. Some general ideas upon the subject have been presented in chapter 2 and here it is necessary to dwell only upon a few practical points of technique.

In the first place hides are often useful as observation posts, not only for hiding the watcher but also for sheltering him in rain and frost. Details of how to construct hides are given in many books on bird photography (e.g. Yeates, 1946; Hosking & Newberry, 1961), while Taylor Page (1957) gives diagrams and details not only of simple and original ground hides but also of tree platforms (*Photograph 22*). The type that is used for watching or shooting deer is built with steps or a ladder leading up to it, which is less fatiguing than the scramble up to the normal bird photographer's hide.

For mammals it is advantageous to have more than one hide, so that a choice is available according to wind direction, but tree platforms help here because they are high enough for the observer's scent to dissipate upwards. Nevertheless, he must still exercise great care in approaching them.

Hides for mammals, especially if they are to be used at dusk or during the night, need not provide quite such an impervious screen as a bird hide. In fact, a simple, elevated platform enables an observer to remain undetected, provided he does not make any sudden movement or noise; from here he has a far better view around him than if he were wrapped about with the canvas of a bird photographer's hide.

It is hardly necessary to offer advice about clothing and camouflage, except, perhaps, to insist on the importance of breaking up or disguising the pale patch of the human face. A wide-mesh net hung over the hat is a great help and hardly interferes with vision, or, failing that, simply a felt hat with the brim turned down all round. On open ground camouflage of the human form may be more efficient than hides. Hurrell (1962) has described how, by disguising himself as a sheep, he was able to move about on the bare moorland on the edge of Dartmoor without alarming Foxes and Badgers.

Having put himself in the way of observing his animals, a naturalist will want to make sure that his field glasses are the best for the purpose. Good advice about this can be found in the British Trust for Ornithology's Field Guide No. 2 (*How to Choose and Use Field Glasses*, by J.R.Hebditch) which can be obtained from their office at 2 King Edward Street, Oxford, for 1s. 8d., including postage. Naturally it is more desirable for watching mammals to have a large object glass and to have all optical surfaces 'coated' or 'bloomed' which will ensure the maximum light transmission in poor or twilight conditions. In fact, it is just in such conditions that coated lenses are most efficient and people who have never tested a modern binocular at dusk will be astonished at how much they will reveal. A glass of any reputable make, either 8 × 30 or 7 × 50 (the first figure denotes the amount of linear magnification, the second the diameter in millimetres of the object glass) will give satisfactory results and, as an adjunct, a light telescope, such as the Ross 20 × 60 'Spottingscope' may be carried. Among more recent improvements may be mentioned field glasses with stainless metal mirrors instead of prisms, making for even more clarity and lightness, made by Hensoldt of Wetzlar.

It is surprising how much detail the human eye can continue to distinguish as dusk falls and the retina becomes gradually dark-adapted. Nevertheless, there comes a time when the observer must pack up and go home unless he has some source of artificial illumination that he can switch on. An infra-red telescope (or, as it has come to be known, a 'Snooperscope') has its own special fascination in that the observer can truly see in the dark. The pros and cons of such an apparatus have been discussed in chapter 2. The latest type, designed for convenience and portability, is not available in this country but can be bought from the United States. For instance, a complete apparatus is advertised by the McNeal Electric and Equipment Co, 4736 Olive Street, St. Louis 8, for somewhere around £25.

But for most nocturnal animals visible red light is quite adequate. The type of lamp to be used must be decided after balancing needs against convenience; a powerful beam from a car spotlight will need a large battery and facilities for recharging it; a moderately powerful beam from a smaller lamp can be run from dry batteries, though these are expensive. For short-range observation an ordinary 3-cell or 5-cell torch with a focused beam, such as the Ever Ready No. 5864 P, is perfectly satisfactory. The bright chromium plate of most torches, however, should be avoided, even at the expense of a coat of dull black paint. Hence those covered in black rubber are a good idea.

Stout celluloid or perspex filters should be fitted carefully to the lamps used so that no white light creeps round the margin. A useful specification for a red light is Ilford No. 205, or near, which is not so deep as the old-fashioned darkroom lamp but is invisible to most nocturnal animals. Infra-red filters can be of the same material, and can also be obtained from photographic firms like Ilford and Kodak. Less expensive colour filter material can also be obtained from the Strand Electric & Engineering Co (see p. 151).

Mammals can often be drawn to an observation point by baits, such as those suggested in chapter 2, or by calls and lures. These may be so simple that they need no apparatus at all, like the 'rabbit squeal' which attracts Foxes and Stoats and can be made by sucking air in between pursed lips. They may need only apparatus that lies at hand and skill, like a foot-long section of giant hogweed for reproducing the rutting call of the Red Deer. Others are on the market and Messrs Young's, Misterton, Crewkerne, Somerset, advertise calls for Rabbits, Fox, Hare and Deer at a few shillings each. In Germany calling up deer has its own mystique and various calls are available, which can be obtained through Messrs Roland Ward.

L

Most observers wish to make an accurate and full record of their observations and there are various aids to this end. A tape recorder is one of the most modern tools and there are now plenty of models on the market which will perform well on dry batteries in the field. Mr D.A.Kempson offers the following advice.

'A moderate range of portable battery operated tape recorders is available from about £75 to as low as £5. If quality is important, as for instance in playback of animal calls in which the maximum fidelity may be necessary, then a tape speed of $7\frac{1}{2}$ in. per sec, provided by recorders in the higher price range, would be essential.

'The majority of recorders are to be found in the £25 to £30 class, having a tape speed of $3\frac{3}{4}$ in. per sec, $1\frac{7}{8}$ in. per sec or a choice of both; a few others are as slow as $\frac{15}{16}$ in. per sec.

'For note recording by speech the slow speeds are perfectly adequate, as indeed they are for musical recording, except for the highly critical user. The main defect in cheap recorders to be looked for is "wow" and "flutter", due to instability in running speed causing frequency distortion. In the very cheap class the drive is incorporated in the take-up spool, whereby the running speed of the tape gradually increases as the tape core gets larger. This simplicity of design limits the tape to being played on the same machine, unless it is re-recorded on to a constant speed model. The total recording capacity in time of a recorder is obviously dependent on running speed, but this can be modified by the type of tape used. These are available in three grades, standard, long play and double play, giving time capacity of 1, $1\frac{1}{2}$ and 2 respectively.'

One drawback to the tape recorder is the ease with which, in the excitement of getting the observations on the tape, one can forget to annotate the account with the essential details of time, place, date and so on. Furthermore, an unedited record leaves one with a poor opinion of the coherence of one's own mental processes. Apart from this there are many situations where the noise involved is inadmissable and an ordinary notebook must be used.

For a repeated survey of numbers and/or distribution on a specific area, a blank map is a great help, especially if copies can be produced cheaply and in quantity by a roneo or mimeograph process. For a survey which is to continue over a period of years, printed maps and record sheets are most valuable, if they are well thought out and not used just for their own sake. Maps may be simply copied from the Ordnance Survey series or may be specially produced by surveying on the spot or by interpreting aerial photographs. Some information about this is given in the *Manual of Game Investigational Techniques*, ed. H.S.Mosby (1960). It is useful to have some of the maps printed in grey or blue so that records made in black will stand out against the grey background or may even appear by themselves, since the blue can be filtered out in reproduction.

TECHNIQUES INVOLVED IN DEALING WITH AND IDENTIFYING TRACES OF MAMMALS

Tracks are important for detecting the presence of some mammals, for identifying their makers and for measuring their distribution and activity. The recording of tracks by means of plaster-of-Paris casts has been dealt with in many publications (see, for instance, Chard, 1936; Murie, 1954; Zimmermann, 1959b; Leutscher, 1960). A convenient method used by Mr J.S.R.Chard is to pour melted paraffin wax into the tracks, allow it to solidify and remove wax and surrounding earth. It is easy to take a plaster impression from the wax, which is finally removed by melting. Where tracks have been made on clay, it is possible to remove a coherent lump and to carry out the cast-making at home.

One of the best ways of finding out what small mammals are present in a neighbourhood is to examine the pellets regurgitated by birds of prey, which contain the bones and the fur of the prey eaten. Collections of pellets can also be made at the same time in different places and at different times in the same place, so that revealing comparisons can be made.

The intactness of the pellet contents varies with the group of predator concerned. Herons have the strongest digestions of all and can eliminate practically all bones, so that the pellets rarely contain anything but a clumped mass of hair. Diurnal birds of prey are not so bad and a careful study recently made by Dare (unpubl. thesis, 1961) on the Buzzard shows that between 20 and 40 per cent of small prey survive in identifiable form.

But the pellets of owls undoubtedly give the best information and the two species most abundantly encountered are the Tawny Owl and the Barn Owl. If both these species can be studied in any region, they will give a fairly complete picture of the small mammals that live there because one hunts in woodland, the other in open country. The pellets of these species are easy to distinguish. Both measure *c.* 1½ in. in length, but those of the Barn Owl are black in colour and have a firm surface, which makes them appear to have been varnished. Those of the Tawny Owl are usually medium to pale grey and are more friable than those of the Barn Owl, often breaking into many fragments if they are cast from high in a tree. Sometimes Tawny Owls produce brownish, hard pellets, which consist of earth and vegetable fibres. These are hardly worth examining for small mammals because they contain mainly earthworm bristles (chaetae).

It is not, however, easy to collect large quantities of Tawny Owl pellets, though the species is ubiquitous, because its pellet stations are frequently changed and are difficult to find. Some hints on how to overcome these difficulties are given in Southern (1954). Barn Owls are far less numerous but, on the other hand, once a territory is found, it may be possible to find a regular cache of pellets, since the birds may use the same barn or hollow tree for roosting and regurgitating pellets for month after month.

Small quantities of pellets can be teased out dry with medium-sized forceps and the important parts to keep of the prey remains are the skulls and the lower jaws. Limb bones and girdles give supplementary information but are normally not worth keeping. Skulls are frequently intact except for the shearing off of the rear part of the cranium which all owls perform by way of a *coup de grâce*, but they may also be found in pieces. If so, one must learn to recognize the very characteristic, but small, L-shaped fragments formed by the maxilla with the upper cheek teeth and the anterior junction of the zygomatic arch. *Photograph 23* shows the easily recognizable shapes that must be looked for.

Since the grinding surfaces of the teeth are often the key to identification, these need to be exposed and cleaned for examination with a hand lens. The fur matrix of the pellet is difficult to clear away from the teeth and it is best to perform this final cleaning by drawing a wet old tooth brush across the surfaces.

Some people soak the pellets in water before they begin to dissect them. This is messy and unnecessary for small collections.

Where there are many pellets to be sorted quickly, some short cut may be necessary and Southern (1954) describes a method based on a machine designed by Dr W.P.Crowcroft in which the pellets are first soaked in water, by batches, stirred with an electrically powered paddle and decanted into a basin of water, when the bones drop to the bottom and the fur floats to the top.

The jaws extracted in this way need checking and examining with a hand lens (magnification ×8 or ×10) or a dissecting binocular until the investigator is sufficiently familiar with the material to dispense with such aids. A small piece of plasticine helps to stabilize the jaw in any position for scrutiny.

On p. 144 a simplified key is given which depends entirely upon the most salient characters still available in owl pellet material. Only the most commonly encountered prey are included, but the following occasional items may be noted.

The skulls and jaws of Brown Rats and Water Voles, even though owls usually capture only young specimens, are notably larger than anything included in the key. If the lower jaws are reasonably intact, as they generally are, those of the Brown Rat are more than 20 mm long (excluding the incisors) and look like an enlarged version of a Wood Mouse's jaw. The lower jaw of a Water Vole, on the other hand, looks like that of a big Short-tailed Vole and measures about 20 mm.

Anything still larger is almost certainly the remains of a young Rabbit, since squirrels are very rarely found as owl prey. A Rabbit's jaw is nearly always in fragments but the five rather similar cheek teeth with fluted sides are easy to identify (see Fig. 2c).

A totally different kind of skull which turns up occasionally in owl pellets is that of a Weasel. The small pointed canines contrast with the slender open-rooted incisors of rodents and one of the cheek teeth in the upper jaw is expanded to shear against a tooth in the lower jaw.

An occasional bat skull will provide a puzzle the first time it turns up. Bat skulls are never more than mouse size, usually smaller, and they have continuous rows of sharp, pointed teeth, like those of insectivores. However, the jaws are not nearly so elongated as those of shrews and look superficially like those of a very tiny carnivore (see Fig. 2b).

Key to Skulls and Lower Jaws of Small Mammals Found in Owl Pellets

1	Incisors not separated by gap from cheek teeth	2
	Incisors separated by wide gap from cheek teeth	5
2	Lower jaw (including incisors) longer than 20 mm	Mole
	Lower jaw less than 20 mm	3
3	Lower jaw *c.* 14 mm long (including incisor), incisor without notches	Water Shrew
	Lower jaw less than 14 mm	4
4	Lower jaw *c.* 12 mm	Common Shrew
	Lower jaw *c.* 9 mm	Pygmy Shrew
5	Teeth with tubercles on grinding surfaces	6
	Teeth with other than tubercles on grinding surface	8
6	Lower jaw (excluding incisor) less than 10 mm	Harvest Mouse
	Lower jaw more than 10 mm, but not more than 15 mm	7
7	Largest upper cheek tooth with 4 roots	Wood Mouse
	Largest upper cheek tooth with 3 roots	House Mouse
8	Cheek teeth with transverse ridges on surface	Dormouse
	Cheek teeth with triangles on grinding surface	9
9	Cheek teeth with roots	Bank Vole
	Cheek teeth without roots (open pulp cavities)	Short-tailed Vole

Unfortunately there is no certain way of distinguishing the Wood Mouse from the Yellow-necked Mouse by the remains of their skulls. The former tends to be rather smaller, of course, but it would be misleading to pretend that this is any practical help in diagnosis.

A final point concerns rodent jaws which have lost their teeth. Mice are still identifiable by the slender sockets for the roots of the teeth; in voles the tooth row has only one orifice all along the jaw but inside this the separate root sockets distinguish Bank Voles unless they are very young.

The same kind of information can also be obtained from the faeces, or droppings, of the mammal predators, though it is much less precise since the prey remains have usually been reduced to fragments. Lockie (1959) describes the best way of dealing with droppings, which is to wash them carefully in a perforated zinc sieve, examining what is washed through for teeth and what is retained for identifiable fragments of fur and bone. A rough estimate can be made of the different proportions each prey species represents in the sample. When the remains are dried, these proportions can be converted into 'weight of undigested matter' for each item. Lockie showed, by feeding stated amounts of food to Foxes and examining the faeces, that this gave the most accurate representation of what they had eaten.

The pellets of diurnal birds of prey come into much the same category and Dare's recent work, on the same lines as that of Lockie, has shown that the diet can be reconstructed from the meagre remains in the pellets of the Buzzard.

Both with mammalian faeces and with the pellets of hawks, the identification of hair assumes primary importance because of the fragmentary nature of the bones which come through. The microscopic structure of hair and the comparison of this structure between different groups is a subject which has received only sporadic attention until recently. Yet it would obviously be valuable to have some firm system of identifying prey species from the fur that is left in faeces or in hawks' pellets. Anybody interested in attempting this would do well to make a reference collection of different mammal hairs.

The long guard hairs which overlie the underfur in a mammal's pelage have several features that can be diagnostic. The body of the hair has usually a central medulla, consisting of individual cells arranged in a column which may be made conspicuous by pigmentation. This medulla may occupy most of the hair or it may be represented by a slender, sometimes interrupted, core; it may take the form of a simple column or it may be compound with more than one strand running parallel to each other. (*Photograph 24 E & F*). Between the medulla and the 'skin' of the hair is the cortex, a layer which is variable in thickness and may or may not be pigmented. Finally the outermost layer, or cuticle, of the hair has a diagnostic pattern of scales, which are thin and transparent and cannot be studied easily without an impression being taken on gelatin or polyvinyl acetate (*Photograph 24 A & B*). These scales may form a series of conical collars round the hair or they may be arranged in various overlapping patterns like tiles on a roof.

The general works which may be consulted on the structure of hair are those of Stoves (1957) and Wildman (1954). Gross differentiation between orders is not difficult; in all insectivores the guard hairs are kinked once or twice and have a spatulate tip and usually a simple medulla; bats are notable because they have no medulla and the cuticular scales usually stand out from the body of the hair. Carnivores generally have a simple, columnar medulla, contrasting with the compound medulla of most rodents. Finally the even-toed ungulates can be distinguished by the honeycomb pattern of the medulla.

But as soon as any attempt is made to distinguish finer differences between families and genera, the task becomes much more complex because, among other things, the variability between hairs from different parts of the body, or even between the different sections of an individual hair, is often considerable. Lever (1959), however, used this method to identify prey species from hairs in Fox faeces and for New World mammals the much more comprehensive task has been undertaken of providing keys for several regions, e.g. Mayer (1952) for California and Mathiak (1938) for southern Michigan. For the British Isles a key is being prepared by Mr M.G.Day as a result of his studies on Weasel gut contents and droppings.

Other works upon analysis of faeces give methods of sorting, identifying and estimating the importance of the contents. Examples are Stephens (1957) on the Otter, Baumgartner & Martin (1939) on identification of finely ground plant material (and many subsequent articles in the *J. Wildlife Management*), Drummond (1960) on Brown Rats and extensive work by W.N.Charles on the Short-tailed Vole, which is not yet published.

PHOTOGRAPHY

Natural history photography is a whole subject in itself and this section does not pretend to do more than (a) recommend some comprehensive books on the theory and practice of photography, both in general and as applied to natural history, and (b) examine some of the methods which are specially applicable to mammals.

Books on photography are legion and the following list is a very brief selection chosen by Mr D.A.Kempson to cover the broad aspects of the subject at different levels from the simple to the complex. As far as possible titles have been selected which are regularly brought up to date.

GENERAL PRINCIPLES
Manual of Photography, Ilford Ltd, Ilford, Essex. 30s.

SPECIFIC
Bird Photography as a Hobby, E.Hosking and C.Newberry. 1961. London. Stanley Paul. 12s. 6d.

DETAILED
Kodak Data Book of Applied Photography, 5 vols, Kodak Ltd, Kingsway, London. (Suggested for reference.) Consists of up-to-date leaflets on a great variety of specialized techniques and subjects. A few selected examples are—'Photography in the Tropics', No. GN 5; 'The Storage of Photographic Materials and Photographic Records', No. RF 6; 'Methods of Increasing Emulsion Speed', No. GN 7, and 'Infra-Red Photography', No. SC 7.

MISCELLANEOUS
The current number of the *British Journal Photographic Almanac* contains a comprehensive list of text-books, leaflets and photo guides on a wide variety of selected subjects for still and cine work. This list also includes 20 or so handbooks on specific cameras and their ancillary equipment.

If the main purpose of photographing mammals is to obtain accurate portraits, then, with medium to small species, the best method is to use animals in captivity. The interest in photographs taken in the wild lies in the records made of habitat, behaviour, food habits and so on and it is not usually possible to obtain really well-lit, close-up studies, like those that can be taken of captive animals.

Many mammals settle down well in captivity and 'natural' photographs can easily be taken with a little patience and ingenuity. However, it is not desirable to have them too 'natural', so a plain background (as recommended below) is better than one fabricated to look like a piece of countryside. Most small mammals are more active and, therefore, more natural at night, so flashlight (especially high-speed (electronic) flash) is a vital addition to the mammal photographer's technical equipment. The efficiency of using flashlight is greatly increased now that we know most mammals can be watched with a red light, to which their eyes are relatively insensitive (see chapter 2). This enables a photographer to judge exactly the moment he wants to make an exposure and avoids the waste of 'flashing blindly'.

Some special box or cage is essential for all but the most docile subjects. For shrews and voles, which can be handled easily, it is sufficient to arrange a piece of branch clamped to a stand and the whole thing placed inside a box or small packing case to contain the animal when it falls or jumps off the branch. Camera and flash can be set up beforehand and prefocused.

The background should be of even tone, either slightly lighter than the animal or a good deal darker—in fact, a black background will often give the best results. Stretched fabric is best because even the blackest-looking paper will return some surface shine from the intense light of the flash.

The design of a special box or cage for photography, in which the animal is to settle down and live, poses certain problems. It must be reasonably large and it must be possible to fit quickly a clean background and glass screen when photographs are to be taken. A painted background is desirable because fabric is so quickly shredded by rodents and it is unwise to alter the appearance of the cage by switching from a fabric to a painted background just when the animals are most wanted to be at ease. The clean glass front should be made of plate glass and the containing grooves should be wide enough to slide this into position in front of the dirty glass, which is then removed.

The flash should, of course, be situated so that no reflections appear on the glass. It may be necessary to cover over shiny parts of camera and tripod which have a way of appearing unexpectedly in the picture. This can be checked first of all, where the camera has a ground-glass screen, with a powerful electric light, or photoflood, in the position proposed for the flash. A good way to avoid reflection is to tilt the glass front of the box vertically.

It is not necessary, with this simple set-up, for camera shutter and flash to be synchronized unless the shutter is noisy and the animal nervous. With any reasonably silent leaf shutter (a Luc shutter, especially) and a dim white or red light, by which to watch the animals, the shutter can be opened and the flash fired independently. A simple cardboard flap covered with velvet and pulled aside by a thread is often quite satisfactory. With restless creatures like small mammals a high proportion of misfires is to be expected but, with a little practice, it is remarkable how swift the photographer's reactions become. With electronic flash giving an exposure of $1/1000$ sec. or less, according to the discharge tube used, there is no question of the animal's movement blurring the definition.

A special cage for simplifying the photography of mammals in captivity has been designed by Dr Ernest P. Walker of 3016 Tilden Street, N.W., Washington 8, D.C., who will be pleased to send diagrams to anybody interested. It is a cage into which animals are introduced for the sole purpose of being photographed, so it is possible that their attitudes may be rather less natural than in a 'living' cage.

There is another branch of mammal photography which is best carried out indoors with captive subjects and that is the photography of bats in flight. The camera is prefocused on to a spot where two pencil beams of light (red or infra-red) cross and, when the bat, weaving around, interrupts both beams at this spot, the shutter and flash are released. Usually by studying the movements of a bat, when it is released in a room, the beams can be arranged to intersect at a point which the bat is likely to pass. This method can be applied to photographing other flying animals and Hosking & Newberry (1961) have used it with great success with birds. They also give details of their apparatus and a circuit for the use of a single beam to release shutter and flash. This can easily be extended for using two intersecting beams.

When we turn to the photography of mammals in the field, it would be possible to write at great length on the subject. Again, we must confine ourselves to certain selected topics.

(1) Trip mechanisms. The method of making the animal take its own photograph by releasing shutter and flash electrically or mechanically has been used for many years, notably, to begin with, on big game. There are many variations to the apparatus which can be used and one of the simplest is to use a beam of red or infra-red rays directed across a runway or path, so that its interruption operates the camera. This is merely a simpler, two-dimension version of the apparatus recommended above for photographing flying bats and Hosking & Newberry's circuit can be used without any modification.

The general drawback to this method is the lack of background knowledge about what is happening. Only too frequently the record does not explain itself and there is no way of remedying this.

Alternative methods are (a) to stalk the animal, as can be done in daylight with deer. At night this method is more difficult but could certainly be tried on Badgers, Foxes and Rabbits, using a red torch. Otherwise (b) a hide can be erected near to a known track or gathering place or to a point where bait has been placed.

Very much the same technical advice applies to working from a hide as to working on captive animals.

(2) Focusing the flash. Electronic flash outfits are designed to illuminate a cone at least equal to that of the angle of view of the normal camera lens and modern outfits also incorporate a simple adjustment to enlarge the cone for use with wide-angle lenses. As far as is known, no provision is made for converging the beam for use with long focus or telephoto lenses, but in some earlier models, in which the reflector is a separate unit and has a polished and not a matt surface, some improvement might be achieved by extending the bulb and reflector separation. A simple adaptation to achieve this and to concentrate the flash into quite a narrow beam is by using a parabolic mirror. It is best to mount flash tube and mirror on a beam of 2×2 in. wood so that the separation brings the flashlight to a focus. This can be tested by substituting an electric light bulb in place of the flash tube. The whole apparatus on its

beam can then be fixed to a tripod with a pan and tilt head and the wooden beam used for sighting the flash on to the spot where the animal is expected to appear. The accuracy of the sighting can be checked by discharging the flash and watching in the ground-glass screen or viewfinder of the camera.

In this way a flash apparatus of relatively low power (100 joules) will give ample illumination at 20–25 ft with an average emulsion speed (33° BS or Scheiner (new rating)) for photographs to be taken at an aperture of f.11 to f.16 in the open where reflecting surfaces are virtually absent, and at a flash speed of about 1/1000 sec.

(3) Cine and floodlights. The use of this method in Britain was pioneered some years ago by Hewer & Neal (1954) who illuminated a Badger set and its surroundings with powerful floodlights, whose intensity could be increased gradually. Thus the Badgers were slowly accustomed to the light. The increase in the speed of film emulsions even since then would make such a task much easier now.

Some tests were made a few years ago by Oliver Hook and H.N.Southern in conjunction with Mr D.A.Kempson to see whether a filtered spotlight would give sufficient illumination to expose cine film. The floodlight used was a German wartime lamp with a parabolic reflector 8 in. diameter and a 200-watt bulb silvered distally. Both orange and red filters ('Cinemoid' flexible material, no. 5A Deep Orange and no. 14 Ruby Red, supplied by Strand Electric and Engineering Co, 29 King Street, London, WC2) were tested. Results showed that with Tri-X film, 16 frames per sec, and a 6 in. lens at a distance of 50 ft, exposure was adequate at an aperture of f.8. At 25 ft with a 3 in. lens an aperture of f.11 could be used. Using the filters required an increase ×3 (orange) and ×10 (red). This leaves plenty of scope for getting satisfactory cine records at night with an illumination that does not disturb the animal. The only limitation is the source of power for the floodlight. If a car with its battery cannot be driven to the observation post, then a heavy battery will have to be carried to it.

AUDITORY RECORDS

Visual recording should have its counterpart in auditory recording. Tape recorders are used widely in the field for bird song but they have not yet been used so extensively for mammals. An exception is the close study of the noises emitted by bats, including the important ultrasonic component which enables them to navigate. This is, of course, a specialized study needing specialized apparatus and anybody interested should consult the fascinating account of his work published by Griffin (1958).

For recording audible noises the naturalist is now well catered for by the lightweight, dry battery-powered, transistor recorders, about which Mr D.A.Kempson gives advice on p. 140. A number of technical points about the use of tape-recorders are discussed by North (1956) in his contribution to *The Ornithologists' Guide*. Although the latest portable recorders had not been perfected when he wrote, his remarks remain generally valid. Another discussion worth consulting, especially about the advantages of using parabolic reflectors to pin-point and magnify a sound, while cutting out distracting noises from other points of the compass, is in Simms (1957).

ACTIVITY RECORDING

The description of an animal's activity pattern—daily, seasonal, year to year—is an essential part of knowledge about its natural history. This pattern tells us about its physiological needs, about its competition with other species, about its reactions to food shortage and many other characteristics which distinguish it as a species.

The perfect way to record the activity of an animal is to sit and watch it (as recommended by Crowcroft, 1959) or to follow it around, as was done very illuminatingly by Gibb for birds (1954, 1956a). Unfortunately, like most counsels of perfection, this is rarely feasible, at any rate with mammals.

Automatic recorders offer the opportunity to collect quantitative data on the intensity and distribution of activity with relatively little trouble after the initial installation of the apparatus. Nevertheless, it is obvious that such gadgets should be used with discretion and should never be allowed to outrun our knowledge of their significance.

Whatever type of activity recorder is used and whether it is applied in the laboratory or in the field, a universal and vital component is the switch or trigger activated by the animal to make the record. A purely mechanical type in which the animal's weight depresses a platform connected in some way with a recording lever is feasible, also a pneumatic type in which its weight displaces air from one rubber bag to another connected to it by a tube. But on the whole, by far the most popular and convenient switch involves an electrical circuit energizing an electro-magnet or solenoid, just as in a battery-operated door bell. In every form and adaptation of this basic design the animal operates by its weight or movement an electrical contact and it is vital that this contact should be efficient. In the field especially, but also in the laboratory, a constant trouble is that the points which make the contact readily become corroded: thus a mercury switch is a great advantage. This consists of a short length of stout glass tube into which two leads are fused side by side with short pieces of wire projecting into the tube. A bead of mercury in the tube rolls across the two wires and makes a contact when the tube is brought to a horizontal position. The tube is evacuated, so that the wires cannot be oxidized when the current passes between them. If the switch is to be used at night a coat of black paint prevents disturbance due to the flash which occurs on contact. Standard switches of this kind can be bought from such firms as I.A.C. Ltd (10 Chase Road, London NW10) for as little as 7s. 9d.

The next point to consider is how the records are to be documented. For some purposes a simple click counter may be sufficient, recording only the number of times an animal passes over a particular spot or visits a bait source. These counters ('Post Office' 4-digit counters, no. 305a 24v.) can be bought complete with solenoid to operate from a battery from H.Franks, 58 New Oxford Street, London WC1 and their cost is approximately 12s. 6d.

The counters measure total activity but give no information about the distribution of that activity in time. The most frequently used method to achieve this is by means of a revolving drum upon which the records are inscribed. The standard meteorological barograph, which can often be picked up second-hand, has such a drum which is driven by clockwork and makes a complete revolution, usually once in seven days. A simple change of gearing will speed up the revolution to about once in every 24 hours. The inscribing of the record is achieved either by an ink pen or pencil tracing a line upon paper which is fastened round the drum or by a needle that pricks a hole in the paper. With ink or pencil the electro-magnet, when energized, draws up the writing arm so that a vertical line is inscribed upon the paper.

Difficulty arises when frequent individual records need to be distinguished. Usually the movement of the drum will not separate recordings made 2–3 minutes apart or less. It then becomes necessary to use paper tape which can be drawn through a machine quite quickly. Fairly complex apparatus can be bought in which a number of parallel recordings can be made on paper tape and the speed of the tape's movement can be adjusted. Such machines are usually too clumsy for use in the field and are generally designed to work on the main electricity supply. A fairly simple moving tape apparatus can be made with an ordinary equipment of tools and a useful discussion of these types of recorder with clear diagrams is given by Gibb (1956b).

The field recording of activity can be carried out at various levels. Often quite a crude method is sufficient, such as placing light twigs across the entrances to burrows and checking at intervals how many have been brushed aside. The preparation of surfaces to take the imprint of feet at strategic points of an animal's home range can give an index to its activity. Furthermore, we must not forget the occasions (rare, indeed, in the south of England) when sufficient snow falls to allow a whole night's activity to be studied from tracks.

Usually a recording machine is a great help and the question of where to place a switch is best left to the ingenuity of the observer. Generally it can be said that any feature of the landscape, whether natural, like the bank of a river, or artificial, like fences and walls, are useful aids to the siting of activity recorders. The switches can be operated preferably by a light wire which is brushed aside or (less satisfactory for obvious reasons) by a platform which is depressed by the weight of the passing animal and is returned by a spring. Tunnels with swinging doors (like the 'smeuses' described on p. 108) can be set in fences and walls and it is easy to fasten a mercury switch to the pivot of such a door.

The record-making drum is best removed some distance away from where the switch is placed. This is usually necessary for the simple purpose of hiding the apparatus in undergrowth away from prying eyes but in addition the operation of the solenoid makes a sharp click which might disturb an animal. For this reason and also for protection against weather, the recording apparatus is best shut into a stout box.

If the drum revolves once every 24 hours, it soon becomes burdensome to visit the apparatus so often for changing the record paper. One method of avoiding this was designed by Mr D.A.Kempson, who hinged the arm with its needle and attached to it a thread which unwound and gradually lowered the arm as the drum revolved. Thus a spiral record is produced which will continue as long as the clockwork mechanism goes (usually 8 days). There is a sketch of this modification in Gibb (1956b).

The more modern type of switch which operates by interrupting a beam of red or infra-red light has already been mentioned. For recording the movements of ground-living animals in the field some care is needed to prevent the beam being accidentally interrupted by wind-blown foliage and herbage.

A logical extension to this kind of automatic activity recording is the use of a cine camera modified to take single still photographs every time the switch is operated. This technique has been exploited in America by Pearson (1959) to measure the activity of several species of small mammals using a runway in grassland. The recording apparatus is set up at one particular place on the runway and, at each passage of an animal interrupting the beam, a high-speed flash photograph is taken not only of the animal concerned but also of a background with a clock, thermometer, ruler and so on. Pearson's apparatus needed about 3 seconds for the high-speed flash to recover after being discharged and it was run on the main electricity supply. Dodge & Snyder (1960), however, give very full details, including circuits, specifications of most of the parts and firms that supply them (though, of course, these are American) of their apparatus which is operated by batteries. This seems almost as good as could be devised and there are many subjects in England waiting to be studied by this method.

The use of radio-active markers and of miniature radio transmitters has obvious applications to the measurement of activity. These methods have already been discussed (see p. 137).

M

WILD MAMMALS IN CAPTIVITY

For studying some aspects of the biology of our small mammals, it is most convenient to keep them in captivity. It cannot be stressed too strongly that this is something easy to embark upon but difficult to keep up at the high standard of care and enthusiasm with which it began. Captive mammals that are proving too great a strain on time and patience should be painlessly destroyed or released rather than given to somebody whose interest is lukewarm.

The surest way to establish a breeding colony of small rodents is to trap a pregnant female in the field and establish her in a cage by herself. Individuals vary enormously in the ease with which they take to captivity and the attempt may have to be made several times. If it is desirable to have a really tame stock, the young should be constantly handled, as soon as this is safe, and any wild or nervous specimens removed.

For those people whose needs are on a simple scale the best small guide is the one entitled *Keeping Wild Mammals in Schools* which was reprinted from the *Schools Supplement of the Transactions of the Suffolk Naturalists' Society*, Volume 11, 1959, and can be obtained from the Mammal Society at the cost of 1s. Much sensible information is contained in this small space on how to keep animals cheaply but efficiently and there is even advice on how to treat bats, which is missing from more elaborate textbooks.

For anybody who is more ambitious one cannot do better than recommend the compendious *UFAW Handbook on the Care and Management of Laboratory Animals*, 2nd ed., edited by A.N.Worden and W.Lane-Petter. This begins with a series of general chapters on cages, equipment, diets, etc., and continues into a long string of sections, each dealing with a different species of laboratory animal. Of course, much space is taken up with dogs and guinea pigs but many species of wild mammals are treated, to which the general information is also applicable.

CHAPTER 7

Systematics

A.J.CAIN AND H.N.SOUTHERN

Mammals are of the greatest interest not only because we ourselves belong to them but also because their fossil record is (considering the unlikelihood of fossilization) remarkably good. The group shows beautifully nearly all the main features of evolution except those connected with any form of asexual reproduction or parasitism. The evolutionary history of the horses (Simpson, 1951), though nothing like as simple as some accounts make it out to be, has long been a classical example, and that of the Proboscidea (elephants, etc.) is also good. The Primates (see, for example, Le Gros Clark, 1955, 1959; Osman Hill, 1953 onwards) do not have as complete a record as one could wish, but nevertheless give an extraordinarily interesting series of indications of our own evolutionary history. *Adaptive radiation*, the production of numerous types specialized for different modes of life from one comparatively less specialized ancestral type, is clearly seen in the mammalian faunas of different continents and ages. The radiation of the Australian marsupials into forms like shrews, anteaters, moles, large rodents, swiftly moving grazers (the big kangaroos), huge ungulates (*Diprotodon*, now extinct), generalized insect-eaters, cats, wolves, etc., is, of course, famous; few have stopped to consider that, correspondingly, there is a striking adaptive radiation in the mammals of the British Isles and the Palæarctic Region, simply because they are more familiar. An even better example than the Australian mammals is given by those of South America (Simpson, 1950) since their fossil history is fairly well known. During the long isolation of South America as an island continent marsupials and placentals paralleled nearly all the orders of mammals known elsewhere, producing even three-toed and one-toed 'horses'. But nearly all succumbed when the great invasion of other mammals from the north took place over the newly emerged Isthmus of Panama, except those which had no corresponding form coming in (the Edentates, mainly) and those which were sufficiently unspecialized to keep going somehow, or even, like the Virginian Opossum, to return the compliment and invade N. America.

So many large mammals became extinct during the Pleistocene, that at the present day we are not in so good a position to see adaptive radiation producing extreme specialization; nevertheless, the comparison of different faunas from this point of view gives a new impetus to zoogeography. A concise account of the zoogeography of mammals is given by Darlington (1957). Much of the fossil history leading up to the distributions at the present day is discussed admirably by Simpson (1953).

Because we know a good deal about the fossil history of mammals, we can be reasonably sure that the accepted groupings (orders, families and so on) within the class are monophyletic, that is, that each 'natural' group, put together on the basic resemblance of all its members, *did* stem from a common ancestor or at any rate was not wildly diverse in origin (polyphyletic), forms only superficially similar being grouped together. We no longer group together the elephant and rhinoceros as pachyderms. And this means that we can appreciate adaptive radiation when it occurs. The hedgehog, shrew and mole are superficially unlike but appear to be specializations of a single type, and are not related to the porcupine, mouse and anteater respectively. Adaptive radiation occurs at all levels, within the South American mammals as a complete fauna, or between the populations of two closely related species within a single wood. If two closely related species coexist within a district, they will be in dangerous competition unless they can do different things—either take, on the average, different food, for example, or take the same sort of food in different habitats, or in different layers of the same habitat. All evolution, even the vast trends over many millions of years that produced the horse, the elephant, or (most bizarre of all) man from comparatively unspecialized types, proceeds by selection acting at particular times for particular reasons on individuals of particular populations. From this point of view, it is of the greatest interest to study exactly what is happening at the present day in different populations of the same species but exposed to different conditions, or in populations of two species competing in the same district. The vicissitudes not only of the native populations, but of introduced species also are important, since these forms are the most likely to show change, immediately in their habits in order to cope with new environments and later in their genetics as selection acts to modify them for their new modes of life.

Yet very little is known about British mammals from this point of view. In America, outstanding work has been done on the deermice of the genus *Peromyscus*, which are abundant all over the continent and resemble our own Wood Mouse, although they are 'voles' (Cricetidae) and not true mice (Muridae). As long ago as 1909, Osgood laid the basis of continent-wide work on this group by a competent systematic survey based on the examination of over 27,000 specimens. These deermice are found in most habitats and have evolved into about 16 species groups, which are totally inter-sterile. On the other hand, within these groups species show a varying amount of crossability, so that inferences can be drawn about duration and directions of species formation.

In the last forty years a comprehensive analysis of the pattern of geographical variation, inter- and intra-specific, has been made, pioneered by Sumner (1932) who carried out many hybridization tests upon laboratory-acclimatized stocks. The genetic control of these variations is not well-explored because, apart from some clear-cut characters, most of the differences are polygenic and show all degrees of variation between extremes. The extensive work carried out by Dice filled in the picture of this variation, tracing the direction and speed of change (geographically speaking) in various characters. It is a complex picture because the species of deermice can vary quite noticeably over only a few miles, probably because their small home-range produces relative isolation between populations which are quite close to each other. Correlation between some of these small-scale variations and the environment (e.g. soil colour) has been established and Dice (1947) showed that predation was probably an important agent of natural selection. The characters studied are mainly size, proportions and coat-colour but genetical investigation has also shown more purely physiological difference, e.g. as evidenced by thyroid size.

The *Peromyscus* work still continues: the latest summary of what is known about the distribution of the species and subspecies and about the patterns of their variation was published by Blair (1950) and the same author (1943) has carried hybridization experiments further by measuring the degree of viability in the products of various crosses.

In the British Isles such work has not progressed far beyond the pioneer stage. The intriguing situation in the Bank Vole with large and distinct island forms on Raasay, Mull, Skomer and Jersey has stimulated tests on hybridization and measurement of F_1 viability (Steven, 1953; Godfrey, 1958), which show parallels with the *Peromyscus* results. The work on mainland populations of Bank Voles has not yet progressed far: Delany & Bishop (1960) have reported on N.W. Scotland and work by Corbet (unpubl. thesis, 1960) indicates some broad gradients of differentiation in mainland populations. Even more work is waiting to be done on the Wood Mouse, which should be more interesting than the Bank Vole, if only for the reason that it is more widely spread in the British Isles. This species has been studied by M.J.Delany but his published results are so far confined to a preliminary report on N.W. Scotland (Delany, 1961).

Naturally the distribution pattern of one or two species in a small area like the British Isles cannot reveal so much about evolution as the *Peromyscus* story over the wide areas of N. America, but the presence of so many fringing islands and the fact that most of our mammal fauna have been derived from Europe by invasion following the retreat of the ice sheet put the British Isles in a situation of great interest.

So it is clear that almost everything waits to be done. We are only beginning to know even the commonest mammals in Britain. What species occur has been determined (for the greatest part), but we are not in a position to discuss their individual and geographical variation except very broadly, still less long-term changes in the characteristics of particular populations. This is mainly because of lack of basic data, although there are now a few good studies such as those mentioned above. Species and subspecies have been named on samples far too small to show what is individual and what is broad geographical variation, island forms have been blithely associated with one or other mainland species on characters only too likely to have arisen independently; and that goal of the systematist, the demonstration of the biological significance of the characters of all his forms, is still far off. We need far more information on the British mammals, so that we know (1) where they are, (2) what they do, and (3) what are their characteristics from place to place and time to time, and this is the kind of information that can often best be obtained by a network of observers all over the country. The Mammal Society is, at the moment, trying out by this method a survey of the Badger's distribution.

Mammals can vary in many different ways. The individual will change as it grows up, matures, and (rarely in the wild) becomes senile. It will change from season to season as it moults, and perhaps as it develops or exaggerates secondary sexual characters for the breeding seasons. In addition, probably all individuals differ somewhat from each other in their genetic make-up (except for identical twins). Most characters are affected by genes at many different loci, so that each character varies almost continuously in value between its extremes, for example, height in Man or body length in the Common Shrew (see p. 74). Occasionally there are single-gene differences that produce rather clear-cut differences in a character, for example blue and brown eye-colour in Man, or the red-brown and sandy brown forms of *Clethrionomys* (Steven, 1953). One of the best-known clear-cut differences is, of course, that of sex, which often carries with it an enormous number of subordinate differences affecting almost every character. When such clear-cut differences occur in any population more frequently than could be accounted for merely by mutation, they constitute a *polymorphism* (Ford, 1945), and this is of particular interest to population geneticists and evolutionists partly because such differences are valuable markers of evolutionary change and differentiation. Again, these may be most usefully surveyed by a network of observers all over the country. The instance of the brown and black phases of the Water Vole has already been noted: there are, similarly, dark phases, whose distribution in time and space are as yet incompletely worked out, in the Grey Squirrel, the Water Shrew and both our species of rat.

As an outstanding example of how interesting these dimorphic distributions can be, the work by Pearson (1938) on the Tasmanian Brush Opossum (*Trichosurus vulpecula*) may be cited. There are two colour phases, grey and black. Only grey animals are present in Australia and on the islands lying to the north of Tasmania. In Tasmania itself there is a gradient from populations with about 25 per cent black animals on the drier high ground and eastern side to 100 per cent on the humid north-west coast. An interesting corollary is the observation of Barber (1954) that the introduced rabbits in Tasmania have sorted themselves into a dimorph-ratio cline in the last 50 years or so with black varieties predominating in the more humid forested areas inland.

Some mapping of dimorphic populations has been done for Europe and a description and discussion of some of these have been published by Timoféeff-Ressovsky (1940).

But the organism is not just an arithmetical sum of characters; it is a coherent self-maintaining and self-regulating whole, and genetic variation in one character may call forth necessary variation in other characters without further genetic change and within the life-history of one individual. The best-known example is allometric growth. The larger an individual is, the more modifications may have to be made, for example, to its skeleton if it is to be efficient. Consequently in large individuals (large either because they are older or because they happen to be genetically larger at a given age) the proportions of many bones are altered, long bones being disproportionally thicker, muscle attachments disproportionally rugose or even drawn out into processes, and so on. A single genetic difference producing large size, therefore, may call out a large number of other differences, the *capacity* for producing which is genetically controlled. It would be tempting, on finding a large individual, or two or three together, with many differences from their nearest relatives in the skeleton, to infer that they had many genetic differences also, and to separate them as a different subspecies or even species; but one must first know the repertoire of variation with size in such forms and whether the sample falls within it or not.

Among the most fantastic examples of allometric growth in mammals are the antlers of deer, culminating in the amazing Irish 'Elk', which was a giant Fallow Deer with horns weighing up to 100 lb and with a span of some ten feet. Many people have felt that so astonishing a creature must have brought itself to extinction by the development of such antlers. Nevertheless, it seems to have been quite a successful animal over much of W. Europe and to have died out, as anything might, because its habitat was changed.

Many allometric skeletal differences are probably adaptive, as are many differences related to sex. But any large single-gene difference probably has repercussions all over the body, some of which may perhaps be only unimportant by-products, but many of which would have important consequences in the wild. Keeler & King (1941) say of the genes controlling various characters of coat colour and hair form in the Norway Rat, that they can be shown to affect also such characters as body weight, dimension of body and skull, size of various glands, weight of the brain, the degree of wildness, the degree of savageness, the amount of voluntary exercise taken, 'and those complex characteristics of behaviour that may be termed "personality" '.

In addition to all this genetic variation with its associated effects there may be, even in mammals with their excellent devices (behavioural and physiological) for self-regulation in the face of variation in the environment, considerable phenotypic variation, simply produced by the direct effects of the environment. Harrison (1959) has shown how complex and extensive this can be under carefully controlled laboratory conditions. A phenotypic change in tail length of a mouse of 2 cm is very large, and although the conditions that produced this change were extreme ones, the results warn us to be careful in comparing far northern forms with far southern ones without breeding them under the same conditions and showing whether their characters are still maintained.

Individuals are members of populations, which can also differ. Small, comparatively isolated populations may differ greatly in average values of continuously varying characters or in the frequency of particular morphs, either because they are responding to selection for different local conditions, or occasionally because of purely random effects. Too many people in the past have found genetic variations which did not seem to them to be correlated with anything obvious in the environment, and so they hastily concluded that because they did not understand them, this must be random. This is to explain on the basis of ignorance, which is seldom very satisfactory. But with careful studies, chance happenings affecting the characters of populations may well come to light.

Large continuously distributed populations of many thousand individuals are highly unlikely to show chance effects—unless they have very recently grown explosively from a few founder individuals—and their characters are most likely to be dominated by natural selection. Introduced forms may be able to increase very rapidly at first, and during this period may show much greater variability than later, when selection becomes more intense. Not much is yet known about selection in British mammals, but climate is well known to affect size, proportions of the extremities, and plumage or pelage colour in warm-blooded vertebrates (Bergman's, Allen's and Gloger's Rules). The amount of response to local conditions will depend on the mobility of the individuals and the intensity of selection at different localities. The absence of a particular competitor or predator over one part of the range of a sedentary species may allow great changes of habit and consequently very different selection pressures in that part of the range. A far wider niche may be occupied, with exposure to different microclimates, acquisition of different feeding habits, different requirements of agility for getting the food, and so on. The absence of a predator may mean the abandoning of a protective colour scheme. Such phenomena are known in birds, and Corbet (1961) has suggested that the increased folding of the teeth of *Clethrionomys glareolus* on Raasay, Skomer and Jersey is related to the absence of *Microtus* there, with a consequent spread of *Clethrionomys* into the *Microtus* niche. Careful studies of island faunas and comparison with near-by mainland ones are likely to give an immense amount of information on the selective significance of all sorts of characters. Equally important are studies of the effects of introducing species. The appearance of an extra form in a district means (except in the rare instance of a truly unoccupied niche) that someone will have to give up something, if the introduced species is to survive. There will be considerable changes of habitat and resulting specialization. The case of the American Grey Squirrel invading the British Isles from injudicious introductions is noted on pp. 29 et seq. We still do not truly understand what has been taking place but there is some indication that nowadays the Red Squirrel holds its own better in coniferous than in broad-leaved woodlands. We do not know what species suffered when the Black Rat invaded the British Isles but when the Brown Rat followed it, there was evidently severe competition between the two species, with the result that now the Black Rat is confined to large ports, like London and Liverpool, and to Lundy off the north coast of Devon. In the ports a division of habitat has taken place, for the Black Rats inhabit the upper storeys of buildings, while the Brown Rat, who is not so good a climber, occupies the ground floor and burrows below ground.

Of the various species of deer which have been introduced into the British Isles, some have spread quickly, some only after a delay and others hardly at all. The progress of these invasions is a subject very well worth studying and suitable for a network of observers such as can be provided by the Mammal Society.

Ideally, the way to show variation in any particular character is by means of an accurate map giving its frequency (in the case of morphs) or mean value and standard error for all the known populations. For no single British mammal do we have the data, but the broad features in variation of some characters in a few species are known. Although the best way of making such a map is to go out and collect for that very purpose, it is often the case that material collected by others is useful. Where nothing is known of a particular character of a given species in seven adjacent counties, finding even a single well-preserved and well-documented specimen in a local museum may come as a pleasant surprise. Everyone should be aware of the desirability of depositing the specimens he comes across or collects in an institution where others can study them as well. Museums are often criticized sharply for not having adequate series of a particular species from many localities. If those who are in a position to collect would do so, we might all be better off.

Perhaps the best-known example of gradients in characters of British mammals is that of increase in overall size from south to north. Maps cannot be used like simple words or phrases in conversation or ordinary text, and it is very convenient to refer to such gradients by Huxley's term *cline*. One can then refer to the south to north cline in body size, without specifying the precision with which it is known or claiming that the gradient is uniform from Thurso to Southampton. Where widespread populations are affected by such a gradient, or by several running in different directions, it is better to refer to the clines than to break off the extremes and give separate scientific names to the resulting arbitrarily distinguished groups of populations. Clines have no formal terminology; it is up to whoever describes one to find the tersest and most expressive name-phrase for it.

Where populations are geographically isolated and differ

noticeably and consistently from their nearest neighbours, then the subspecies terminology can often be used. Every species has a two-word name, the first word being the name of the genus in which it is placed, the second its own name within that genus. For example the weasels, stoats and polecats are in the genus *Mustela*, as distinct from the martens (genus *Martes*), and the Weasel is distinguished as *Mustela nivalis* from the Stoat, *Mustela erminea*. Such names are binominal (International Code, 1961). When a geographically definable population, or group of populations, is consistently different from others in that species, it can be given a third name, a subspecific name, to distinguish it from others in that species. A subspecies therefore has a trinominal name. For example, the British Stoat has been separated from the Continental and Asian populations as *Mustela erminea stabilis*, the Irish one as *M. e. hibernica*, and the Islay stoat as *M. e. ricinae*. The Scandinavian populations from which Linnaeus originally described the species are referred to as the nominate subspecies, and this is always named by repeating the second as the third name, thus: *Mustela erminea erminea*. (There is nothing specially important or biologically typical about the nominate subspecies. Which population happens to be named first may depend on politics, economics or religious wars.) Where the range of a sub-species is a single island or archipelago, the geographical name is as good a way to refer to it as any—thus the Raasay Bank Vole, the Orkney Vole, the Irish Hare. These names have the great advantage of *not* forcing a decision on the taxonomic status of the populations—whether they are really distinct enough to warrant a subspecific separation, or so distinct as to constitute a different species, a matter very difficult to decide for isolated populations (see Cain, 1954). When the geographical range is not easily nameable, the subspecific name may be very convenient for reference. (The best example I know is one subspecies of a bird in the South-west Pacific. It has become adapted to life on small islands and its range wriggles along the coasts of northern Australia and Papua, and in and out among the larger islands which are occupied by other subspecies.)

It must be said that far too many authors, rather excited by the hope of getting their names into print, have named far too many subspecies on far too small samples. Since the formal nomen-clature is the reference system, internationally agreed, by which we know what form an author is talking about, and by which we hope to find all the information in the literature on any given aspect of a form or group, by far the best that the amateur and most professionals can do about nomenclature is to leave it alone, to choose a standard list and work from that, and make no 'improvements' on the names.

The great advances that can be made in the study of British mammals (apart from their use as laboratory animals for physiological and genetical research) will be in the determination of the characters of different forms and populations and their significance in the lives of their possessors. The results will be of the first importance to science generally, and everyone can help to produce them.

CHAPTER 8

Wild Mammals and the Law

VALERIE WORRALL

The law relating to wild mammals, i.e. mammals living in their natural state and neither captive (e.g. a lion in a zoo), nor reclaimed (e.g. deer in an enclosed deer park), may be considered most easily by examining it under four heads: (1) ownership, (2) preservation, (3) control, and (4) protection from cruelty. These concepts sometimes overlap—for instance certain measures against cruelty affect those prescribing control—but such overlapping will be readily apparent.

It should be remembered that the value set upon the animals varies considerably; for example, in relation to deer, questions of ownership have an importance which they do not have in relation to mice, and similarly, certain mammals are pests, while others are not and measures of control operate accordingly.

OWNERSHIP

In English law there is no ownership of wild animals in the sense of an absolute right to them, but certain qualified rights are given to a number of people. The owner or occupier of land may maintain an action for the recovery of the animal or damages against persons stealing the young of wild animals on his land while they are still so immature as to be unable to escape. A person who captures a wild animal is given similar rights although they are extinguished if the animal regains its natural liberty. Under the Larceny Act, 1916, s. 1 (3), living wild animals which are the property of any person in the above limited sense and which have value are capable of being stolen. The owner of land may retain the exclusive right to hunt, kill and take the wild animals on his land or may grant such rights to others. This is subject to the right of the occupier of land to take and kill rabbits under the Ground Game Act, 1880. The owner or

168

occupier of land, or a person to whom he has granted sporting rights, has a right to dead wild animals on the land.

Deer are an exception to the general rules in that it has been held that if they are reclaimed from their wild state and kept on enclosed ground a person may acquire a qualified right of property in them with the result that they will form part of his estate, passing on death to the executors and subject to be taken in distress for rent.

Laws against poaching enforce the rights of owners of land and those to whom they grant sporting rights. There are a number of nineteenth-century Acts prohibiting the poaching of rabbits (the Game Act, 1831, the Night Poaching Acts, 1828 and 1844 and the Poaching Prevention Act, 1862) but these have now lost much of their significance, because of the change in status of the Rabbit and the decline in its numbers. Under the Larceny Act, 1861, there are penalties for the unlawful hunting, snaring, taking, killing or wounding of deer and for the unlawful possession of deer or venison.

PRESERVATION

Private persons may seek to preserve certain species of mammals but the law recognizes little such need. An exception exists in relation to Grey Seals. These seals remain on land with their young for three weeks and because of raids which used to be carried out on their breeding grounds, the Grey Seals Protection Act, 1932, imposes a maximum fine of £5 on anyone who kills, wounds or takes a Grey Seal between 1 Sept and 31 Dec in any year, or such other dates as may be determined by the Minister of Agriculture, Fisheries and Food and the Secretary of State for Scotland.

Although there is no close season for hares, they are given a measure of protection during their breeding seasons by the Hares Preservation Act, 1892, which prohibits the exposure for sale of hares and leverets during the months of March to July, inclusive.

CONTROL

A number of British wild mammals are now classed as pests. In the case of rats and mice their outright extermination is sought, while in the case of others such as the Fox and deer only a measure of control is exercised. The Rabbit is in a peculiar position; it was once preserved, but it is so destructive to agriculture that our attitude towards it has now changed and it is now generally regarded as a pest with stringent provisions for its control.

The serious pests of agriculture and food stores are rats, mice, rabbits, hares, moles, squirrels, short-tailed voles, coypus, mink and foxes. Other mammals, such as badgers, wild cats, otters, stoats, weasels, seals and deer are sometimes destructive, but cannot be classed as outright pests of agriculture or fisheries.

For the most part the responsibility for enforcing the control of mammalian pests rests ultimately with the Minister of Agriculture, Fisheries and Food, who is given wide powers by the Agriculture Act, 1947, and the Pests Act, 1954, and more limited ones under the Prevention of Damage by Pests Act, 1949, and the Destructive Imported Animals Act, 1932. In Scotland the responsible Minister is the Secretary of State; and in Northern Ireland, Eire, the Isle of Man and the Channel Isles, the appropriate agricultural Minister.

Under section 98 of the Agriculture Act, 1947, which applies to rabbits, hares, various rodents, deer, foxes and moles, the Minister may by notice require the person having the right to do so to take such steps as may be necessary for the killing, taking or destruction of the animals specified in the notice. The Minister has power to extend these provisions to other animals, but has not yet done so. Any person failing to comply with such a notice is liable to a fine, and moreover the Minister may make arrangements for the necessary steps to be taken for compliance with the notice.

The Prevention of Damage by Pests Act, 1949, makes local authorities responsible for keeping their area free from rats and mice, and they have power to issue directions and to act in default if the directions are not complied with.

Under the Prevention of Damage by Rabbits Act, 1939 (now repealed), local authorities were also responsible for the control of rabbits, but power to require the destruction of these animals was transferred to the Minister by the Agriculture Act, 1947. Under the Pests Act, 1954, which extends his powers, the Minister may declare any area a 'rabbit clearance area', i.e. an area to be freed as far as practicable of wild rabbits by the occupier of the land. Almost the whole of Great Britain has now been designated under this Act. Failure to comply renders the occupier liable to a fine, and the Minister again may act in default and secure compliance with the requirements.

The Destructive Imported Animals Act, 1932, enables the Minister to make orders prohibiting or controlling the importation and keeping of specified non-indigenous mammals, with an obligation on occupiers to notify the presence of any of such animals on their land. The Minister may destroy any such animals that are at large. The Act has, so far, been applied to musk rats, grey squirrels, non-indigenous rabbits, mink and coypus.

PROTECTION FROM CRUELTY

The principal methods of controlling and destroying these animals are trapping, snaring, shooting, poisoning and gassing. All these methods are subject to criticism on the ground that they involve cruelty and certain measures have been passed to give some protection to the animals.

Trapping is the method most commonly used to kill or take wild animals. As from 31 July, 1958 the only spring traps which may be used are of a type and make approved by the Minister of Agriculture either generally or subject to conditions as to the animals for which or the circumstances in which they may be used (Pests Act, 1954, s. 8). Penalties are imposed for the wrongful use, sale or possession of other spring traps, save those specified by the Minister as being adapted solely for the destruction of rats, mice and other small ground vermin. The Minister may licence the use of other spring traps for experimental purposes so as, for example, to enable a trap to be developed or tested with a view to its being approved.

Spring traps cannot be set for hares and rabbits elsewhere than in a rabbit hole except where permitted either by statutory instrument or licence by the Minister of Agriculture and Fisheries (Pests Act, 1954, s. 9). The Committee on Cruelty to Wild Animals (Cmd. 8266) pointed out the difficulty of enforcing the law against open trapping (then contained in the Prevention of Damage by Rabbits Act, 1939, s. 75, 76), but with the decrease in the number of rabbits this provision has at least for the time being lost much of its importance. Open trapping of other animals remains legal, nor is there any requirement for the inspection of traps set for them as there is in the case of rabbits and hares under the Protec-

N

tion of Animals Act, 1911. Under section 10 of that Act any spring trap set for a rabbit or hare or so placed as to be likely to catch them must be inspected at reasonable intervals and at least once each day between sunrise and sunset, but the provision is again difficult to enforce (s. 82, 83).

In England and Wales there are no laws governing the use of snares. The Committee on Cruelty to Wild Animals recommended that it should be made illegal to set a snare to catch a deer but this has not so far been given effect. In Scotland snares set for rabbits and hares must be inspected at reasonable intervals (Protection of Animals (Scotland) Act, 1912).

As to shooting, although persons wishing to use guns must possess the necessary licences, no proof of their skill is required and no protection afforded to wild animals against bad shooting.

The Protection of Animals Acts, 1911 to 1960, in general apply only to domestic or captive animals and not to wild animals at large, but under section 8 (b) it is an offence to lay poison or any poisonous food for any animal save rats, mice or other small ground vermin. In the Protection of Animals (Scotland) Act, 1912, the exception is wider and allows the use of poison for the purpose of destroying vermin. Where it is pleaded that poison was lawfully laid under either of these Acts the defendant must prove that he took all reasonable precautions to prevent access to it by dogs, cats, fowls and other domestic animals and wild birds. Poisonous gas or substances generating poisonous gas by evaporation or when in contact with moisture may be placed in any hole, burrow or earth for the purpose of killing rabbits, hares and various rodents, foxes and moles (Prevention of Damage by Rabbits Act, 1939; Agriculture Act, 1947, s. 98 (3), (4)).

The Animals (Cruel Poisons) Act, 1962, enables the Home Secretary to prohibit or restrict the use for destroying animals of poisons likely to cause undue suffering in circumstances where other suitable methods of destroying them exist.

Myxomatosis proved very effective in eliminating the rabbit pest in this country and certain people were tempted deliberately to spread it. The Pests Act, 1954, sought to prevent the deliberate spread of this disease by making it an offence for any person knowingly to use or permit the use of a rabbit infected with the disease to spread it among uninfected rabbits. How effective this provision has been it is difficult to assess.

Attempts to render hunting and coursing illegal have proved unavailing so far, and the conduct of these sports is unregulated by law. Wild animals may be kept in captivity and then let loose to be hunted or coursed, provided they are not let loose in an injured or exhausted condition.

CHAPTER 9

How to Read more about Mammals

H.R.HEWER

This short chapter is written for those who would like to know more about some aspect of mammalogy than they can find in the text of this book. The first thing they will do is to refer to the list of literature or bibliography at the end and there they will probably find something that they would like to read. It may be part of a book or an original paper in a scientific journal. The problem then arises of how to get hold of it.

First it must be identified. References are always abbreviated for economy and there is a standard abbreviation for the titles of journals which are internationally recognized (to be found in the *World List of Scientific Periodicals,* further reference to which is made below). The rest of the reference varies slightly in form from journal to journal but the usual abbreviations and conventions are easily interpreted. A simple example will suffice:

NEMO J.F. (1950) Observations on the breeding behaviour of the Common Shrew. *Proc. zool. Soc. Lond.* **329:** 63–117.

The title of the paper follows the author's name and the date of publication. The journal is the *Proceedings of the Zoological Society of London,* volume 329, and the paper is quite substantial because it has 54 pages. Sometimes a figure in brackets follows the volume figure and this indicates the part of the volume. In this case the colon follows the number of the part. Sometimes 'pp.' prefixes the page numbers. Literature cited falls into two classes: the first comprises books or journals which may be obtained through Public Libraries (some of them you may eventually wish to have on your own shelves). This approach should always be made first as some Public Libraries may be able to borrow volumes through the National Central Library scheme from sources which would not otherwise be open to you.

The second class consists largely of references to papers in journals which are normally only available in national libraries or in university departments. These national libraries do not usually loan books other than to accredited borrowers or Fellows of the Society to which the library belongs. Most, however, are well aware of the needs of the *bona fide* amateur and will allow persons to consult these periodicals on the premises. Another source for this type of reference is the larger provincial museums. These vary, of course, in their interests but all will have some mammalian literature available—at least the English part.

The two national societies with considerable libraries containing mammalian literature are the Zoological Society of London, Regent's Park, NW1, and the Linnean Society of London, Burlington House, Piccadilly, W1. Their libraries are open on week-days (except Saturdays) usually from 10 to 5 and *bona fide* readers are given facilities even though they may not be Fellows. The Science Museum, Imperial Institute Road, South Kensington, SW7, also allows readers to consult books and periodicals on their premises. The Library at the British Museum (Natural History) is not a loan library and is primarily for the use of the scientific staff. It is possible, however, to obtain a reader's ticket through the personal recommendation of a member of staff who has to vouch for the *bona fides* of the intending reader. The same is true of the Library of the Bureau of Animal Population at Oxford, which has an extensive collection of literature on mammals and on general ecology. Would-be readers may apply to the Director.

The problem of finding out what journals are kept in what libraries is made simpler by the existence of a valuable publication called the *World List of Scientific Periodicals*, 3rd ed., edited by W.A.Smith and F.L.Kent with the assistance of G.B.Stratton. Most libraries will have a copy of this book and the entry of each journal is annotated with the libraries in the British Isles where it can be consulted and the 'run' of years that each library possesses.

Papers dealing with mammals may, as will be seen in this book, be published in a variety of scientific journals, only some of which are devoted solely to mammalian matters. This is because the subject of the paper may be concerned with, for example, physiological or ecological principles, in which mammals happen to be the animals investigated. Every so often there appear books or reviews which gather together all the important literature on a subject and from these still further references can be found dealing with more detailed information. For British mammals Harrison Matthews's volume of that title in Collins' New Naturalist Series (1952) performs the task admirably and those requiring further literature beyond that quoted in the present volume cannot do better than refer to it. Copies are usually available in most Public Libraries.

Mention must be made here of the important periodical published by the Zoological Society of London entitled *The Zoological Record*, which lists all papers and books about all groups of animals published in each year throughout the world. For each class there is given first a list of all the works concerned arranged by alphabetical order of authors. Next—and this is the most valuable part of Zoo Record (as it is affectionately known)—come indexes at the end of each issue arranged under three headings—subject, geography and species in systematic order. In the section Mammalia, we can swiftly look up in the first index what has been published during the year in question about, e.g. populations or genetics; in the second index what papers have dealt with, e.g. Danish mammals; and in the third one what has appeared about Carnivora in general or about *Vulpes vulpes*, the Fox, in particular.

These three indexes give the author only, but the full reference can then quickly be looked up in the first part of the section, which is arranged under authors' names.

The Zoo Record can be subscribed to, either complete or in sections (those for different classes can be bought separately), but is probably best consulted in the libraries which take it (see World List).

If you are a member of the Mammal Society, you will receive its *Bulletin* (which is for private circulation) and this contains each year a list of books and papers that have been published about British mammals.

There are, of course, other ways of finding mammalian literature. Three journals of some size are devoted to it: (1) *The Journal of Mammalogy* (U.S.A.), (2) *Mammalia* (France), (3) *Zeitschrift für Säugetierkunde* (Germany). Also members of the Mammal Society will find in *Bulletin* no. 9, p. 17, a list of Societies and Journals which deal with mammals outside the British Isles.

Too much emphasis cannot be put on the necessity of becoming conversant with the literature of a subject to be studied before undertaking more than superficial field-work of an observational character. Such field-work is a necessary preliminary to understanding the literature, but any attempt to break new ground cannot be begun until the student is certain that a real gap in knowledge exists. Even when the scientist says that 'practically nothing is known about so and so' there is usually quite a bit of literature available. Study of it may disclose the reason for the lack of knowledge: practical difficulties, for example, which more modern methods or facilities can now overcome. It is then possible to begin planning investigations economically without encountering all the stumbling blocks of earlier workers or wasting time making observations of well-established facts. Of course, sometimes confirmation of observations is necessary but this only comes at a later stage, when one's own experience leads one to suspect previous statements or when one is making comparisons.

Science lives by reason of the publication of all new knowledge so that those who follow may profit. Often publication of small articles is difficult although many journals, particularly of local societies, have provision for 'Notes'. Sometimes the material gathered cannot be conveniently put together in publishable form. Nevertheless, even voluminous field-notes may have their value to later workers and a means of storing these is essential. The British Museum (Natural History) Library contains many such diaries and note books. The Nature Conservancy is also willing to place such documents among their records. The Bureau of Animal Population, University of Oxford, will consider storage of unpublished information about mammals.

When a number of people become interested in a subject there is always a danger of duplication of effort unless some means of interchange of ideas and information exists. In this country, for mammals, the Mammal Society of the British Isles has been founded to provide just this medium. Its *Bulletin*, issued about twice a year, is privately circulated so that members may put into it 'progress reports' on their work which keep others up to date with what is going on. Short notes and records of British mammals are published from time to time in the *Proceedings of the Zoological Society of London*. These are permanent records of completed work.

Often one would like to have in one's possession for constant reference, papers on the subject that is being studied. Authors usually have a small number of copies of their papers for personal distribution (known as 'separates' or 'reprints') and are willing to send one on request from a serious worker. A word of warning, however, is necessary lest you should become a 'separate' collector. We have all suffered from the person who devotes all his energies to collecting other people's work and not to doing anything original himself.

Progress in knowledge can only be achieved by the workers in a field getting to know each other and their work. Belonging to a local Natural History Society or a national society of special character (such as the Mammal Society) is the usual method followed by the keen amateur so that he can meet fellow specialists, amateur and professional alike.

CHAPTER 10

The Mammal Society of the British Isles

T.J.PICKVANCE

Honorary Secretary, 1954 to 1962

Our native and introduced mammals have been much neglected by naturalists in the past. The recent revival of interest in them is due, in part, to the Mammal Society of the British Isles, and the purpose of this chapter is to show just how this has come about.

What we have been witnessing is the renewal of an interest which, early in the century, was strong and developing on sound lines, but which lost its impetus between the wars.

The reason becomes plain if we examine long runs of national and local natural history journals from about 1830 when they were becoming established. For over 30 years the notes on mammals were short, sparse and mainly anecdotal, but in the 1870's a change can be detected. In 1874, Tomes and Alston's much improved revision of Bell's *British Quadrupeds* appeared. This proved a useful standard work for the next 30 years. In 1877, J.E.Harting took over the editorship of *The Zoologist*, the national journal which had previously devoted most of its space to birds. To this period the beginnings of a serious and widespread interest in mammals can be traced. Harting, in his first editorial preface of 1877, wrote: ' ... the Editor who certainly cannot be accused of indifference to its great fascination [i.e. that of ornithology], would yet remind his correspondents that for this journal justly to maintain its title of "The Zoologist", many other groups of animals deserve attention as well as Birds'. During his 20 years as editor Harting set a good example with his own pen, and gradually articles on particular species appeared, county lists of mammals were published, and notes improved much in quality. Interest continued under the editorships of W.L.Distant (1897–1914) and Frank Finn (1914–16).

In 1904, J.G.Millais's three large volumes on *The Mammals of*

Great Britain and Ireland appeared. In 1910, G.E.H.Barrett-Hamilton published the first part of his *History of British Mammals* and, after his death, this was continued by M.A.C.Hinton, but the work was unfinished when the last published part appeared in 1921, leaving carnivores, whales and ungulates untreated. Over 30 years were to elapse before the publication of L.Harrison Matthews's *British Mammals* (1952). Lack of interest during these years was partly due to the disappearance of *The Zoologist*.

Frank Finn, announcing 'the cessation of this journal as a separate publication' in 1916, stated that 'Although the flow of literary contributions has been fully maintained ... the increased support from Subscribers which, as we said at the beginning of the year, was necessary, has not been forthcoming'. *The Zoologist* was incorporated with *British Birds* and disappeared without trace.

So the journal was a financial casualty of the 1914–18 war. The gap left in the literature has never satisfactorily been filled and the Committee of the Mammal Society has often debated how best to meet the need for publishing articles like those in *The Zoologist*.

The rebirth of a general interest in mammals dates from the end of the 1939–45 war. For many, the first stimulus was the publication of *The Badger* by E.G.Neal (1949). Neal's book showed what could be done by patient, careful observation. L.Harrison Matthews's general survey followed in 1952.

Soon after this R.S.R.Fitter and others formed a 'Bat Group' and a 'Deer Group' under the respective secretaryships of M.Blackmore and F.J.Taylor Page.

The suggestion that a society was needed to perform for all British mammals what the British Trust for Ornithology had done for birds was put to me by the late G.B.Hindle in the early summer of 1953. He suggested that it could be launched at a university extra-mural lecture school that I was planning for the following year.

Charles Elton, Director of the Oxford Bureau of Animal Population, and one of his Senior Research Officers, H.N.Southern, promised support.

Since the war, the Zoological Society of London has been the natural meeting place of people interested in mammals and in Sept 1953 a small group met to discuss the proposal for a new society. Those present were: L.Harrison Matthews, Scientific

Director of the London Zoo, T.C.S.Morrison-Scott, now Director of the British Museum (Natural History), H.V.Thompson, of the Pest Control Division of the Ministry of Agriculture, Sir William Taylor, a member of the Forestry Commission, of the Nature Conservancy and of the National Parks Commission, Oliver Hook of the Hampshire Field Club, also H.N.Southern and G.B.Hindle, with myself as Convener in the chair.

It is interesting to recall some of the arguments *against* the formation of such a society. Three years after this meeting I summarized them at the British Association for the Advancement of Science in the following words: 'No one will question the statement that birds hold pride of place in the affections of naturalists today ... In comparison with birds ... mammals are uninteresting creatures: they are not brightly coloured, nor given to overt display. They are perforce, if not by nature, of nocturnal or retiring habits, and therefore observed with difficulty. Besides, there are not many of them, a mere sixty species on the British list, a number that does not justify the existence of a society devoted to them alone. It seems extremely unlikely ... that mammals will gain a place in popular affection even approximating to that held by birds.'

All these arguments required careful thought because they questioned the equivalence of the B.T.O. and the proposed society.

However, the replies to a questionnaire sent, after this meeting, to nearly a hundred naturalists and biologists dispelled any remaining doubt about the wisdom of the project.

The Mammal Society was formed at Easter 1954 at a conference held in the University of Birmingham. The first President was the Earl of Cranbrook and the first Chairman was A.N.Worden, who was succeeded a year later by L.Harrison Matthews.

From the outset the Committee has been widely representative of many interests and a balance between amateurs and professionals has always been preserved.

The declared aim of the Society is 'to promote the study of mammals, especially those found in the British Isles and in the adjacent seas'. The official leaflet continues ' ... the main purpose of the Society is to provide facilities for co-operation between professional and amateur observers'.

The response to this announcement was immediate and

enthusiastic, and, at the end of its first year of existence, the Society had enrolled just over 200 members. Since then, growth has continued at a slower but steady rate and the present membership is between 600 and 700.

We can now see that the rapid initial growth of the Society was due to the fact that from the outset it drew into membership people already belonging to groups with special interests, groups that were large and nation-wide in distribution. Examples are the staffs of the Ministry of Agriculture, Fisheries and Food Infestation Control Division, of the Forestry Commission and Nature Conservancy, farmers and landowners, research workers, veterinarians, museum curators, teachers in universities, colleges and schools, and the staffs of zoos. Also represented in the Mammal Society are lecturers and writers on mammals, photographers, people connected with animal welfare and training, and also groups associated with field sports.

The traditional interest taken in our native mammals arises both from some of them being large, gregarious animals and from others being small and economically harmful. Obviously the large ones may also be economically harmful, so for these reasons alone, mammals will continue to demand our attention. The large size of some also ensures that they are objects of economic exploitation: as sources of food, fur, bristle and pelts.

The place that mammals occupy in the nation's thoughts and activities is, indeed, a remarkable one. They are not only a subject for study and research, but they are bred, trained, caged, petted and stuffed; hunted, shot and dug out; introduced for ornament, treated as vermin, exterminated, preserved, conserved, controlled, cropped; snared, trapped and released; keepered and poached; raced, coursed, and it must be admitted, often cursed.

Half of our first 300 members were amateur naturalists. Most of them are connected with natural history societies, among many of which mammals have barely begun to be studied. Mammal Recorders have been appointed only in recent years, if at all. Yet the possibilities for amateur study of mammals are great; indeed certain questions will remain unanswered until enough amateur observers are available.

It is hardly surprising that the first task of the Committee of the newly formed Mammal Society was to decide upon priorities among the many things that called for action.

First, attention was given to publications. The earliest, and still continuing, production of the Society was a mimeographed *Bulletin*, edited by G.B.Hindle, through which requests for co-operation can be published, information of common interest exchanged and summaries of papers read at meetings communicated to members.

The compilation of a *Handbook of British Mammals* was originally suggested by A.N.Worden, and in 1955 L.Harrison Matthews produced the first skeleton of the present book. In 1957 a *Field Guide to British Deer*, edited by F.J.Taylor Page, was published by the Society and has by now run through two editions.

A need was also felt for published records of short notes on British mammals. Dr Harrison Matthews arranged that occasional batches, collated by the Scientific Secretary of the Mammal Society, should be published in the Notes and Abstracts of the Zoological Society's Proceedings and reprints are distributed to all members. Reprints of articles of general interest on British mammals that have appeared in scientific journals have also been distributed.

Annual week-end conferences have been held, ever since the inaugural meeting at Birmingham, at university towns in the following order: Exeter, Cambridge, Durham, Reading, Bristol, Oxford, Aberdeen, Leicester and Southampton. At each meeting a programme of lectures, field excursions, films and an exhibition has attracted a substantial proportion of the membership. The lectures cover a wide range of levels and younger members especially are encouraged to give short communications. The excursions have been particularly valuable for the beginner and many members have had their first sight of some of the less widespread species in this way, e.g. H.G.Hurrell's Pine Martens at Wrangaton, Horseshoe Bats in Devon caves, Roe Deer and Mountain Hares in Aberdeenshire, wild Red Deer at Balmoral and Muntjac on the Chilterns.

The most important function of these annual conferences has been to provide opportunities for people to meet and discuss common problems. Sometimes information has been exchanged about techniques, localities, books, etc.; sometimes the subject of common interest is one on which conflicting and controversial views are held. To meet one another on friendly, neutral, scientific ground is beneficial to all concerned.

Scientific meetings are also arranged and, to date, these have taken the form of one-day symposia, held each autumn at the London Zoo. Reports are circulated in the *Bulletin*. The following topics have so far been dealt with: myxomatosis, deer, the field study of mammals, mammals in British history and pre-history, whales, and the economic importance of mammals.

The Constitution of the Society provides for the encouragement and co-ordination of field studies throughout the country. The first task of this kind arose immediately after the Society's founding.

In 1953, myxomatosis had begun its spread through the southern parts of Britain and soon reports were coming in that, in certain districts, the Brown Hare had markedly increased in numbers after the Rabbit had vanished.

At this point the Nature Conservancy asked one of its officers, N.W.Moore, to investigate any possible connection, and a request was sent to members to collect relevant facts. This was among the earliest examples of co-ordinated field observations by the Mammal Society. Others, notably some on deer, have taken place since.

In 1956, the Society adopted the national scheme for bat-ringing, or bat-banding, with M.Blackmore continuing to act as Secretary. Up to 1947 individual bat-ringers had tested various ring designs in aluminium and devised their own systems of code letters and numberings. The disadvantages of using private code letters for identification were obvious. Bats were being found in various parts of the country bearing rings whose owners were untraceable. A scheme was devised, therefore, by the Mammal Society, for rings to be stamped 'Lond. Zoo' and supplied to ringers at half the cost of manufacture. The London Zoo has helped by acting as a clearing house for returns of all ringed bats.

Further experimental rings in different sizes and metals have been tested but a completely successful type has not yet been evolved. Hence uninstructed people, especially school pupils, cannot be encouraged to take up bat-ringing. At the present stage, trials of new rings are best left to experienced ringers, but anyone interested in the work is invited to write to the Secretary.

Another way of encouraging field studies has been the giving of advice on technical matters, e.g. by teaching live-trapping methods for small mammals and by buying a stock of traps for lending to members. The 'Longworth' trap for small mammals, which was designed at the Bureau of Animal Population, Oxford, is convenient to use but expensive to buy. The loan scheme has made them available at all levels from schoolboys to professional zoologists.

Individual attempts to design new and simpler traps for small mammals have been encouraged and there is still plenty of room for ingenuity here.

The Society also provides research grants. These normally cover only travel, equipment and, exceptionally, some of the expenses of publication. Under this head, contributions have been made towards completion of a survey of seal colonies in Northern Ireland, and of another around the Cornish coast; also to trapping expeditions visiting South Rona, Skomer Island and Lundy.

From the earliest days, the formation of groups with special interests within the Society has been encouraged.

The Deer Group continued a separate existence for some time and then became incorporated as the Deer Group of the Mammal Society. With F.J.Taylor Page as Secretary it has shown what excellent work such a group can do. Its activities include compiling all available information about deer in the British Isles. The spread of introduced species is kept under observation and new information about all aspects of deer is communicated through News Letters. F.J.Taylor Page has prepared a bibliography on deer in the British Isles from the fourteenth century.

'Meets' are held in parts of the country with special interest to deer enthusiasts where their general biology, control and management can be studied. The influence of the Deer Group has not been limited to stimulating scientific study but has contributed to a more enlightened attitude to deer generally.

The Mammal Society's constitution does not allow it to indulge in propaganda for the protection of mammals. There is no special body dealing with this and for most British species, at present, none is needed. But with deer, especially Red and Fallow, the situation is very different and the need for proper treatment and management is urgent.*

Recently the Society undertook to sponsor a nation-wide survey

* Since this was written the British Deer Society has been formed with F.J.Taylor Page as its Secretary. A Deer Group within the Mammal Society is, therefore, no longer necessary, though of course, the scientific study of deer remains within the province of the Mammal Society.

of Badgers with the aim of co-ordinating local surveys already begun. For this purpose a system of county and local recorders has been set up. Such a survey can contribute to knowledge in various ways. The distribution of the Badger can be worked out in detail and the factors that determine it studied. The instruction sheets include a question about damage done by Badgers and the control measures taken. By gathering information on these points it should be possible to discover how much damage is caused by the Badger and what proportion of the animals are responsible. At present the Badger is persecuted for reasons that many naturalists believe to be unsound. The present survey should reveal the facts of the case.

Local censuses, undertaken in areas where sufficient people are available for simultaneous watching, should tell us more about Badger densities.

In conclusion, something should be said about the Mammal Society's attitude to the protection of British mammals, to animal welfare and to the controversial subject of hunting.

The policy of the Society is clear and has been followed consistently, with the full endorsement of the Annual General Meeting. With regard to legislation for protection, the policy is that members are entirely free as individuals to support or decry proposals for such legislation, but the Society should, normally, confine itself to giving advice on matters of fact when consulted.

In other words, the Mammal Society is a scientific body and desires to be known to the public as such. To allow itself to be drawn into debate about issues which are not scientific questions, but are decided on grounds other than scientific, would be detrimental to the Society's true function and likely to diminish its influence in matters in which it can properly give an opinion based upon the facts. Protection is occasionally necessary; so is animal welfare work, since unnecessary suffering arouses our resentment. But some body is needed which can be trusted by all to produce unbiased facts.

If I may judge from puzzled inquiries that came to me while I was Secretary of the Mammal Society, the Society is thought to have preserved a façade of masterly inactivity in all such debates. On the contrary, animal welfare questions are not infrequently discussed by the Committee. If the inner history of constructive action taken during the last decade to secure better treatment of

Photo: D. A. Kempson

1. The Longworth live trap for small mammals assembled for use (p. 99)

Photo: D. A. Kempson

2. A light aluminium carrier for Longworth traps (p. 100)

Photo: H. N. Southern

3. A Wood Mouse about to enter a Longworth trap, positioned on a runway (p. 100)

Photo: D. A. Kempson

4. The way to hold a small mammal while determining sex and breeding condition (p. 102)

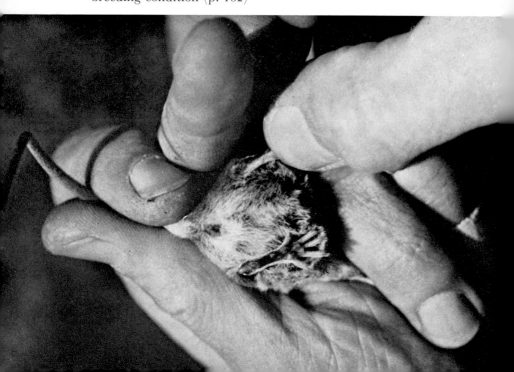

Photo: H. N. Southern

5. A smeuse with box trap fitted into a wire-netting fence round a rabbit warren (p. 108)

Photo: D. A. Kempson

6. Weighing and recording data about a small mammal in the field (p. 115)

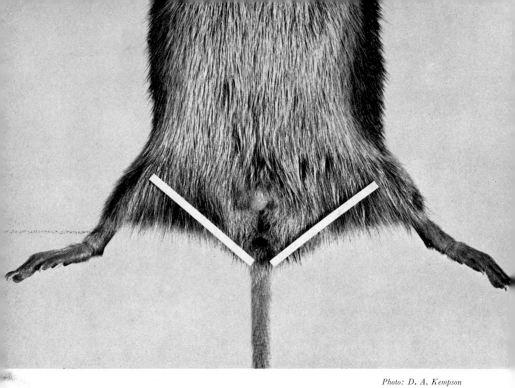

Photo: D. A. Kempson

7. Preparing a flat skin: position of cuts (p. 118)

Photo: D. A. Kempson

8. Preparing a flat skin: withdrawing the left hind leg from the skin (p. 119)

Photo: D. A. Kempson

9. Preparing a flat skin: the right hind leg has been cut and the skin round the base of the tail has been freed (p. 119)

Photo: D. A. Kempson

10. Preparing a flat skin: the tail vertebrae have been withdrawn. Note the sawdust which helps the fingers to grip (p. 119)

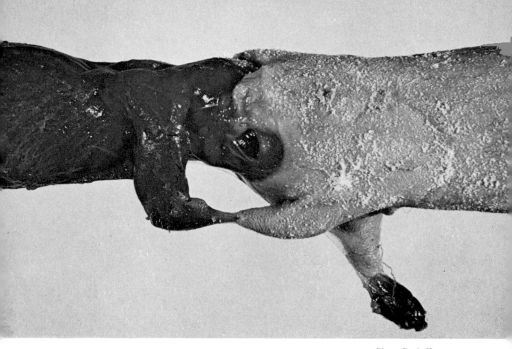

Photo: D. A. Kempson

11. Preparing a flat skin: the skin has been peeled back to expose the fore-limbs and back of the head (p. 119)

Photo: D. A. Kempson

12. Preparing a flat skin: 'cutting neatly inside the eyelids . . .'

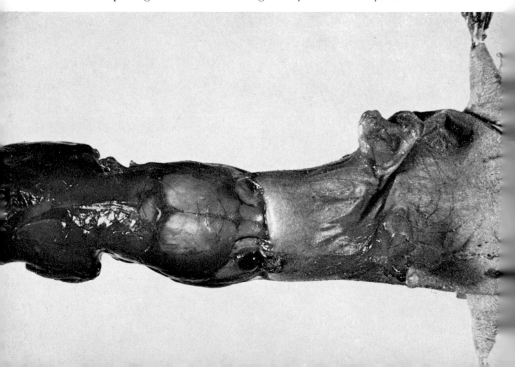

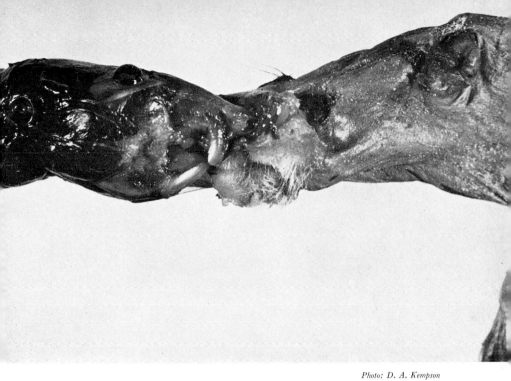

Photo: D. A. Kempson

13. Preparing a flat skin: ' . . . sever the skin from the body by cutting inside the lips '

Photo: D. A. Kempson

14. Preparing a flat skin: rubbing in preservative (p. 119)

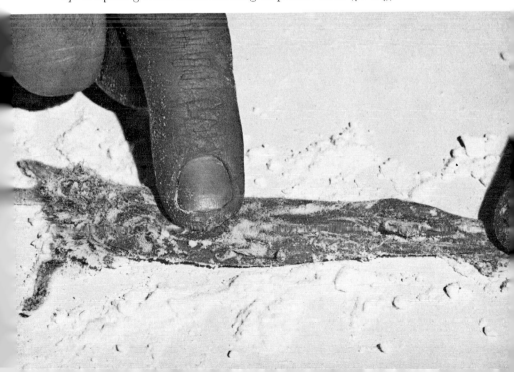

Photo: D. A. Kempson

15. Preparing a flat skin: '... roll the skin on to the card' (p. 119)

Photo: D. A. Kempson

16. Flat skin below and round skin above with data attached (pp. 116 & 120)

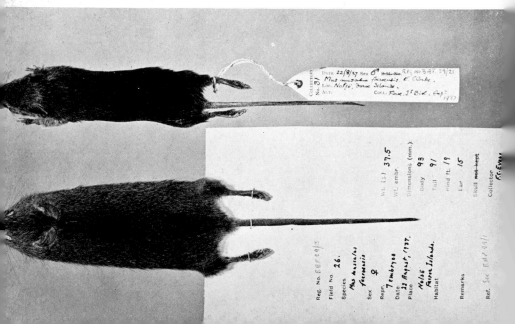

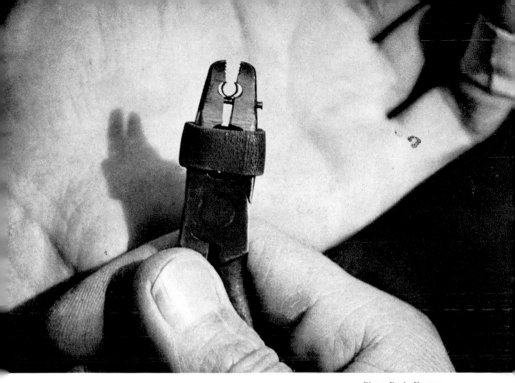

Photo: D. A. Kempson

17. Special pliers with ring in position ready for fitting (p. 132)

Photo: D. A. Kempson

18. A numbered monel ring fitted to the hind leg of a Wood Mouse (p. 133)

19. A numbered disc pinned to a Rabbit's ear. This can be read at a distance (p. 134)

20. A number tattooed inside a Rabbit's ear (p. 134)

Photo: D. A. Kempson

21. Using a Geiger-
Müller counter to
follow the move-
ments of Short-
tailed Voles
(p. 134)

Photo: O. Hook

22. An observation
post for watching
deer (p. 137)

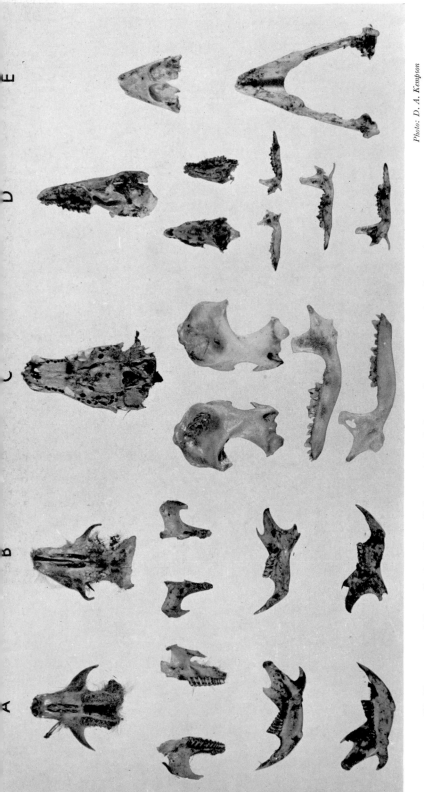

Photo: D. A. Kempson

23. Skulls recovered from Owl pellets. Column A (top) shows the most complete form of a Vole skull, while below are the characteristic bits left after further disintegration. Below these again are the lower mandibles. Column B shows the same details for the Wood Mouse. Column C shows the remains of a Mole's skull (top) and (below) the curiously shaped humeri. Under these again are the lower jaws. Column D shows similarly the skulls and lower jaws of Common and Pygmy Shrews, distinguished by the differences in size and Column E shows what remains of a Chaffinch's skull, the upper mandible above and the lower jaw below. All *c.* twice natural size.

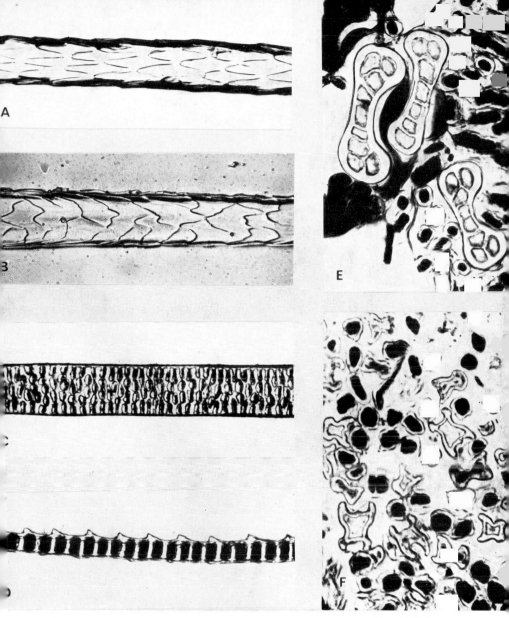

24. Features of mammalian hairs:

A gelatine cast of guard hairs of a Weasel—V-shaped scale pattern:

B gelatine cast of the base of a guard hair of a Vole—irregular scale pattern:

C whole mount of the top section of a guard hair of a Vole—smooth outline (no scales) and several rows of medullary 'cells':

D whole mount of the base of a guard hair of a Shrew—protruding row of scales and single row of medullary 'cells':

E cross section of hairs of a Rabbit—many compartments in the medulla of (large) guard hairs:

F cross section of the hairs of a Shrew—single compartment in medulla of (large) guard hairs (p. 146)

Photo: Jane Burton

25. Hedgehog depositing saliva on its back and sides (p. 198)

Photo: G. Colin Butler

26. As the Mole burrows, the tail is carried erect and brings into play the sensory hairs on its tip (p. 202)

Photo: J. H. D. Hooper

27. Greater Horse-
    shoe Bat in flight,
    showing the
    thumbs, interfem-
    oral membrane
    and the nasal
    membranes
    (p. 224)

Photo: S. C. Bisserôt

28. Serotine in flight.
    The young is
    carried on the
    mother for about
    the first three
    weeks of life
    (p. 242)

Photo: S. C. Bisserôt

29. Serotine eating ghost-swift moth caught in flight. Note the moth's scales on the head of the bat (p. 242)

Photo: G. Kinns

30. Leverets of Brown Hare in form (p. 258)

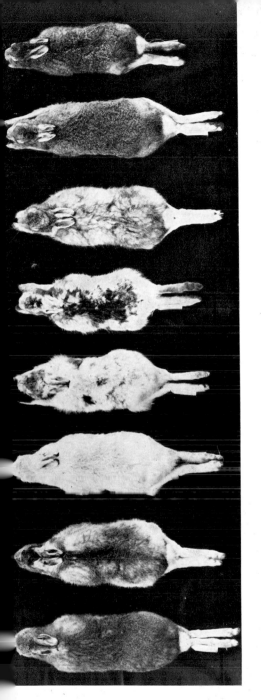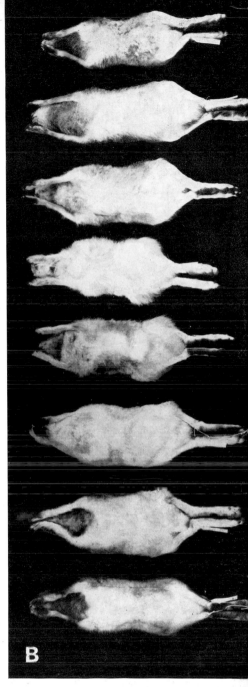

B

Photo: A. Watson

31. Moult changes in Blue (Mountain) Hare.
   A Upper side; *B* under side.
      Bottom to top—autumn, winter, spring, summer.

Photo: G. Kinns

32. Grey Squirrel
with pine cone.
Bracts are re-
moved and the
seeds eaten. Sur-
plus food is
frequently
buried (p. 274)

Photo: G. Kinn

33. Wood Mouse
suckling young.
An unusual view;
when the nest is
disturbed the
female usually
removes the
young elsewhere

Photo: G. Kinns

34. Water Vole
removing young
from a disturbed
nest. This is the
more usual reac-
tion of voles and
mice, cf. *Photo-
graph 33*

35. Black Rat smears
in a London
warehouse. A fine
example of the
crescentic smears
left under success-
ive joists (p. 303)

Photo: G. Kinns

36. Water Vole diving. Note the blunter head of the Vole compared with the Brown Rat in *Photograph 37*. Also cf. *Photograph 44*.

Photo: Jane Burton

37. Brown Rat swimming. Although the general posture is similar to that of the Water Vole, the pointed head and ears are distinctive.

Also cf. *Photograph 44*

38. Young Brown Rat approaching bait. The tentative nature of the approach is well shown by the posture. Taken by infra-red light (p. 305)

99. Coypus huddled together in a bunch characteristically found in winter. Young animals are particularly prone to this habit.

40. Fox pouncing upon what is probably a small mammal. A very characteristic attack (p. 355)

41. Fox cubs playing in mock fight. Play is an important aspect of the behaviour of many carnivores (p. 355 & *Photograph 43*)

Photo: Jane Burton

42. Weasel in charac-
teristic posture,
investigating
surroundings by
scent and sight.
This posture is
also seen in Stoats
and Otters (p. 370)

Photo: E. G. Neal

43. Badger family
at play soon after
emergence at
nightfall. Note
the cub climbing
up the elder
trunk.

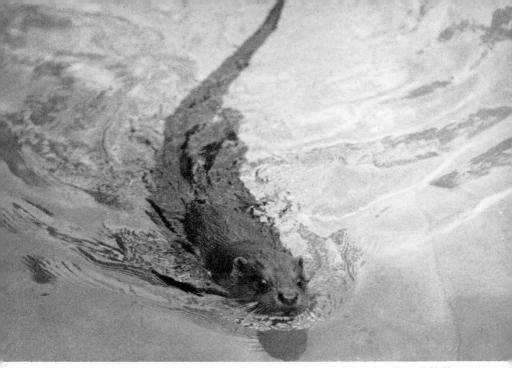

Photo: E. Hosking

44. Otter swimming on the surface. Apart from the larger size, the broad, flat head and heavy tail are distinctive, cf. *Photographs 36 & 37* (p. 382)

Photo: G. Kinns

45. Wild Cat lair in Cairngorm Mountains, Inverness-shire. These lairs always have several entrances and are often situated at the base of a tree.

Photo: Camera Press

46. Typical haul-out of Common Seals on a sand bank. Note the tracks left by those which have already entered the water (p. 391)

Photo: H. R. Hewer

47. Bull Grey Seal coming ashore and challenging: another, on left, is preparing to retreat, while a cow, extreme left, is hooting at interference (p. 397)

Photo: J. Woolston

48. Grey Seal rookery in Orkney, bull in foreground, cows and pups nearer the sea (p. 397)

49. Haul-out of bull
Grey Seals at
moulting period.
Dark seals fully
moulted, others
unmoulted or
partly so (p. 398)

50. A typical Roe
Deer feeding area
in Thetford Chase
with denser
forest in the back-
ground (p. 419)

Photo: G. Kinns

51. Fallow buck in early summer. Antlers almost full-grown but velvet not yet stripping (p. 409)

Photo: Rex Ashby

52. Fallow buck challenging, accompanied by his does, in autumn (p. 409)

53. Young Red
Deer stag in
early velvet in
May. Probably
in the third year
of life (p. 412)

54. Red Deer stag
stripping velvet
in August (p. 412)

Photo: G. Kinns

55. Red Deer stags fighting at approach of rut in early September
(p. 413)

Photo: K. Whitehead

56. Red Deer stag and hinds at time of rut, September to October
(p. 413)

Photo: G. Kinns

57. Red Deer hinds and calves. In winter, spring and summer they remain apart from the stags (p. 413)

Photo: F. J. Taylor Page

58. Typical Red Deer wallow used particularly during rut (p. 413)

Photo: F. J. Taylor Page

59. Roe Deer ring
    formed by the
    buck chasing the
    doe during the
    rut (p. 419)

Photo: O. Hook

60. Roe Deer fraying
    stock to mark
    buck's territory.
    A source of
    damage to
    forests (p. 420)

animals were written, it would be found that individuals close to the counsels of the Mammal Society have often taken a prominent part. But in every instance these persons have been firmly directed to the appropriate organization to take up the case, e.g. the Fauna Preservation Society or the Universities' Federation for Animal Welfare and so on. As for hunting, if questions about it were ever raised within the Society (which they have never been), those for and against would be equally firmly directed to the appropriate societies and as straitly charged not to associate the Mammal Society's name with either attitude.

But there is a way in which the Mammal Society contributes directly towards animal welfare, and I think it is, in the long run, the most important way.

As more and more people learn how to observe mammals in the field, intelligent curiosity is aroused, especially in the large species. Admiration follows upon interest, and a desire to protect these fine animals is produced. Therefore the Society is having, incidentally, a valuable educational effect as well as pursuing its primary object of extending scientific knowledge about British mammals.

PART TWO

A SYSTEMATIC ACCOUNT OF BRITISH MAMMALS

A Systematic Account of British Mammals

The following pages are the complicated production of a number of authors. Their respective responsibilities have been apportioned, as precisely as possible, in the Editor's General Introduction.

Treatment has inevitably varied between the orders, mainly because of differing personal approaches to the task but also because of the differences in characteristics between the orders and in the state of knowledge about them. The Editor has made every effort to unify the style and system of presentation without trespassing too much upon the personal traits of the authors.

References to literature have had to be chosen with some obvious limitations. The policy has been to mention most works that are comprehensive and authoritative and, in addition (though here the treatment varies between orders), to document particularly important, or recently discovered, information. Every effort has been made to cover the literature to the end of 1962.

The separate accounts of the different species of British mammals are prefaced by a note on the Class Mammalia, and the order, family and genus to which each species belongs are considered briefly in terms of their world distribution and importance.

In addition, the systematic account of each order is prefaced by the 'Field Identification Characters', to which readers can turn for quick diagnosis based on field characters.

The following signs and conventions have been used:

* before a species name indicates an introduced species.
† before a species name indicates an extinct species.

'British Isles' is used to cover the whole archipelago, including the Channel Islands.

Measurements are given in the form of the average followed in parentheses by the number and range of the observations, wherever sufficient data have been found to justify this. The metric system has mainly been used and where other measurements may be more familiar, these also are given in parentheses.

Down to genera, Simpson's (1945) classification has mostly been preferred. Any departure from it has been noted. For species and subspecies the Check Lists indicated at the beginning of the Bibliography have been consulted.

Class Mammalia

The world's mammals are by now fairly completely known taxonomically, if we except fossil forms. The class embraces primitive forms like the Monotremes, of which the Platypus is the best known, and highly developed forms like the primates which include man. The latest classification (Simpson, 1945) divides the class into 18 living and 14 fossil orders. Of the former the 3 most abundant are the rodents with 344 living genera, the bats with 118, and the carnivores with 114. There follow, at a lower level of abundance, the insectivores (shrews, moles, hedgehogs, etc.) with 71 genera, the primates (apes, monkeys, lemurs) with 59 genera, the even-toed ungulates (deer, antelopes) with 86 genera, the marsupials with 57 genera and the whales with 35 genera. These include all the best-known mammal groups, showing the widest adaptive radiation and spread over most of the world. Other orders, containing only a few genera, are the edentates (sloths, anteaters), rabbits and hares, elephants, hyraxes, sea-cows and odd-toed ungulates (horses, etc.).

Of the 8 major orders mentioned above the bats have specialized in flight and echo-location, the whales in marine life, the deer and antelopes in vegetarianism and speed, the rodents in being inconspicuous and small and the carnivores in eating, among other things, their fellow mammals. Other groups have either been isolated, like the marsupials, and have evolved adaptations in way of life which parallel those in other groups of mammals or they have remained relatively unspecialized, like the insectivores and primates. The last-named group, by avoiding blind-alley specialization, has culminated in that 'piece of work'—Man.

All these 8 major orders, except the marsupials, are represented in Britain.

Order Insectivora

Mainly small, carnivorous mammals with many primitive features. Most groups traceable back to Eocene, shrews being recognizable as such back to Oligocene. Probably close to earliest primates; tree-shrews (Tupaiidae) formerly classified as insectivores now removed to that order.

Eight recent families, falling into five superfamilies, which are all widely separated and may have little to connect them except their ancient lineages. Families occurring in the British Isles are hedgehogs (Erinaceidae), moles (Talpidae) and shrews (Soricidae), the last two being closely related and connected by the curious Asiatic shrew-moles. Other families are Tenrecidae (tenrecs, which have had their own adaptive radiation in Madagascar into surface-living, burrowing and aquatic forms), Solenodontidae (like large rats with long, bewhiskered noses; W. Indies), Potamogalidae (giant water-shrews, otter-like animals from C. and W. Africa), Chrysochloridae (Cape golden moles from southern half of Africa, highly specialized for burrowing life), Macroscelididae (elephant shrews, rat-size animals with small mobile trunks from relatively dry parts of Africa). Of the families which do not occur in Britain the first three are clearly related, the last two highly distinct groups.

Insectivores are important members of the fauna of most habitats throughout the world, excluding Australasia and Antarctica. Small forms like shrews and moles extraordinarily abundant and widespread. Characteristics vary between the generalized and primitive, e.g. little reduction in digits and dentition unspecialized, often complete (44), and the bizarre and specialized, as in hedgehogs, golden moles and so on.

Field Identification Characters

(1) Hedgehog (*Erinaceus europaeus*). A compact animal rather smaller than rabbit with pointed face, conspicuous ears, tiny tail not often visible, and dense, thick coat of spines. Often first heard snuffling about at night in open country and in gardens and road-sides of built-up areas. Defence is to roll itself into a ball, which accounts for frequency with which it is run over. Nevertheless, can run quite swiftly. In winter, may be found hibernating in leafy nest in hedge bottom.

(2) Mole (*Talpa europaea*). Usually identified from traces of its activities in form of mole-hills: sometimes, course of tunnels near surface can be seen in arable land. Size like small rat, body tubby, immensely heavy digging fore-limbs with strong claws, rounded head with tiny eyes and invisible ears, pointed snout, short tail like bottle-brush carried upright, very characteristic black fur with no set, like velvet. Seen above ground now and again, or can be dug out of surface runs. Main tunnels deeper down and nests below ground with network of runways round them. Latter often contain largest and most spectacular British flea, *Histrichopsylla talpae*.

(3) Shrews. Abundant, tiny and very active animals, often to be heard rustling and twittering in leaf litter of woodlands and in grass and scrub. All our species have velvety fur, like Mole, tiny eyes, long and mobile snout and are about mouse-size or smaller. Teeth are small with needle-like cusps, tipped with red enamel in *Sorex* and *Neomys* and form a continuous row along each jaw, unlike rodents. Ears little noticeable except in *Crocidura*, tail with hairs. Very short life span, adults usually breeding during one season, then dying.

Most usual species are Common Shrew (*Sorex araneus*) (absent however, from Ireland), size of small House Mouse with light-brown to chocolate fur on top, greyish white underneath, tail about half length of head and body (never more than two-thirds), and Pygmy Shrew (*Sorex minutus*) about two-thirds as long in head and body as Common Shrew (it is our smallest non-flying mammal) but with tail about same length (always more than two-thirds as long as head and body and looks relatively heavier than that of Common Shrew). Pygmy Shrew also paler and less variable in colour than Common Shrew. Difference in size between two species always obvious because young shrews are full size before they leave nest. Water Shrew (*Neomys fodiens*) is largest and heaviest of our shrews with very black fur on back, clear white, grey or almost black underside and white spots near eyes and ears. Tail and hind feet have fringes of hairs which help in swimming, but Water Shrew often found far from water. All three are members of sub-family Soricinae.

Other British species of shrews belong to other sub-family, Crocidurinae, white-toothed shrews, and only found in Scillies and Channel Islands. Distinguished from *Sorex* spp. by triangular head with more prominent ears (giving foxy appearance), by spaced-out white hairs on tail which project well beyond general surface of tail fur and by lack of red pigment on teeth. White-toothed Shrew (*Crocidura russula*), common Continental species, found in Guernsey, Herm and Alderney, is greyer than *Sorex* spp. Lesser White-toothed Shrew (*C. suaveolens*), smaller than *C. russula*, occurs in Jersey and Sark and, as distinct race (*C. s. cassiteridum*), in Scillies.

FAMILY ERINACEIDAE

True hedgehogs (sub-family Erinaceinae) distributed over Palaearctic and into Ethiopian Region; also into India, but not further into Oriental Region: five genera. One other sub-family (Echinosoricinae) now confined to Oriental Region, with four genera, 'hairy hedgehogs' rather like large shrews, e.g. *Echinosorex*, the Moonrat of Malaya. The two sub-families have overlapped widely in geological history, and one occurred in N. America up to the Pliocene.

GENUS *Erinaceus*

Opinions vary as to number of species, especially in Asia, but seems wise, at present, to follow E.&M.-S. in admitting only two species, *E. europaeus*, which, in spite of its name, covers practically all Palaearctic Region (excepting only Himalayas and N. Africa) and *E. algirus* from N. Africa, Canary Islands and Balearics, and also overlapping with *E. europaeus* into Spain and S.E. France.

Hedgehog (Urchin) *Erinaceus europaeus* L.

DISTRIBUTION Range abroad extends over most of Palaearctic Region up to *c.* 63° N. E.&M.-S. give 17 subspecies, including British form, *E. e. europaeus*. E. European forms darker than western and have more distinct markings on face. Analysis of geographical variation in Europe given in Herter (1938) who recognizes two species, *E. europaeus* and *E. roumanicus*. Introduced into New Zealand 1880–90, where it has flourished. Widespread throughout mainland of British Isles, though more thinly spread in Scottish Highlands; sporadic on islands and presence sometimes result of recent introduction, e.g. Canna (Campbell, 1955). Known to be on I. of Wight, I. of Man, Anglesey, Shetland, Orkney, Skye,

Bute, Mull, Coll, Canna, Jersey and Guernsey though in some of these probably introduced.

DESCRIPTION See Field Identification Characters. Spines dark-brown to black with white bases and tips, *c.* 20 mm long, normally lying flat but can be erected at will. Eyes black, fairly large. Nose pointed, reminiscent of dog's and similarly moist on surface. Feet with five digits, all with strong claws. Front feet larger than hind. Legs appear short and gait crouching, but when unalarmed, Hedgehog can move fast and evenly and well clear of ground. Fur of underside, head and tail harsh and brittle, yellowish-white to dirty-brown. Some variation in colour, most animals being brown, but in others colour diluted culminating in rare, very light specimens. Albinos not uncommon. Nothing certain known about moult, though B.-H.&H. quote evidence that older spines become superficially seated and may be shed. However, Knight (1962) suggests spines are fewer in young, increase to *c.* 100 per sq in. in adults and then decline as they wear off. Herter noted clipped spines still visible after 2 years. At birth they are white and soft but harden and colour by 4 weeks. No constant difference between sexes, though Knight considers snout generally longer in males. Skull and teeth fairly primitive.

MEASUREMENTS B.-H.&H. give following: h.&b. ♂ 230 mm (7 meas., range 188 to 263 mm), ♀ 217 mm (10 meas., range 179 to 257 mm); tail, ♂ 26 mm (7 meas., range 17 to 35 mm), ♀ 23.5 mm (10 meas., range 17 to 31 mm). Weight varies widely. Herter found from captive Hedgehogs that seasonal changes in weight differed in sexes: females (7 observed) lowest in Jan (800 g), highest in July (1025 g); males (7 observed) lowest in June (900 g) and highest in Sept–Oct (1200 g).

HABITAT Rare in dense woodland, marshes and high moorland, common in most open country which has some cover for making nests and shelters: grassy heaths, cultivated land, open wood and scrub, and sand dunes. Also notably abundant in gardens and parks in built-up areas.

GENERAL HABITS Gait usually hesitant, with frequent stops to sniff the air: when moving swiftly has a curiously clockwork action. Will crouch and begin to erect spines at least sign of danger, reacting especially to noise: head is depressed with spines on crown presented forwards and circular muscle tightens around and underneath body. If gently handled, can be persuaded to uncurl (Ranson, 1941a) and soon becomes tame.

Almost entirely nocturnal, unless ill, though may be seen active at dusk and dawn. Noisy when foraging for food in leaf litter, emitting stream of grunts and snorts: also has loud wail, when hurt or alarmed. Eyesight not keen; smell and hearing acute.

FIG. 19. Hedgehog (*Erinaceus europaeus*) illustrating how it lifts the body well clear of the ground when it is walking rapidly. When it is moving around tentatively investigating things, the attitude is more crouching, while real alarm causes the animal to curl up.

Swims and climbs well and claws quite efficient for digging. Droppings cylindrical, *c*. 1 cm diam., several cm long, with pointed ends. Usually black with many insect fragments.

Nests, built of dry leaves, grasses and moss and placed in bottoms of hedgerows or in bramble thickets or burrows, vary in size, breeding nest being large, hibernating nest compact and well hidden.

Hibernation not so profound as in rodents: may not begin until Dec and ends March–April; even during this period Hedgehogs occasionally active. Beginning associated with increase in size of so-called hibernating gland, lymphoid and fatty tissue disseminated around neck and shoulder regions (see summary in Matthews, 1952).

Movements small: Herter marked 4 with bird rings, only 1, recovered 1 year later, had travelled any distance (c. 1 km). Not known whether territory or home range defended but males certainly aggressive in breeding season. Remarkable habit described by Herter is production of frothy saliva (when stimulated by chewing certain things like leather and tobacco), which is placed on spines all over body (*Photograph 25*).

BREEDING Males fecund early April to late August; females pregnant from May to Oct with early peak May to July, and later peak Sept (Morris, 1961). Ovulation spontaneous, early cycles often infertile. Gestation 31–32 days (Morris, 1961), 34–40 days (Herter, 1938, animals in captivity). Embryo rate 5.0 (Deanesly, 1934, 10 obs., range 4 to 7), 4.6 (Morris, 1961, 42 obs.). Both authors record only slight losses of embryos (0% and 3·3%). Two peaks of pregnancies suggest two litters per year, but perhaps late-born females do not become pregnant until late in following year. Lactation about 4 weeks; no post-partum oestrus. Sex ratio about equal or slightly favouring males (54% of 249 (Herter, 1938); 50% of 271 (Allanson, 1934; Deanesly, 1934)). Young born blind, weighing 11 to 25 g. Male takes no part in rearing them; female moves them to new nest if disturbed. Eyes open at 14 days and at 3+ weeks they start to leave nest; finally they forage in a string following mother. Weight doubles in 7 days, ×10 in 47 days, ×40 in 98 days. Growth uneven: one family at 128 days ranged from 650 to 1,125 g. No evidence of sexual maturity ever occurring in year of birth.

POPULATION Very little known. No satisfactory studies yet on age determination. Only figure for absolute density is Zimmermann (quoted in Herter), who estimated 40–50 Hedgehogs living on 400 ha of woodland +24 ha of open ground (c. 1,275 acres). Road mortality used as index to population shows far greater density in New Zealand than in England; Brockie (1960) and Davies (1957b) show difference of the order of ×50. Known to live at least 7 years in captivity.

FOOD Very little systematic work. In British Isles known to eat wide range of invertebrates, including many apparently distasteful such as slugs and carabid beetles. Earthworms, snails and insect larvae and pupae also eaten. Kalabukhov (1928) gives analysis from N. Caucasus and Ukraine in which insects are 97% by bulk; mammals, birds and reptiles 2%. Brockie (1959) found in New Zealand main items of food were slugs, beetles, millipedes, snails, earthworms and moth larvae. Herter (1938) gives figures for food consumption in captivity: one, weighing 675 g, ate, in 24 hr, 144 g of bird + 85 g of milk; another, in 10 days, ate 1,880 g of mealworms (it increased in weight from 679 g to 1,155 g during the test!) and in the following 10 days same animal ate 1,462 g of sparrows and lost 63 g in weight! Also eats some vegetable matter, e.g. acorns, berries.

PREDATORS No precise information. Dogs and man obviously important. Otherwise Fox, Badger, Polecat and Tawny Owl. Foxes and Badgers do not seem to have much trouble in opening up Hedgehogs and occasionally leave skin of victim turned inside out.

RELATIONS WITH MAN For many years now considered as serious predator of game birds and still extensively persecuted. At least known that diet mainly invertebrates, but proper assessment badly needed. Easy to keep and breed in captivity if allowed sufficient space (Herter, 1938; Ranson, 1941); important animal for experimental work on viruses and is used in investigation of foot-and-mouth, influenza and yellow fever (Edwards, 1957). Foot-and-mouth outbreaks are recorded as arising in Hedgehog populations, presumably from endemic condition (McLaughlan & Henderson, 1947).

FAMILY TALPIDAE

Closely related to following family (Soricidae), both together forming superfamily Soricoidea. Holarctic in distribution (one genus just reaching into Oriental Region), with 17 genera divided into 5 sub-families; the shrew moles (Uropsilinae) from Asia which live above ground and look superficially like shrews; the desmans (Desmaninae) from Europe and Asia, mole size or somewhat larger, aquatic; the Old World moles (Talpinae) from Palaearctic Region, true burrowers; the American moles (Scalopinae) from N. America and E. Asia, with genera ranging from the burrowing moles to creatures like shrews; and finally the remarkable star-nosed moles (Condylurinae) from N. America with only one genus and species, distinguished by a rosette of pink 'tentacles' on its nose.

GENUS *Talpa*

Distributed over most of Palaearctic Region and down to Malaya; only genus in Europe. E.&M.-S. recognize only two species in Europe, *T. europaea* in north and *T. caeca* in the south, and one, *T. micrura*, in Asia. Recent revision by Stein (1960a) gives three species in Asia and four in Europe. *T. hercegovinensis* and *T. europaea* more northern species and *T. caeca* and *T. romana*, both rather smaller, southern in distribution (S. Italy, Iberian Peninsula and S. France). Distinguished from other genera by having complete dentition (44 teeth).

Mole *Talpa europaea* L.

DISTRIBUTION Europe northwards to S. Sweden and Finland, southwards to N. and E. Spain, N. Italy, Yugo-Slavian hinterland, eastwards to Asia—Siberia and Mongolia (Stein's *T. hercegovinensis*). Few subspecies, but situation not satisfactorily investigated yet. Stein separates a central European *T. e. europaea* from west European *T. e. cinerea*, but is undecided about British moles, which otherwise come under *T. e. europaea* (in E.&M.-S.).

In British Isles distributed widely, isolated populations being found high up (B.-H.&H. say almost to 3,000 ft in Lakeland). Absent from Ireland, I. of Man, Outer and many of Inner Hebrides, Orkney and Shetland. Present on I. of Wight, Anglesey, Skye, Mull (introduced into last island in early 1800's). Was also introduced Ulva (off Mull) but now vanished. In Channel Islands, present on Jersey and Alderney, but not on Guernsey (Godfrey & Crowcroft, 1960). Characteristics extremely stable and no geographical variation reported within British Isles.

DESCRIPTION See Field Identification Characters. Fur velvety and black at all ages and seasons, though in strong light slight greyish or brownish cast. Sometimes yellowish markings on ventral surface. Muzzle pointed but without protruding snout of shrew, eyes tiny and usually hidden by erect hair, which, however, can be drawn back at will to expose eye; ear without external pinna. Fore limb with five strong and enlarged claws. Tail stumpy, narrow at base so that it will hold a metal marking ring (Pavlinin, 1948; Godfrey, 1955). Skull narrow like that of large shrew, 44 teeth, upper molars expanded to give large grinding surface. Fore limb and girdle remarkably modified for digging, with humerus expanded like figure of 8 (very noticeable in owl pellets) and extra bone (sesamoid) in wrist. Sternum with keel for attachment of digging muscles.

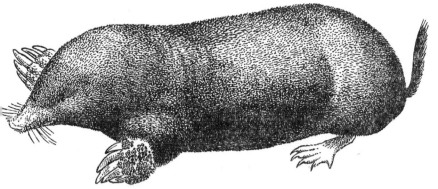

FIG. 14. Mole (*Talpa europaea*). Note the cylindrical body with heavy fossorial fore-limbs and small tail carried vertically.

Sexes identifiable only by external genitalia, though males usually 10% longer than females and weigh 10 to 20 g more.

Three moults, one in spring when males almost month later than females, another (intermediate) July to Sept which may not be completed, and third in autumn from early Oct to Dec, occurring in all age groups and both sexes at about same time (Godfrey & Crowcroft, 1960). Young are already like adults when they leave nest. Variant forms not uncommon (Skoczeń (1961b) notes 51 in 50,000 in Poland) and are mainly (i) pale, varying from rare, true albinos through cream to apricot or rust-coloured, (ii) piebald or patched, and (iii) grey or silver-grey.

MEASUREMENTS Great variation according to locality, year, sex. May be partly genetic. Fairly representative sample of 99 animals from Suffolk given in Godfrey & Crowcroft (1960): h.&b. ♂ 143 mm (42 meas., range 121 to 159 mm), ♀ 135 mm (57 meas., range 113 to 144 mm); tail ♂ 33 mm (range 26 to 40 mm), ♀ 32 mm (range 25 to 38 mm); weight ♂ 110 g (range 87 to 128 g), ♀ 85 g (range 72 to 106 g). Stein (1950b) shows moles from higher altitudes and poorer habitats lighter and smaller than those from lowland and rich habitats. Larkin (unpubl. thesis, 1948) found substantial differences between neighbouring localities; also showed weights varied seasonally, reaching maximum Feb to April. Juveniles reach adult size and weight within 2 to 3 months of birth.

HABITAT Found in almost every habitat except barren mountains, sand, and, possibly, conifer forests. Very abundant, and noticeable, in permanent pasture but also abundant in woodland where much less noticed. Spends almost entire life in tunnels from a few inches to a few feet below the ground.

GENERAL HABITS Degree to which sight used not clearly understood, but certainly not completely blind. Smell poor, only useful at short range (1 to 2 in.). Reacts to wide range of sounds. Touch, apparently, most important sense, and vibrations in soil detected in this way. Makes almost inaudible twitter when excited and single raucous squeaks when fighting. Vibrissae replaced by groups of tactile hairs on chin and muzzle and top of latter with highly sensitive receptors (Eimer's Organs); also sensitive hairs on tip of tail (*Photograph 26*).

Locomotion by sideways thrusts of fore-limbs (above ground they only touch ground with their inner edges): said to travel backwards using hind-limbs alone. Swims well. Method of burrowing disputed but now known by use of fore-limbs: surplus earth forced up, making mole-hills, by pressure from one fore-limb (Skoczeń, 1958). Burrows probably variable in diameter but much of system tight fit for Mole which squeezes its fur clean as it travels along (Earl of Cranbrook, unpubl.). Deeper burrows (1 to 2 ft down) indicated by mole-hills: shallow burrows, often seen in arable fields in summer, visible as ridges on surface; and simple, open furrows sometimes found.

Burrow systems usually belong to single Mole of either sex. Length of home range area in pasture (Larkin, Godfrey & Crowcroft, loc. cit.) fairly constant for females at 30 to 40 yds; in males smallest in winter (50 yds), increasing with onset of sexual activity in spring (153 yds). Both sexes have branching systems, but in spring males often make long straight tunnels entering systems of females. Possibly some sharing of burrow systems, subordinate animals coming out when dominant ones rest (Stein,

1950a). Nests, for resting or breeding, built in runway system, sometimes under 'fortress' (very large mole-hill). Apart from mating, only association is between female and young. Latter expand into poorer habitats in summer, making conspicuous shallow burrows and becoming easy prey to predators, e.g. Tawny Owl (Southern, 1954). Some deep permanent burrows used as highways by many Moles, e.g. between fields otherwise separated by ditches.

Active day and night: periods of almost continuous activity last c. 4½ hr and alternate with periods of c. 3½ hr in nest (Godfrey, 1955). Periods in nest involve quite deep sleep in upright position with head tucked between fore-limbs.

Food sought in burrows and in loose soil, occasionally above ground. Held in fore-limbs and pulled with jaws: with earthworms this motion cleans earth from outside and inside of worm.

Nests made from any dry material, usually dead leaves and grasses, pulled below ground by short sallies out from burrow. Usually have fairly complex tangle of burrows around them (Adams, 1909), though these not so stereotyped as once thought.

BREEDING General account of breeding given by Godfrey & Crowcroft (1960). Special accounts are by Matthews (1935), Larkin (1948) and Stein (1950a). In both sexes season usually very short and involves radical growth and involution of sexual organs. Testes and prostate glands increase rapidly from Dec, reaching peak in Feb–March and declining to minimum in late May. Matthews showed that female has two parts to ovary, one 'interstitial' which is homologue of testis and active during anoestrus. In Feb and early March rapid swing to ovarian activity and secondary sexual organs grow rapidly. After very short period of heat practically all females pregnant and sexual organs decline again swiftly. However, occurrence of second oestrus in small proportion of females recorded in British Isles and on Continent, perhaps related to abundance of food. Oestrus may last only 20 to 30 hours and possible that ovulation may depend upon copulation.

Gestation probably c. 4 weeks. Embryo rate, assembled from various sources by Godfrey & Crowcroft, fairly constant at about 3.8, contrasting with higher numbers up to 5.7 in Russia. Single litter per year usual: occasional second litter rare and reproductive

P

rate perhaps controlled more by absorption of embryos. Larkin found loss of 6% and Morris (1961) 25%, including 20% of litters being totally absorbed. Latter also found embryo rate 3.9 (70 observations).

Lactation probably 4 to 5 weeks: Godfrey (1957) found one litter marked with radio-active rings first left nest 33 days after birth.

Sex ratio approximately 50%, though males tend to come into traps first and, during breeding season, may exceed females in trap catches by 2 or 3 : 1. Godfrey & Crowcroft give details of growth of young, which begin to grow fur at 14 days and open their eyes at 22 days: at birth they weigh *c.* 3.5 g and at 3 weeks have increased to 60 g. Growth may be much slower if food is scarce. Nest abandoned when young are *c.* 5 weeks old. Sexual maturity not attained until Feb following birth.

POPULATION Many attempts made to relate mole density to mole-hills but with poor success. In some fields, where burrow systems can be distinguished, counts of individuals can be made, but represent minimum figures. Most careful work by Larkin who estimated, for grassland, 4 per acre in winter and 8 per acre in summer.

Life span *c.* 3 years: in some populations 3 year-classes distinguishable by wear of teeth (see Larkin), but in others this is too variable. About two-thirds of population must die each year, giving mean expectation of further life *c.* 1 year, if mortality evenly spread among age groups. Figures from Larkin suggest this may be correct, though first-year mortality may be unevenly spread.

Little known about importance of different mortality factors. Predation evidently heavy (see below) but indications that intra-uterine and nestling mortality may be heavy when food scarce, e.g. in drought when earthworms hard to obtain. Populations, wherever studied, seem reasonably steady, compared with fluctuations of small rodents. Clearly man, as predator, can exert sufficient pressure to keep populations low: now that mole-catching no longer lucrative, numbers have increased, especially in open, cultivated land.

FOOD Difficult to assess accurately from stomach contents because of different rates of digestion according to chitinization of items. Diet almost confined to larger members of soil fauna, especially earthworms and insects (mainly larvae of beetles and flies). Two other constant items (but not nearly so abundant) are myriapods and molluscs, latter mainly slugs. Occasional vegetable matter. Larkin showed how earthworms predominated in winter (90 to 100% by volume) and declined in summer (c. 50%), when percentage of insects increased; also how general percentage of insects increased during dry weather; and how this percentage also varied from place to place (see also Schaerffenberg, 1940). From mean weight of stomach contents (3 to 6 g of food) Godfrey & Crowcroft suggest 40 to 50 g of food eaten daily and Hawkins & Jewell (1962) from laboratory experiments on energy requirements state that mole of c. 80 g needs some 50 g of earthworms per day (= c. 0.5 Kcal/g/body-wt/day). This result suggests insectivores have no higher energy requirements than rodents (cf. Hawkins, Jewell & Tomlinson, 1960). Importance of steady food supply (cf. effect of observed food shortage on survival and growth of young) suggests desirability of maintaining daily ration throughout year, and, therefore, of storing food, habit now known to be widespread in Moles (Evans, 1948), and Skoczeń (1961a) has records of many such stores, one in Feb containing 470 earthworms (820 g). Grulich (1959) suggests that moles eat 9–16% of soil fauna during a year, but obvious that this may vary widely.

PREDATORS Moles, especially young ones, have wide variety of predators, whose combined effect may be serious, though they may only rarely coincide. Small carnivores and some birds of prey (e.g. Tawny Owl (Southern, 1954)) take significant numbers at certain times of year, particularly when young animals are dispersing in search of unoccupied areas (May to August).

RELATIONS WITH MAN Much dispute about value of Mole's activities to agriculture, many people, following Darwin (1881), believing earthworms of utmost importance and, therefore, predation of Mole detrimental; others maintaining that Moles aerate and drain soil with their burrows. Farmers find mole-hills great nuisance in pastureland, and, since mole-catching now no longer profitable, destruction by poisoning with strychnine allowed. Moles not easy to keep in captivity, needing much fresh animal food, particularly earthworms, but, for those who do not mind expending patience and labour, moles become quite tame (see Godfrey & Crowcroft, 1960).

FAMILY SORICIDAE

A widespread family, containing a multitude of small forms, all carnivorous or insectivorous, which live mainly in leaf litter and soil. Important element in any animal community, breaking down animal tissue and returning raw materials to soil. Three sub-families: (i) Soricinae (red-toothed shrews) with 8 genera distributed over Holarctic Region and with one of them (*Cryptotis*) extending to northern S. America. Two groups in this sub-family have become aquatic, *Sorex palustris* from N. America and the genus *Neomys* in Palaearctic Region. Both have swimming hairs on the feet. (ii) Crocidurinae (white-toothed shrews) which have their main centre in Africa, where many species varying in size up to animals of genus *Crocidura* almost rat-size. Twelve genera, in Palaearctic and Oriental Regions, including two aquatic, *Chimarrogale*, with swimming hairs and *Nectogale* with webbed feet. *Suncus murinus*, the House Shrew, in Oriental Region is commensal: *S. etruscus* from Mediterranean is smallest known mammal, weighing, when adult, 1.5 to 2 g. (iii) Scutisoricinae with one remarkable form, *Scutisorex*, from central Africa, having an elaborate girder-like backbone. Useful survey of family with extensive bibliography by Pruitt (1957).

GENUS *Sorex*

A very difficult genus for systematists because such wide variation between splitters and lumpers. Many cognate genera which may be considered as subgenera of *Sorex*. E. Palaearctic forms specially difficult; some of these may be conspecific with Nearctic ones. Spread widely over Palaearctic and Nearctic Regions. Mostly small, some very small, e.g. *Sorex minutus*, Pygmy Shrew, and one, at least (*S. pacificus*) large for a shrew (h.&b. *c.* 6 in.). E.&M.-S. give 9 species in Palaearctic Region; Miller & Kellogg (1955) give 38 for Nearctic.

Common Shrew (Shrew-mouse, Ranny) *Sorex araneus* L.

DISTRIBUTION European Continent except Iberian Peninsula (Van den Brink, 1955, gives three small patches in Spain) and Mediterranean Islands. Through Asia to Pacific, northwards to tundra, often to Arctic Ocean, southwards to Caucasus, Mongolia, Manchuria, China, Kuriles. Systematics so tangled that number of subspecies cannot be determined: Miller (1912) gives eight in W. Europe, but more have been suggested since. In British Isles abundant and widespread throughout England, Scotland and Wales. Definitely missing from Ireland, Scillies, Lundy, I. of Man, Outer Hebrides and some of Inner Hebrides (e.g. Eigg, Muck), Orkney and Shetland. Present I. of Wight, Skomer, Anglesey, Islay, Jura, Gigha, Arran, Bute, Mull, Skye, Colonsay, Raasay, S. Rona, Scalpay, Ulva and Jersey (only, of Channel Islands). Further information needed. Form in British Isles duller in colour than those on Continent and separated as *S. a. castaneus*. On Islay Common Shrews often lack second upper premolar and have striking grey flanks; they have been named *S. a. granti*. Similarly the Jersey form, *S. a. fretalis*, given subspecific status, though now known that it resembles French races in chromosomes, being unlike British (Meylan, 1960).

DESCRIPTION See Field Identification Characters. Usual back colour very dark brown, varying with strength and angle of light. Underside greyish white; demarcation line along flank variable, may be sharp or diffuse. Generally yellowish tinge to underside. Tail conspicuously haired and bicoloured, dark above, light below; rarely with white tip. White ear tufts not uncommon (20% in population studied by Crowcroft, 1957). 'Grey patch' on occiput of some parous females probably indicates where she was held by male during copulation. Skeleton slenderly built, all feet have five digits, unlike rodents. Skull thin and tapering with no zygomatic arch and conspicuous red-tipped teeth. Height of brain-case decreases between Oct and Jan, increases from Feb to July and then declines again just before death (Crowcroft & Ingles, 1959). No external distinction between sexes except by genitalia during breeding season: Becker (1955) has shown for several members of Soricidae, including Common Shrew, that pelvic girdle is heavier and more irregular in male with uneven margins to pubis and ischium.

Two moults during lifetime: first in autumn to dark, long winter coat; starts at posterior end and moves forward to head, dorsal surface being ahead of ventral. Spring moult is to coat of same colour but with shorter fur: proceeds in opposite direction to autumn moult. By autumn rare survivors from previous year do not moult. Pelage of young lighter than that of adults (Crowcroft, 1957).

FIG. 15. Four species of British shrews—the Water Shrew (*Neomys fodiens*), bottom left, is the largest and blackest; the Common Shrew (*Sorex araneus*), top left, is fairly dark and is the species most generally encountered; the Pygmy Shrew (*S. minutus*), top right, has a relatively long tail and is the smallest British mammal; and the Scilly Shrew (*Crocidura suaveolens cassiteridum*), bottom right, has more prominent ears and outstanding hairs on the tail.

As with many insectivores, lateral subcutaneous scent glands present, more highly developed in males and anoestrous females. Produce the familiar musky smell. Variants, e.g. albinos, melanics, sandy colour, white spots and patches all recorded: Crowcroft found 1 mutant in *c.* 1,000 specimens.

Chromosome number variable, 22 to 27 in male, 22 to 25 in female (Sharman, 1956). Subject complex and still under investigation (Meylan, 1960).

MEASUREMENTS Vary through life: Crowcroft (unpubl. thesis, 1954) gives following: June–July immat. h.&b. 69.5 mm (77 meas., range 62 to 75 mm), tail 39.7 mm (76 meas., range 32 to 45), weight 7.2 g (77 weighed, range 5.4 to 9.0); some slight growth is made in summer and autumn and by Oct–Nov figures are, h.&b. 71.8 mm (68 meas., range 66 to 75 mm), tail 39.8 mm (67 meas., range 35 to 47 mm), weight 7.0 g (64 weighed, range 5.8 to 9.3 g). Between then and Feb a drop occurs, viz. h.&b. 66.7 mm (65 meas., range 57 to 71 mm), tail 40.2 (64 meas., range 35 to 45 mm), weight 6.0 g (64 weighed, range 4.8 to 7.7 g). Finally there is burst of growth at sexual maturity (May), h.&b. 79.3 mm (38 meas., range 74 to 85 mm), tail 38.3 mm (37 meas., range 34 to 42 mm), weight 10.4 g (37 weighed, range 8.5 to 13.6 g). The winter drop in weight varies with severity of weather.

HABITAT Found in practically every habitat from sea-level to at least 3,000 ft. Most abundant in dense, low herbage, e.g. thick grass but common in woodland, scrub with bushes and bracken, hedgerows, banks. Relatively more common than Pygmy Shrew in woodland (see under that species). Lives mainly in runways which it makes in and above litter and soil; also uses mouse and mole tunnels. Climbs well and has been found 8 ft up in a hollow tree (H.N.Southern, unpubl.).

GENERAL HABITS Two main types of noises, (a) soft twittering used in exploration or when moving around home range, and (b) shrill screaming used during contacts. This latter is aggressive and will sometimes drive away another shrew without fighting. Screaming of female less raucous than that of male (Crowcroft, 1957). Movements swift and bustling, exploring busily with mobile snout and vibrissae and, now and again, rearing up and appearing to sniff the air. Touch, hearing and probably kinaesthetic sense more important than sight and smell. Runways may be made in litter and regular tunnels, recognizable by small size and flattened cross section, are driven with vigour, by use of nose and front paws, through soil. Large objects like stones removed in the mouth. Burrows of other animals used but tight fit of its own burrows keeps a shrew's fur polished and clean. Swims readily and is recorded as prey of Grayling in Russia (Teplov, 1943).

Except during actual mating period and when young still with mother, shrews are solitary and aggressive. Method of fighting which drives away neighbour or newcomer described in Crowcroft (1957): contests often confined to screaming, then posturing, then biting but wounding rarely severe. Victor will never pursue vanquished, so several can share range and avoid discommoding each other by keeping contest formal. Size of range varies with age and sex, as well as with individuals: J.Shillito (unpubl. thesis, 1960) gives following rough figures for average distances moved between recaptures: juveniles and subadults 8 to 54 m, dispersing juveniles 70 to 119 m, resident females 24 to 56 m, roaming males 79 to 144 m. In spring most males moved right off study area. All shrews occasionally shift centre of range.

Active throughout 24 hours with c. ten periods of almost continuous activity alternating with shorter periods of rest. Peaks of activity about 10 p.m. and 10 a.m.; most active at night, least active early afternoon (Crowcroft, 1954a). Active periods mainly occupied in seeking food, which is held down by fore-legs and eaten on spot. Surplus food stored. Feeds from anus by everting rectum.

Nests woven of grasses into form of loose ball; placed either below ground or on surface under cover. Normal refuge may be flimsy affair but breeding nest more substantial.

BREEDING Sexual organs swiftly reach maturity after winter, males late Feb to early March and females March to April. Later on Continent: females mature mid-April to first week May in Poland (Tarkowski, 1957). Breeding ceases in both sexes August to October, mainly because parent generation is rapidly dying off. Brambell (1935) showed that ovulation probably followed copulation and that a high percentage (nearly 100) of females became pregnant shortly after first oestrus. Details of mating behaviour in captivity given by Crowcroft (1957). Gestation not certainly known, but between 13 and 19 days (Brambell, 1935) and one probable instance of 21 days recorded by Crowcroft. Some evidence that number of ova shed at one ovulation vary during season: Tarkowski gives 8.6 in May, dropping to 5.9 in second half of July and then rising to 6.8 in August and 6.3 in Sept. Embryo rate shows steady drop throughout season first through decline in ova ovulated, later through increased foetal mortality. Data from British Isles show similar decline in embryo rate, e.g. Crowcroft (1954b) found mean of 7.7 embryos (16 examined) in May, 6.7 in June (6 examined) and 5.7 in August (6 examined). Foetal mortality cited as 21% in August and 18% in Sept (Tarkowski, 1957) and was higher in conifer than in deciduous woodlands.

Number of litters per season variable. Normally most females conceive at post-partum oestrus, but later lactation dioestrus becomes more extended until breeding declines in Aug and Sept. J.Shillito (1963) studied reproduction of females on 2¾ acres for 2 years: in first year 7 present, of which 2 died after 1 pregnancy, 2 had 2 pregnancies, while evidence about the others was not clear. In second year 12 present, of which 6 had two litters, 4 had 1 and 1 had 3 (the last was not traced). Tarkowski (1957) believes 5 litters in a season maximum. Lactation lasts c. 22 days. Sex ratio approximately 50%, though at some times, e.g. spring, males more trappable. Pucek (1959) suggests females preponderate when populations are low.

Young grow linearly to about 18th day, being just under 0.5 g at birth and c. 7 g on day 18 (Crowcroft, unpubl. thesis, 1954). Since litter may contain 7–8 young and parent may not weigh more than 10–12 g, this means quite an efficient transfer of energy. Female eats voraciously during this time. Nevertheless development of young is slow and eyes are not open until 18 to 21 days after birth, only a day or two before weaning.

Usually Common Shrews mature in year after birth, but Pucek (1960) and Stein (1961) show that small percentage of females in first litters may become sexually mature in year of birth, when population density is low and food abundant. Such precocious breeders stay at immature length and weight.

POPULATION J.Shillito (unpubl. thesis, 1960) gives population

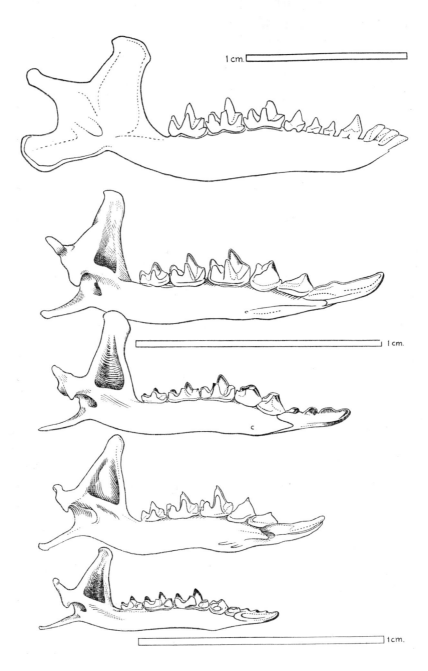

data over 2 years for small wood ($2\frac{3}{4}$ acres) in Devon. Numbers determined by intensive live trapping and marking (Linn & Shillito, 1960). Seasonal swing showing peak numbers each June to August (25 in 1958, 70 in 1959) and lowest numbers towards end of winter (25 in 1958/9, 25 in 1959/60). Each year showed influx of new males in April. Changes in abundance from year to year occur (see above) but not so violent as in rodents. Numbers trapped on 250 acres of deciduous woodland over 4 years (H.N. Southern, unpubl.) began at <10 in 468 trap nights in winter 1948/9, rose to big peak (c. 60) in summer of 1949, stayed at low figure (c. 10) over most of 1950 and 1951, then climbed to another peak (c. 40) in autumn 1951; finally after staying at c. 25 in 468 trap nights throughout winter, crashed to 2 in June of 1952. Trap catches like this form useful index to density: so do contents of owl pellets.

Brambell (1935) and later Crowcroft (1957) and others showed that Common Shrews of adult generation in any year all die off in late summer and early autumn after breeding. Overwintering population, therefore, consists of young born in that year. Summer population can be separated into new and old generations by size and by wearing down of teeth. Recently shown (Pucek, 1960; Stein, 1961) that small percentage (<2%) of young females breed in year of birth. Shillito showed mortality heavy on young shrews, some 25% dying of those 1 to 4 months old, but survival improves thereafter, only further 14% dying up to 10 months of age. Heavy 'mortality' at 11 months (onset of breeding) perhaps partly due to migration; thereafter survival drops steeply. Mean expectation of life decreases gradually from 6 months at 1 month of age to about 3 months at 9 months of age and then drops suddenly. This convex survivorship curve suggests many shrews live out their physiological life-span. Certain facts suggest food supply may

FIG. 16. Lower jaws, viewed from inside, of small British insectivores—that of the Mole (*Talpa europaea*), top drawing, is far the largest of these (note the different scale) and has small incisors; the Water Shrew (*Neomys fodiens*), second from top, is distinguished from other shrews by having a heavy articular process which partly obscures the triangular hollow in the ascending ramus of the jaw; the lower jaws of Common Shrew (*Sorex araneus*), third from bottom, and of Pygmy Shrew (*S. minutus*), bottom, have long, projecting first incisors with serrations and the teeth are tipped with red pigment; the Scilly Shrew (*Crocidura suaveolens cassiteridum*), second from bottom, lacks this pigment.

exert important influence on population, e.g. loss of weight in winter when litter fauna goes deeper into ground, foetal mortality higher in poorer habitats.

FOOD Mainly invertebrates of soil and litter, especially beetles and earthworms; also carrion, if fresh, including other shrews. Systematic studies rare but Mezhzherin (1958) examined stomachs of 265 *S. araneus* in Russia and found beetles, especially carabids, more than 50% of food all year round; spiders and flies also important. Crowcroft (1957) describes food preference, showing shrews greatly prefer *Philoscia* of 4 species of isopods offered, also that some millipedes and beetles are distasteful, while grasshoppers and spiders are eagerly eaten. Some vegetable food regularly taken and *Sorex* spp. in N. America eat sufficient Douglas fir seeds to influence regeneration (Moore, 1942). J.Shillito (unpubl. thesis, 1960) compared invertebrate fauna in samples of litter experimentally exposed to and protected from shrew predation. Mainly removed were springtails, spiders, beetles and flies, discrepancy being greatest in late autumn and winter, and again in June and July. Animals eaten as second choice were woodlice, pseudoscorpions, myriapods and lumbricid oligochaetes. Those rejected were enchytraeid oligochaetes, mites and small beetles. Crowcroft (1957) reckoned common shrew ate three-quarters of its weight per day of food—up to $1\frac{1}{2}$ times when lactating: Hawkins & Jewell (1962) found shrew of 8 g ate its own weight of wet food (= 2–4 g dry wt) per day, or about 2 Kcal/g body wt/day.

PREDATORS Many mammals, including domestic cats, kill shrews, but not certain how many refuse to eat them on account of distastefulness. Birds more important, especially Barn Owl on open ground. Üttendörfer (1939) reckons shrews are 25% of diet. In woodland Tawny Owls take only about 5% by weight in total diet (Southern, 1954) and some evidence of distastefulness.

RELATIONS WITH MAN Shrews not liable, as once thought, to die of shock if brought into captivity and handled, but often half starved when found in trap, unless traps visited every hour. Thrive on diet of fresh meat or earthworms and little oatmeal and can be kept on tinned dog food (Crowcroft, 1957).

Pygmy Shrew (Lesser Shrew) *Sorex minutus* L.

DISTRIBUTION Over Palaearctic Region mainly as Common Shrew but totally lacking from Spain and does not reach so far into Arctic. Present on some islands off Brittany. Distribution in British Isles most widespread of all small mammals except Wood Mouse, suggesting early immigration after glaciation; ascends to highest mountains (4,400 ft on Ben Nevis). Present most islands, including Lundy, Skomer, I. of Man, Outer and Inner Hebrides, Orkney. Absent Scillies, Channel Islands, Shetland. Over most of range two subspecies recognized, *S. m. minutus* extending over most of Europe, including British Isles, and into Asia; the second race in Italy: various far Eastern races described.

DESCRIPTION See Field Identification Characters. Sandy-brown, dirty white on underside, less variable in tone than Common Shrew. No difference between juvenile and adult pelage: white ear tufts never present. Tail relatively and absolutely longer and thicker than that of Common Shrew, densely haired; body elongated and snout vibrissae long (up to 16 mm). Skull and lower jaws conspicuous by tiny size and delicate construction. In upper jaw the 5 unicuspid teeth, i.e. those between large front incisor and molariform teeth, decline in size evenly from front to back, contrasting with Common Shrew, where sudden decrease in size of third tooth. In lower jaw, angle between horizontal and ascending rami nearly perpendicular (Fig. 16). Height of brain case varies seasonally as in Common Shrew (Dehnel, 1949). No sexual dimorphism. Two moults, spring and autumn. Young not notably distinct from adults and reach adult weight before leaving nest. Albino and cream-coloured specimens mentioned.

MEASUREMENTS Similar changes to those observed in Common Shrew. Crowcroft (unpubl. thesis, 1954) gives following: immature (July to Feb) h.&b. 52.9 mm (39 meas., range 41 to 58 mm), tail 39.0 mm (38 meas., range 37 to 44 mm), weight 2.8 g (40 weighed, range 2.4 to 4.2 g); mature (March to June) h.&b. 57.8 mm (27 meas., range 53 to 63 mm), tail 38.1 mm (27 meas., range 33 to 42 mm), weight 3.5 g (27 weighed, range 2.4 to 5.6 g). Range of mature weights increased by pregnancies which were not distinguished. J.Shillito (unpubl. thesis, 1960) found mean weights of trapped samples varied sharply between 3 g for immature and 5 g for mature shrews.

HABITAT Widespread in all types of habitat which have plenty of ground cover. Relatively less abundant than Common Shrew in woodland. Crowcroft (1957) notes in trapping results *c.* 4% of shrews caught in forest are Pygmy Shrews, but in grassland 10 to 16%. J.Shillito found 10% and over in wood strip and Heydemann (1960) found gradient from woods and wood edge (12% Pygmy Shrews) to dunes (35%).

GENERAL HABITS Voice as Common Shrew, aggressive squeaking and exploratory twittering. Moves about very swiftly and reactions very quick: for this reason Crowcroft (1957) found Pygmy and Common Shrews lived together without casualties, the rapid avoidance of contact by Pygmy giving little chance of encounters. If these did occur, Pygmy behaved much as Common except that fighting did not progress beyond screaming. Pygmy Shrew does not burrow but uses runways of other animals. Climbs well. Social arrangements apparently much as in Common Shrew. J.Shillito found, from recaptures of marked shrews, that length of range varied from 16 to 45 m with an average of 31 m. Shorter and more frequent periods of rest and activity than Common Shrew and relatively more active during day (Crowcroft, 1954a). Feeding and nest-making habits much as Common Shrew.

BREEDING Season in both sexes begins (April) and ends (August) abruptly (Brambell & Hall, 1937), but occasional pregnancy to October. First oestrus and ovulation apparently always followed by pregnancy, but in some animals lactation anoestrus occurs. Thus peak of breeding about June. Dehnel (1949) finds breeding season extends over same time in Poland, but believes shrews born late in year do not mature sexually until summer of following year. Pucek (1960) found variable proportion of females (1 to 8%) became pregnant in year of birth. Gestation period not certainly known; probably about same as lactation which is *c.* 22 days (young were seen to take solid food for the first time at this age by Crowcroft). Brambell & Hall give embryo rate as 6.2 (31 observed, range 2 to 8). Litters per season probably about 2, some females having one immediately after the other, others with anoestrous period interposed. Sex ratio probably about equal, though, as with Common Shrew, more males obtained in spring. Young take same time to weaning as Common Shrews but reach full weight more quickly: from 0.25 g at birth they reach *c.* 2.5 g at 14 days and remain about this weight until following year.

POPULATION Data about body weights (see above) and tooth wear (Crowcroft, unpubl. thesis, 1954) show Pygmy Shrew has annual turnover like Common Shrew. No figures for absolute density but index shows Pygmy Shrews less abundant (proportions graded according to habitat) than Common (see under Habitat). J.Shillito using index of catches per trap per trapping period found a peak in numbers in summer and early autumn but with some erratic fluctuations. Little known about how population controlled: predation perhaps important (q.v.); Pucek (1960) and Stein (1961) believe proportion of females breeding in year of birth linked with abundance of food.

FOOD Probably similar to that of Common Shrew but no systematic information. Crowcroft (1957) offered choice of different woodlice and found Pygmy Shrew ate more of smaller *Trichoniscus* than did Common Shrew. J.Shillito, using technique with litter samples described under Common Shrew, found high proportion of woodlice, especially *Trichoniscus*, removed by Pygmy. Also selects spiders and beetles (as does Common Shrew) and rejects (relatively) springtails and insect larvae. Hawkins & Jewell (1962) found a high intake of food, 5.5 to 9 g wet weight per day or 3.1 Kcal/g body wt/day.

PREDATORS From information collected from pellets over 8 years (Southern, 1954) Pygmy Shrews composed 13% of shrews eaten by Tawny Owls in deciduous woodland. Probable that species of owls which hunt open ground, e.g. Barn Owl, Short-eared Owl and Long-eared Owl may take number of Pygmy Shrews.

RELATIONS WITH MAN Crowcroft (1957) gives some notes on keeping in captivity.

GENUS *Neomys*

A fairly distinct genus of the red-toothed shrews, having one less unicuspid tooth in the upper jaw than genus *Sorex*. Also, instead of being equal, the two hooks on the first upper incisor are very unequal, the anterior one being far larger and longer than the posterior one. Confined to Palaearctic Region (the Nearctic aquatic form *Sorex palustris* resembles it by convergence) having only two species, one, *N. fodiens*, occupying north and east of the range, the other, *N. anomalus*, which lacks the keel of swimming hairs on the tail, occupying mountain areas in Europe (high ground in Spain, Alps, Carpathians, Balkans) and steppe areas in E. Europe, and Asia Minor.

Water Shrew *Neomys fodiens* Pennant

DISTRIBUTION Over much of Palaearctic Region to Arctic Ocean in Europe and to about Arctic Circle in Asia; south, on lower ground to Pyrenees, S. France, Italy, N. Caucasus. Occurs east to Pacific coast and Sakhalin but details not known. E. & M.-S. give 5 subspecies, but eastern ones dubious yet; type subspecies covers most of continental range and British subspecies, *N. fodiens bicolor*, distinguished by generally more dusky appearance, found on mainland of British Isles only, being absent from Ireland and all islands, except Anglesey, I. of Wight (?), Arran, Kerrera, Islay and Skye (for last, see Gordon, 1951). On whole, continental Water Shrews have clearer white on underparts eastwards, but situation is complicated by frequent melanism (see below). Not known how high it occurs but on continent up to 6,000 ft. Frequent in prehistoric deposits, presumably owl pellet contents, back to Upper Pleistocene. Perhaps drainage and pollution have restricted it.

DESCRIPTION See Field Identification Characters. Upperside usually slaty-black with sometimes tinge of brown, but notably blacker than other British shrews. Conspicuous tufts of white hairs near eyes and ears frequently occur. Underside white, greyish-white or cream with straight and clear demarcation line. Various stages of melanism occur on underside to extreme with dusky tone all over. Tail dark-brown on top, whitish below including fringes of swimming hairs which form 'keel' below tail. Similar pale fringes on digits of fore and hind limbs. Skull and lower jaws notably heavier than in genus *Sorex* and triangular hollow inside ascending ramus of lower jaw almost occluded by expanded articular surface. Red tips of teeth not so extensive as in genus *Sorex* and may wear away with age. No sexual dimorphism. Moult not described in detail but change to long and lustrous winter coat in autumn and back to shorter coat in spring. Various authorities, including J.Shillito (unpubl. thesis, 1960), mention anomalous summer moult, proceeding from head towards tail, which is usual direction of spring moult in shrews. Young much like adults but black fur has iridescence which is lost later. Pelage very variable in degrees of melanism, in tingeing of underside with yellow or reddish and in white ear and eye tufts. Albinos very occasionally.

MEASUREMENTS Same course of seasonal change as in two preceding species but obscured by much greater individual variation, especially in weight. Price (1953) determining maturity from sexual organs, gives range of weight for adults 12 to 18 g, for immatures 6 to 19 g. Long series of measurements from Polish material (Dehnel, 1950) gives: h.&b., immat., 80.0 mm (135 meas., range 70 to 88 mm), mature 85.1 mm (119 meas., range 76 to 96 mm); tail, mature and immature, 61.2 mm (202 meas., range 52 to 72 mm). J.Shillito, dealing with some 16 Water Shrews that invaded her trapping area for some months and were marked, found weight might alter by as much as 6 g between captures. Mean weights were c. 12 g from June to Oct, c. 10 g Nov to Jan, rising to 13 g by April.

HABITAT Found by clear streams and especially known to frequent water-cress beds. Also widely known to spread into other habitats far from water (especially woodland), rare specimens being encountered regularly and larger numbers, almost amounting to invasions, at sporadic intervals. Near Oxford turned up as prey of Tawny Owls in territories up to two miles from water (H.N. Southern, unpubl.) and nest found at about same distance (J.Godfrey, unpubl.). Dehnel (1950) found, in Poland, range extended into conifer and deciduous woods, in contrast to *Neomys anomalus*, which remains by water in this area.

GENERAL HABITS Voice a shrill chattering much like that of two preceding species. Movements very rapid and, on land, sometimes bounding. In water swims with alternate strokes of limbs and with laterally undulating movements of body: appears to walk over bottom under water like Dipper. Mostly makes short excursions into water, returning to bank for grooming fur: Lorenz (1957) believes constant grooming necessary to keep fur waterproof. Crowcroft (1957) found that squeezing through tight-fitting tunnel completely restored bedraggled fur. Makes extensive burrow systems with flattened cross section as in Common Shrew,

Q

but larger. Little known about social organization but almost certainly solitary with overlapping home ranges as with other species. J.Shillito studied temporary population in small wood (2¾ acres) in summer and autumn of one year and found some moved about all over wood and probably outside it. Length of range as shown by recaptures longer than in other species, up to 160 m. Short-term activity periods like those of Common Shrew but active periods rather longer. Night has generally higher level of activity (Crowcroft, 1954). Feeding habits of considerable interest: known that injected secretion of sub-maxillary gland will kill small rodents swiftly (M.Pucek, 1959) though not known whether this enables large prey to be tackled regularly, as with American *Blarina*. Cranbrook (1959) found earthworms were partially paralysed when treated to quick bites along their length; also large snails attacked at foot and soon cleaned out, presumably by paralysis of muscles.

BREEDING One substantial account by Price (1953) based on 190 shrews, mainly from S. England. Season begins mid-April and lasts until Sept, with peak in May–June. Suggested ovulation stimulated by coitus. Gestation *c.* 24 days, perhaps longer in lactating females, since lactation lasts up to 37 days. Mean number of embryos 6.8 (18 records, range 3 to 8). Probably all females have 2 litters, most becoming pregnant a second time at post-partum oestrus. Sex ratio variable, males predominating Nov to May, females rest of year: overall 48% males. Growth of young described by Crowcroft (1957): weight at birth just over 1 g; rate of growth about same as Common Shrew but weaning takes longer, 4 weeks, at which time they have reached weight of 10 g. Time of weaning best determined by change of colour of faeces from bright green to brownish-black. According to Price sexual maturity not attained until second year. Dehnel (1950) and Stein (1961) maintain small number of females breed in year of birth on Continent.

POPULATION No reliable figures for density: J.Shillito had *c.* 7 living on 2¾ acres for a month and *c.* 5 for 2 months, but this was transient summer population. Over 8 years investigation of owl pellets in deciduous woodland Water Shrews were about 3% of total shrews preyed upon (Southern, 1954). Little known about mortality and regulation of numbers.

FOOD No systematic investigation. Records of many aquatic invertebrates (snails, crustaceans, insects) and of larger species, fish and frogs. On land probably eat much same as other species with addition of larger prey, perhaps even small vertebrates. Hawkins & Jewell (1962) showed *c.* 8 to 12 g wet weight of food needed per day (= 1.1 to 1.4 Kcal/g body wt/day).

PREDATORS As for Common Shrew. Presumably more vulnerable to predacious fish.

RELATIONS WITH MAN   Accused of eating spawn of fish but total effect must be small. Notes on keeping in captivity in Crowcroft (1957) and Lorenz (1957).

GENUS Crocidura

Sub-family Crocidurinae (white-toothed shrews) most abundant in tropics of Old World but reach also into southern and central part of Palaearctic Region. Only one species reaches to Baltic and presence of two species in Channel Islands and one in Scilly Isles is peculiar. Both *Suncus* and *Crocidura* very large genera, latter having 110 species listed for Africa, and nearly 90 for Palaearctic and Oriental Regions. Probably these will be much reduced when further work done. E.&M.-S. reduce Palaearctic and Indian list to 14 species. Skull distinguished from that of *Sorex* and *Neomys* by lack of red pigment on tips of teeth and by reduction of unicuspid teeth in upper jaw to three.

White-toothed Shrew (Musk Shrew) *Crocidura russula* (Hermann)

DISTRIBUTION Extends over most of C. and S. Palaearctic Region, reaching north to Baltic, Caucasus, Turkestan, over to Japan. About 28 subspecies named. In British Isles confined to Alderney, Guernsey and Herm in Channel Islands. Form on Guernsey has been distinguished as separate subspecies (*C. r. peta*) but re-examination with further material confirms they belong to nearest mainland subspecies (*C. r. russula*) (Cranbrook & Crowcroft, 1958, 1961).

DESCRIPTION See Field Identification Characters. Species difficult to separate from slightly smaller Lesser White-toothed Shrew except by careful study of teeth. First large upper tooth (only premolar) more expanded on lingual side and last two unicuspids larger (see drawings in Cranbrook & Crowcroft, 1958).

MEASUREMENTS From specimens on all 3 islands (Cranbrook & Crowcroft): h.&b. 74.0 mm (51 meas., range 60 to 80 mm); tail 40.0 mm (51 meas., range 36 to 45 mm); more recent data (Bishop, unpubl. thesis, 1962), h.&b. 74.7 mm (140 meas., range 62 to 89 mm); tail 40.6 mm (141 meas., range 34 to 46 mm); weight 8.2 g (123 weighed, range 6 to 10 g).

HABITAT Abundant in all habitats on coast and inland on Alderney (Matthews, 1947); equally distributed over Guernsey habitats (farmland, arable and rough pasture, Bishop, unpubl. thesis, 1962); on Herm occurs abundantly wherever there is low cover (Cranbrook & Crowcroft, 1960)

GENERAL HABITS No information from Channel Islands. Little from Continent: said to be less agile than *Sorex* spp. and more resistant to starvation. More nocturnal than *Sorex* spp. (Saint-Girons, 1959). 'Caravan' behaviour (young following behind mother in Indian file each holding tail or fur of preceding one) recorded for this species (Zippelius, 1957).

BREEDING Data from Guernsey and Alderney for one season (Bishop, unpubl. thesis, 1962) show breeding season begins in March, reaches peak (90% pregnant or lactating) in June, falls off sharply in August and concludes with an odd record in October. Mean number of embryos 4.1 (9 records, range 3 to 6).

POPULATION Bishop determined age from degree of wear of last lower molar, showing that young come into population from June onwards, predominating from August and overwinter without coming into breeding condition. Parent generation almost died off by October, completely so by Jan. Population, therefore, has yearly turnover, as in *Sorex* spp.

Lesser White-toothed Shrew *Crocidura suaveolens* (Pallas)

DISTRIBUTION Distributed over central and southern parts of Palaearctic Region, much as preceding species but absent from most of Iberian Peninsula and northern parts of France and Germany (though information from France, at least, is scanty). Nineteen subspecies described. In British Isles present on Jersey and Sark of Channel Islands (presumably French race *C. s. mimula*) and on Scilly Isles with form originally named as separate species but now reckoned as subspecies, *C. s. cassiteridum*.

DESCRIPTION See Field Identification Characters. Very like preceding species in external appearance; distinguished by teeth (see *C. russula*). Small constant difference in teeth of Scilly subspecies.

MEASUREMENTS Channel Islands (Cranbrook & Crowcroft, 1958; Bishop, unpubl. thesis, 1962) h.&b. 67.8 mm (29 meas., range 60 to 76 mm); tail 42.7 mm (28 meas., range 35 to 50 mm); weight 5.8 g (20 weighed, range 3 to 11 g). Scilly Isles, h.&b. 69.4 mm (16 meas., range 57 to 73 mm); tail 33.1 mm (16 meas., range 26 to 38 mm).

HABITAT Channel Islands. On Sark shrews were caught all over the fallow farm land and hedge-banks with a concentration in a small patch of wood. On Jersey, Morrison-Scott (1937) examined owl pellets which suggested the Common Shrew occurred inland and the 'Musk' Shrew around the coast. Bishop's (1962) results failed to confirm this but he found both shrews notably scarce. On Scilly Isles widely distributed in all habitats from pebbly beaches to bare pine plantations; prefers most of all heathland vegetation with bracken and bramble and deep leaf litter. Found on St Mary's, Tresco, St Martins, St Agnes, Bryher, Tean, Annet, Samson and some, but not all, of the smaller islands (I.Linn, unpubl.).

GENERAL HABITS Little known. Spencer-Booth (1956) observed refection in captive Scilly Shrew. Frequently caught in traps during daytime. Habit of 'caravanning' known for this species (I.Linn, unpubl.).

FOOD Spencer-Booth found insects taken most readily, including sandhoppers which were abundant on stony shores. Hawkins & Jewell (1962) measured food intake and found 7.4 g per day wet weight (1.9 Kcal/g body wt/day).

RELATIONS WITH MAN Easier to keep in captivity than *Sorex* spp.; can survive longer and recover more quickly if short of food.

Order Chiroptera

Bats are one of the most distinctive groups among mammals and only ones that can fly. They have many affinities with the order Insectivora from which they may have evolved. Fore-limb shows most obvious modification for achievement of true flight. Radius or forearm long and curved; first digit (thumb) with its hooked claw free and relatively short, but remaining digits much elongated (especially the third) and form supporting framework for membrane of skin which continues to ankle (sometimes to base of toes) and thence to tail (Fig. 17 & *Photograph 27*). Thin spur of cartilage, the *calcar*, attached to inner side of ankle, supports part of outer border of interfemoral membrane, which lies between hind-limbs. In some non-European bats, whose tails are very short or absent, there is usually reduction in interfemoral membrane; in some species it is only a narrow flange on inner side of legs. It is also insignificant in a few foreign families whose tails are well developed but free.

Several adaptations for flight in internal anatomy. Upper part of sternum, or breast-bone, has well-developed keel to which powerful pectoral muscles are attached. These pull wings downwards during flight, shoulder muscles being used for up stroke. Clavicle, or collar-bone, which connects top of sternum and shoulder joints strong and curved, and provides firm support for humerus, or upper arm. Bones of neck and back robust and some of them may be fused together for extra strength. In some bats first and second ribs fused not only with sternum and backbone but also with each other, thus making solid ring.

In contrast to upper part of skeleton, bones of pelvis, legs and tail relatively weak. Thigh-bones twisted round and knees therefore bend in opposite direction to that of most mammals.

Classified into two suborders: (1) Megachiroptera, comprising only one family Pteropidae, common 'flying foxes' and fruit-bats, of Asia, Africa and Pacific; (2) Microchiroptera which include rest of order, divided into 16 families, of which only two represented in British Isles. Megachiroptera essentially fruit-eaters, though some feed also on berries, buds and other vegetable matter. Microchiroptera mostly insectivorous (entirely so in Europe), but few families have mixed diet of insects and small vertebrates. Others have become specialized as fruit-, fish-, or pollen-eaters,

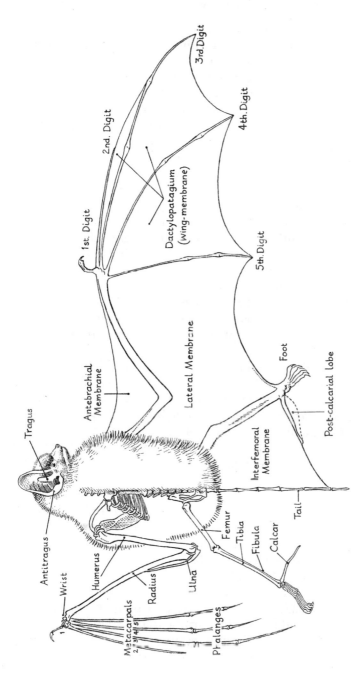

FIG. 17. Diagram of a generalized bat to illustrate the terms used in the Key. The post-calcarial lobe is shown with a dotted outline because it is absent from some species.

and one is sanguinivorous. Modifications for various feeding habits are chiefly in shape and number of teeth, and sometimes in shape of jaw and structure of tongue.

Two families of Microchiroptera, Rhinolophidae and Vespertilionidae, occur in Great Britain. Rhinolophidae contain two sub-families, Rhinolophinae and Hipposiderinae, the former with one genus, *Rhinolophus*, and the latter with seven (non-European) genera.

Rhinolophidae have prominent cutaneous nose-leaf (Fig. 18) consisting of three parts: (1) *horseshoe*, which covers most of face above mouth and surrounds nostrils; (2) *sella*, protruding from central part of horseshoe; (3) *lancet*, a pointed and erect piece of skin, surmounting other two sections, in region of forehead. Ear without tragus but has prominent antitragus (Fig. 18). Tail short and interfemoral membrane shallow. Wing and antebrachial membrane broad. Two rudimentary pubic nipples present. Rhinolophid bats alight by rolling sideways in air and grasping resting-place with feet. They hang suspended by toes, rest of body being free of its surroundings. When asleep they wrap wings round body, almost completely covering dorsal and ventral surfaces.

Vespertilionidae contain six sub-families, of which Vespertilioninae is the largest and the only one found in Great Britain, where it is represented by seven genera: *Myotis*, *Vespertilio* (vagrant), *Eptesicus*, *Nyctalus*, *Pipistrellus*, *Barbastella* and *Plecotus*.

Vespertilionid bats have lobe of skin, known as *tragus*, which arises from anterior base of outer ear, its shape differing in the various genera. No nose-leaf and nostrils relatively simple in shape.

Bats now known to find their way about and to detect prey by echolocation. Since pioneer experiments of Lazaro Spallanzani in Italy in 1794, ability of bats to avoid objects in path of flight in total darkness studied widely. Formerly held that some tactile sense associated with wing-membrane, tragus or nose-leaf responsible; but in 1920 Hartridge suggested bats might emit short-wavelength squeaks or pulses, the reflected echoes from which could give information about nature and position of surrounding objects. Tests made later by Griffin and Galambos in U.S.A. confirmed this theory and more recent work by Griffin and others has revealed many aspects of echolocation in several families

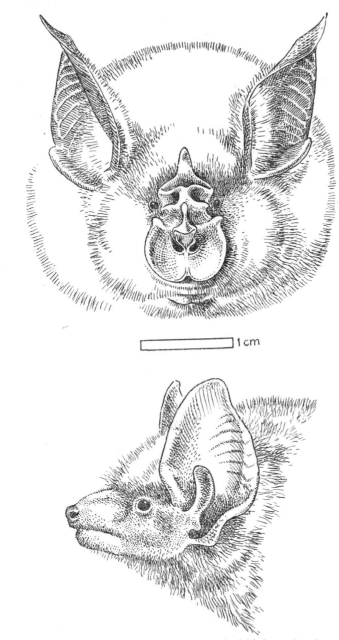

1 cm

FIG. 18. Heads of (above) a Rhinolophid bat, the Greater
Horseshoe (*Rhinolophus ferrumequinum*), and of (below) a Vespertilionid bat, the Serotine (*Eptesicus serotinus*), showing details of
characteristic nose-leaf in the former and of tragus and shape of
the ear in the latter.

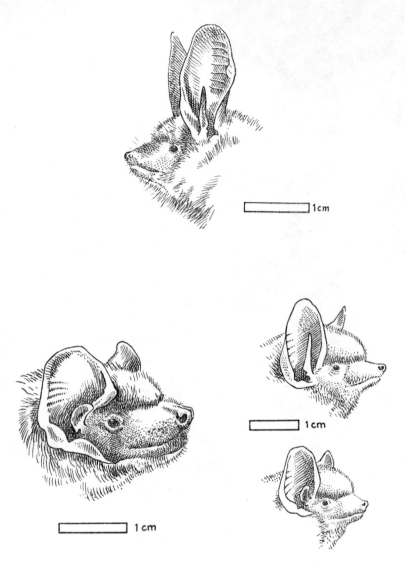

Fig. 19. Heads of (top) Bechstein's Bat (*Myotis bechsteini*), (lower left) Noctule (*Nyctalus noctula*), (upper right) Natterer's Bat (*M. nattereri*), and (lower right) Pipistrelle (*Pipistrellus pipistrellus*), showing diagnostic details of ears and tragus (see text).

(Griffin, 1958). Pulse-repetition rate of Vespertilionidae may rise to 50 or 60 a second when flying bat approaches stationary object; in some Vespertilionidae increases to 200 a second when bat is in active pursuit of insect. Each pulse lasts average of 2 milliseconds (1/500 second) in Vespertilionidae, maximum intensity frequency being about 50 kc. Pulse, which is emitted through open mouth, scans about one octave (frequency modulation) during its short burst. Rhinolophidae emit pulses of almost constant frequency through nose, the horseshoe concentrating sound along narrow beam. Repetition rate in this family seldom more than five or six a second, each pulse lasting about 65 milliseconds (1/16th second) at frequency of 80 or 100 kc according to species (Möhres, 1954).

Certain objections to this theory as explained above. For example, intensity of squeaks so great that they might deafen bat and prevent it hearing fainter returning echo. Moreover, pulse and frequency overlap at high repetition rate so that former masks latter. Perhaps bat does not listen to echoes themselves but to beat frequency, which is audible when overlapping occurs (Pye, 1960), but other theories have been proposed.

Some echolocating pulses have audible component ('tick', 'buzz' or 'click' sounds) at lower end of frequency scale; these should not be confused with audible *signalling* cries described later under 'General Habits'.

Breeding habits of very few British bat species studied in detail. Copulation, apparently promiscuous, observed under natural conditions during autumn and winter, sperm being stored in female genital tract until hibernation ends in spring. Fertilization then occurs and is effected by stored sperm. This seems to be usual sequence, with at least one regular exception. Young, usually single in Great Britain, born blind; young of Vespertilionidae hairless, but that of Rhinolophidae with sparse down on back at birth. Offspring (both families) sometimes carried by mother in flight during first day or two, then left in roost when adult goes hunting. Eyes open after about seventh day. First flight when about 20 to 22 days old, but no exact data for most species. Father takes no part in rearing of young and adult males of some species tend to form separate colonies during parturition season, but more observations needed to confirm. Age at which bats first copulate not studied in detail, probably in second autumn for most species.

Weights vary widely according to age, season of year, whether captured with full stomachs and (for females) whether pregnant when captured. Specific conditions mentioned in text where known.

Several British species have shown themselves adaptable to captivity for varying periods. Soon become tame and may even learn to fly to owner's hand for food. Mealworms usually given as staple diet, but, unless other food offered, bats sooner or later lose condition and eventually die owing to lack of vitamins or trace elements. Spiders, moths, beetles, grasshoppers and other insects necessary for preserving health, but satisfactory results have been obtained by supplementing mealworms with slightly moistened mash of hard-boiled egg, biscuit-meal and cream cheese. Water must be given regularly. May be necessary to feed by hand in early stages of captivity. Most bats soon learn to find food if shallow feeding-dish placed in same spot in cage, which should be kept draught-proof and made preferably of wood. Small inner sleeping-box, or pieces of bark, should be provided for Vespertilionid species. Rhinolophid bats prefer to hang suspended from roof of cage, to which small twigs or pieces of rough sacking should be fixed to afford footholds.

FIELD IDENTIFICATION CHARACTERS

Most British land mammals present few difficulties of identification. Bats are exception; therefore dichotomous key provided. Brief account below of structures, some specialized, upon which identification based, together with the illustrations in Fig. 17, should make key straightforward to use. To avoid confusion, only those external characters which are diagnostic included in key. As few technical terms as possible have been used and these are explained below.

Nose-leaf Cutaneous outgrowth above upper lip covering most of face.

Tragus Lobe of skin at anterior base of outer ear. May be bean- or spear-shaped and resembles small inner ear in front of ear-channel. Should not be confused with posterior base of ear, on upper side of which is anti-tragus.

Interfemoral membrane Expanse of membrane stretching between hind-limbs and embracing most of tail.

Calcar Spur of cartilage arising from inner side of ankle and running along part of outer edge of interfemoral membrane.

Post-calcarial lobe Flat extension of skin on outer edge of interfemoral membrane near its junction with ankle.

1. Nose-leaf present; no tragus (Rhinolophidae) 2
   Simple nose; tragus present (Vespertilionidae) 3

2. Forearm over 50 mm ... ... GREATER HORSESHOE BAT
   Forearm under 41 mm ... ... LESSER HORSESHOE BAT

3. Tragus broadest at top 4
   Tragus longer than broad 5

4. Forearm 49 mm and over ... ... NOCTULE
   Forearm 38 45 mm ... ... LEISLER'S BAT

5. Ears joined at inner bases; nostrils open upwards 6
   Ears separate; nostrils open forward ... ...' 7

6. Ears 34 37 mm long ... ... LONG-EARED BAT
   Ears 14–16 mm long ... ... BARBASTELLE

7. Post-calcarial lobe present; forearm under 33 mm PIPISTRELLE
   Post-calcarial lobe small; last two vertebrae of tail project about 6 mm
   beyond interfemoral membrane... ... ... SEROTINE
   No post-calcarial lobe 8

8. Forearm 57–64 mm; ears 27–28 mm long ... MOUSE-EARED BAT
   Forearm under 45 mm 9

9. Interfemoral membrane has fringe of hairs on extreme outer border
   near tail; ears 14–17 mm long ... ... NATTERER'S BAT
   Interfemoral membrane not fringed 10

10. Ears 18–26 mm long and extending for about half their length beyond
    muzzle, when laid forward ... ... BECHSTEIN'S BAT
    Ears under 18 mm long, reaching to tip of muzzle, when laid forward 11

11. Calcar extends half-way along outer border of interfemoral membrane; foot half as long as tibia ... ... WHISKERED BAT
    Calcar extends two-thirds along outer border of interfemoral membrane; foot more than half length of tibia ... DAUBENTON'S BAT

FAMILY RHINOLOPHIDAE

Monogeneric according to Simpson, though others, e.g. E.&M.-S., follow Miller and include the seven genera of the Hipposiderinae. Contains only one very large and specialized genus, *Rhinolophus*.

GENUS *Rhinolophus*

Distinguished by peculiar and highly developed nose-leaf and by absence of tragus in ear. Many species and subspecies spread throughout Old World: Allen gives 50 species in Ethiopian region. E.&M.-S. give 21 species in Palaearctic Region and India. Believed Oriental in origin. Teeth $\dfrac{1.1.2.3}{2.1.3.3} = 32$.

Greater Horseshoe Bat *Rhinolophus ferrumequinum* (Schreber)

DISTRIBUTION Range abroad over C. and S. Europe, eastward through S. Russia and Asia Minor. Occurs in Palestine, Persia, Himalayas, China, Korea and Japan. Several subspecies named, among which *R. f. insulanus* of England and Wales. Diagnosis based on forearm measurement not exceeding 55 mm, but British specimens with forearm of 58 mm (as in typical European race) not uncommon and therefore separation of these two seems invalid. Locally common in S.W. England, S. and W. Wales. Occurs in most southern counties eastward to Kent. One record for East Anglia. Absent Scotland and Ireland.

DESCRIPTION See Field Identification Characters. Dorsal surface ashy brown, underside pale buff. Immature greyer than adult. Female usually larger than male.

MEASUREMENTS H.&b. 65 mm (up to 68 mm); forearm 54 mm (up to 58 mm); wing-span 330 to 385 mm. Weight varies considerably through year, with maximum in December when average male weighs 20.6 g (heaviest 23.4 g) and average female 21.6 g (heaviest 27.3 g). By April weight decreases by 23% (males) and 28% (females) (Hooper & Hooper, 1956).

HABITAT Caves and tunnels during hibernation. Often frequents lofts and attics May to October. Some habitats (both types) used throughout year.

GENERAL HABITS Voice a loud, high-pitched, penetrating squeak. Very noisy in colonies with young. Emerges rather late and flies at intervals throughout night. Flights observed in all months in south-western counties. Ringing by various workers shows movements usually local (under two miles). Longest flight recorded in England forty miles (Hooper & Hooper, 1956).

Gregarious. Usually flies low (2–3 ft), but sometimes higher (10 ft). Flight heavy and butterfly-like, with frequent glides.

BREEDING Copulation in Oct, and sperm stored during winter in uterus, also in white translucent plug, probably formed of urethral gland secretion from male, which completely occludes vagina. Ovulation during April with consequent fertilization by stored sperm from uterus. In British Isles blastocyst seen entering uterus third week in April (Matthews, 1937). Plug shed later and all sperm stored therein appear to have undergone phagocytosis. Single young born late June to mid-July. Milk teeth stated to be absorbed before birth but does not always happen. Young observed to fly short distances when about 22 days old, before being weaned. Lactation period unknown, but by mid-August most juveniles independent. Some segregation of sexes apparent in nursing colonies, where parous females usually accompanied by non-breeding immature females and a few immature males. Female does not breed until at least second autumn, more probably third.

FOOD Beetles, moths, other nocturnal insects and spiders. Some prey caught by bat dropping on ground with outstretched wings. This observed in N. Devon where bat was seen to settle on grass and seize dor-beetles feeding on cow-dung (M.Blackmore, unpubl.). Prey usually taken to resting-place where dismembered and eaten. Small insects devoured on wing.

PREDATORS Both Barn and Tawny Owls will roost during winter in disused mine-borings occupied by Horseshoe Bats. Examination of pellets in two mines showed hibernating bats formed large part of diet in December and January.

RELATIONS WITH MAN Difficult to keep in captivity but can be successfully tamed on mixed diet of mealworms, moths and plenty of water. Male and female captured in Feb 1933 died after 643 and 671 days respectively (M.Blackmore, unpubl.).

Lesser Horseshoe Bat *Rhinolophus hipposideros* (Bechstein)
DISTRIBUTION Ranges throughout Europe as far east as S. Russia; also in Asia Minor, Persia, Arabia, N.W. and N.E. Africa (Morocco, Sudan and Abyssinia). British race has been described as *R. h. minutus*, but differences in length of forearm and

skull between three named European subspecies so slight that they are virtually indistinguishable. In British Isles range includes all areas where Greater Horseshoe is found, but also extends into Midlands and Yorkshire. Recorded in three East Anglian localities. Common in parts of S., W. and N. Wales. Occurs in Ireland where confined to west, but prevalent in some limestone districts.

DESCRIPTION See Field Identification Characters. Dorsal surface greyish-brown; underside paler. Fur of immature noticeably grey. Little difference in size of sexes.

MEASUREMENTS H.&b. 35 mm (up to 39.5 mm); forearm 37 mm (up to 40 mm); wing-span 228 to 250 mm. Weight of small series, weighed between Oct and April by Hooper & Hooper (1956) showed average of 5.3 g in Oct, increasing to 6 g in Dec, with decrease to 4.9 g in April.

GENERAL HABITS Voice a high-pitched squeak. Activity rhythm like that of Greater Horseshoe but emerges earlier. Gregarious but usually in smaller colonies than Greater Horseshoe. Flight low to medium (4 to 15 ft). No defined beat; erratic and rapid, with sudden alterations in height. Short glides.

BREEDING As for Greater Horseshoe, but young often born at beginning of July in West Country and sometimes during last week in June. Late births up to fourth week in July. Some females may bear young when one year old (Sluiter, 1960).

POPULATION Bezem, Sluiter & van Heerdt (1960) give expectation of life for adult 1.8 years, life-span 8 years.

FOOD Small beetles, moths and spiders. Method of capture and disposal similar to Greater Horseshoe.

RELATIONS WITH MAN Does not survive captivity for more than a few weeks.

FAMILY VESPERTILIONIDAE

Contains one very large sub-family, Vespertilioninae, distributed all over world, and five small sub-families with one or two genera each, also very widely spread.

Simple nose, without nose-leaf; ear with tragus. Tail fairly long and interfemoral membrane well developed. Third finger has three phalanges, of which the distal one cartilaginous.

GENUS *Myotis*

Contains more species than any other genus in the order, and is represented practically throughout the world. Species vary considerably in size. All have slender muzzle, ear and tragus.

Myotis is most primitive of Vespertilionidae. Teeth $\frac{2.1.3.3}{3.1.3.3} = 38$.

Whiskered Bat *Myotis mystacinus* (Kuhl)

DISTRIBUTION Range abroad covers most of Europe and Asia. Nearly twenty Asiatic subspecies described. Common in most of British Isles. Apparently rare in Scotland but may have been overlooked. Said to be rare in East Anglia but two colonies recently recorded in Norfolk.

DESCRIPTION See Field Identification Characters. Dorsal surface brown with long, silky hairs, often paler at tips. Underside greyish-white in adults, dark in immatures.

MEASUREMENTS H.&b. 46 mm (up to 50 mm); forearm 34 mm (up to 37 mm); wing-span 225 to 245 mm. Weight 4.5 to 6 g (Ryberg, 1947).

HABITAT Buildings and trees in summer. Often hibernates in caves, rock-fissures and cellars.

GENERAL HABITS Voice a low buzzing squeak. Emerges early. Specimens observed on wing at all hours of night but evidence suggests activity intermittent. Sometimes makes short flights by day, especially in spring. Usually found alone but sometimes gregarious both in summer and winter. Flies low to medium (4 to 13 ft) often near foliage. Not very rapid; somewhat fluttering.

BREEDING Copulation observed in Dutch cave in Jan (van Nieuwenhoven, 1956). Single young in British Ises born June or July.

POPULATION Results from 13 years' ringing of hibernating population in Holland by Sluiter, van Heerdt & Bezem (1956) show some 40% die in first 6 months of life, after this *c.* 20% annually (mean expectations of life 4.4 and 4.9 years). Life-span 20 years.

FOOD Small insects and spiders. Prey usually picked from foliage and fences, but also taken on wing.

R

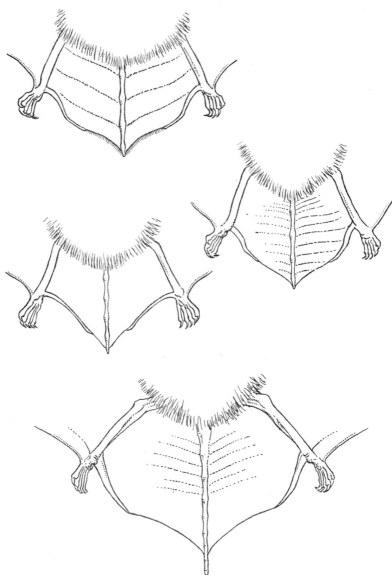

Fig. 20. Tail area of Natterer's Bat (*Myosotis nattereri*), top left; Whiskered Bat (*M. mystacinus*), top right; and Daubenton's Bat (*M. daubentoni*), middle left; showing diagnostic details in this genus of calcar, interfemoral membrane, etc. (see text). The tail area of the Serotine (*Eptesicus serotinus*), below, shows how the last vertebrae of the tail project beyond the margin of the interfemoral membrane.

RELATIONS WITH MAN Can be tamed fairly easily and will survive captivity for several months on diet of moths and small beetles.

Natterer's Bat *Myotis nattereri* (Kuhl)

DISTRIBUTION Occurs throughout most of Europe and Asia east to Japan. Few subspecies. Fairly common in most of England and Wales. Recorded occasionally in southern half of Scotland and in many parts of Ireland.

DESCRIPTION See Field Identification Characters. Dorsal surface medium greyish-brown; underside white with distinct line of demarcation from base of ear to shoulder.

MEASUREMENTS H.&b. 43 mm (up to 50 mm); forearm 40 mm (up to 43 mm); wing-span 265 to 285 mm. Ryberg (1947) gives extremes of weight as 5 to 9.5 g for Swedish specimens but without dates or details of age and sex. Adult British examples in winter vary between 8 and 9.5 g. One female weighed in September 1937 was 10.3 g.

GENERAL HABITS Voice a shrill squeak, sometimes heard when bat is hunting. Emerges early and flies at intervals through night. Active on mild nights in autumn and winter but probably for short period only. Gregarious in summer but often solitary during hibernation. Flight low to medium (4 to 15 ft) and rather slow. Frequents woodlands and well-timbered parks. Long series of electronic highspeed flash photographs by Eric Hosking and S.C.Bisscrôt show that, when bat is flying with body approximately on horizontal plane, tail is directed downwards at angle of at least sixty degrees and *not* held in straight line behind body as sometimes stated.

BREEDING Copulation observed during Dec in cave (Gilbert, 1948). Single young born in British Isles at end of June or early July.

FOOD As for Whiskered Bat. Preys much on moths. Some food is picked off foliage.

RELATIONS WITH MAN Adapts itself to captivity easily.

Bechstein's Bat *Myotis bechsteini* (Kuhl)

DISTRIBUTION Central and S. Europe east to S. Russia; also S. Sweden. No subspecies. Regarded as rare throughout range.

Rarest of native British bats. Until 1946 was recorded only in Hampshire, I. of Wight, Berkshire and Sussex. Specimens have since been found in Dorset (several), Gloucester, Shropshire, Somerset and Wiltshire.

DESCRIPTION See Field Identification Characters. In colour similar to Natterer's Bat.

MEASUREMENTS H.&b. 50 mm (up to 53 mm); forearm 41 mm (up to 44 mm); wing-span 237 to 252 mm. Ryberg (1947) gives 9 to 11 g as extreme weights of non-pregnant Swedish specimens.

HABITAT Holes in trees during summer. Three British specimens taken after entering houses in autumn and one apparently had regular roost in roof. Frequently hibernates in caves.

GENERAL HABITS Voice a low buzz; also loud, high-pitched squeals when excited. Little information except that it is said to emerge late on Continent; but Vesey-FitzGerald (1949) who watched small Hampshire colony in August saw them on wing about fifteen minutes after sunset. Gregarious in summer, living in small colonies. Flight low to medium (4 to 15 ft) and rather slow.

BREEDING Single young born in June (C. Europe).

FOOD Probably preys mostly on moths. A bat, almost certainly this species, watched at close range in Shropshire on moonlight night, 2 September 1955, flew round oak tree for twenty minutes catching moths both on wing and resting on leaves. Food preferences in captivity not reliable as indication of behaviour in natural state, but one specimen showed marked choice for moths, some of which it snatched from walls of room.

RELATIONS WITH MAN One British specimen quickly became tame and fed from hand immediately after capture. Survived for 172 days and frequently drank on wing from filled bath.

Mouse-eared Bat *Myotis myotis* (Borkhausen)

DISTRIBUTION Common in many parts of European Continent. Ranges east to Russia; China, Persia, Afghanistan, Israel. Status in British Isles uncertain; perhaps rare winter immigrant but may be resident. Doubtfully recorded London, before 1835. Authentic occurrences in Cambridgeshire, 1888, and Dorset (Blackmore, 1956), where several found subsequently.

DESCRIPTION Average size larger than any native British species. Medium-brown dorsal surface contrasts strongly with greyish-white underside. Clear line of demarcation from base of ear to shoulder.

MEASUREMENTS H.&b. 65 to 79 mm; forearm 57 to 64 mm; length of ear 27 to 28 mm, width 17.5 to 19 mm (when laid forward, ear extends about 5 mm beyond muzzle); wing-span 355 to 412 mm (exceptionally 450 mm).

HABITAT Buildings and caves.

GENERAL HABITS Loud strident shriek when handled or alarmed. Known on Continent to travel considerable distances, up to 260 km (Eisentraut, 1937); therefore no reason to suppose that British examples mentioned above accidentally imported.

RELATIONS WITH MAN Has been kept in captivity quite easily for periods of up to two years on Continent.

Daubenton's Bat *Myotis daubentoni* (Kuhl)

DISTRIBUTION Covers most of Europe and several parts of Asia east to Japan. Fewer than six subspecies. Locally numerous in most counties of England, N. Wales and Scotland. Recorded in nine Irish counties and has probably been overlooked in many others.

DESCRIPTION See Field Identification Characters. Dorsal surface medium to dark brown with tips of fur paler. Underside greyish but often with pale yellowish tint. Immature specimens darker than adults.

MEASUREMENTS H.&b. 46 mm (up to 51 mm); forearm 36 mm (up to 38 mm); wing-span 220 to 245 mm. Sexes about equal in size. Weight of non-pregnant Swedish specimens 7 to 10 g (Ryberg, 1947). Two British females in Sept were 8.5 and 11 g.

HABITAT Buildings, caves, hollow trees and rock-fissures in summer. Hibernates in caves and buildings.

GENERAL HABITS Voice, an angry buzz when alarmed; usually silent on wing. Emerges rather late and hunts over water, often in large numbers. Can be observed throughout night but each individual not continuously active. Frequent returns made to roosting-place and after midnight periods of rest may be prolonged but no precise information available. A colony of over 200 in Ulster seen hunting over lake for 150 minutes when all left suddenly and moved across open ground to another lake about a mile away, where followed by observer. In Hampshire several bats were active at midnight on River Avon on warm September night, but on following night when cold breeze was blowing none seen although other species were present. Extremely gregarious in summer when colonies of several hundreds not unusual. During winter, when it often hibernates alone, small clusters of three to six bats may be found. Flight very low over water in wide circles. Lacks abrupt 'jerking' movements of Pipistrelle which also often flies over water.

BREEDING Copulation observed in German cave in Oct; male hung close behind female and apparently tried to stimulate her by biting neck and back of head (Eisentraut, 1949). Another pair, in Dutch cave, copulated in February and attracted notice by loud squeaking (van Nieuwenhoven, 1956). In British Isles young seen second week in June but births occur up to early July. No segregation of sexes when females have young.

POPULATION Results from marking hibernating cave populations (Bezem, Sluiter & van Heerdt, 1960) in Holland suggest mean expectation of life 3.5 years for adults after first 6 months and life span of 16 years.

FOOD Mainly small aquatic insects, eaten during flight.

RELATIONS WITH MAN Will survive in captivity for a few months.

GENUS *Vespertilio*

Palaearctic. Restricted by Miller (1907) to two species, one of which vagrant to British Isles (see below). Teeth $\dfrac{2.1.1.3}{3.1.2.3} = 32$.

Parti-coloured Bat *Vespertilio murinus* L.

DISTRIBUTION Northern and C. Europe; Asia. Rare vagrant to British Isles. Three British records; Plymouth, and Yarmouth Roads (both before 1835), Whalsay, Shetland (1927).

DESCRIPTION Dorsal surface dark brown with pale white tips marbled with patches of pale yellowish-brown. Underside whitish-cream.

MEASUREMENTS H.&b. 56 to 63 mm; wing-span 260 to 286 mm. Short rounded oval ear about as broad as long (12 to 16 mm), which does not reach nostril when laid forward. Short, bean-shaped tragus.

HABITAT Buildings, holes in trees.

GENUS *Eptesicus*

Another widespread genus with similar world distribution to foregoing, but not so many species. Also closely related to *Vespertilio*. Teeth as *Vespertilio*.

Serotine *Eptesicus serotinus* (Schreber)

DISTRIBUTION Ranges widely over Europe and Asia. South-western limit of range Algeria and Tunisia. Several subspecies described. In British Isles confined to England, where locally not uncommon in Kent, Surrey, Sussex, and Hampshire (including I. of Wight). Extends west through Dorset, Devon and Cornwall, and east to Essex and Suffolk. Recorded also Middlesex, Buckinghamshire (probably), Hertfordshire and Cambridgeshire.

DESCRIPTION See Field Identification Characters. Dorsal fur long, dark brown, sometimes with chestnut tinge. Underside paler.

MEASUREMENTS H.&b. 74 mm (up to 80 mm); forearm 50 mm (up to 54 mm); wing-span 348 to 380 mm. Ear longer than broad. Weight of non-pregnant Swedish specimens 13 to 17 g (Ryberg, 1947). English free-flying juvenile male 24 g; adult nursing female 33 g. Juvenile male reared in captivity weighed 10 g at 14 days, 15 g at 21 days and 24 g at 7 weeks when weaned (Earl of Cranbrook, unpubl.).

HABITAT Buildings and hollow trees. Has very rarely been found hibernating in caves.

GENERAL HABITS Usually silent, but strident *tick, tick, tick* sometimes uttered during flight when two bats meet. Time of emergence variable, from sunset until about seventy minutes after. Experiments with marked male show intermittent activity throughout night (H.E.Jenner, *in litt.*). Hibernates from mid-Oct to mid-March, sometimes until beginning of May. Flight medium to high (8 to 40 ft). Sometimes dives very low. Noticeably broad-winged. Gregarious. British colonies of up to fifty specimens noted.

BREEDING Single young observed in British Isles 5 July; it was fluttering 'somewhat uncertainly' in roost 8 August (H.E.Jenner, *in litt.*). Pregnant females taken in Dorset on 9 June gave birth on 16 and 22 June. Young were able to fly after about 20 days (M.Blackmore, unpubl.) (*Photograph 28*).

FOOD Beetles and moths. Specimens observed to settle heavily on branches, with wings 'spread-eagled', to snatch prey from foliage. Insects eaten during flight and at rest (*Photograph 29*).

GENUS *Nyctalus*

Palaearctic and Oriental. About six species, four of which occur in Europe. Closely allied to *Pipistrellus* (see p. 245), with shortened fifth finger and long narrow wing. Teeth $\dfrac{2.1.2.3}{3.1.2.3} = 34$.

Leisler's Bat *Nyctalus leisleri* (Kuhl)

DISTRIBUTION Ranges over C., S. and E. Europe; also N. India. Few subspecies described. Usually regarded as rare in England but status hardly known. Wide distribution indicated by records from Yorkshire, Cheshire, Warwickshire, Worcestershire, Northamptonshire, Gloucestershire, Somerset, Devon, Cambridgeshire, Hertfordshire, Essex, Kent and Surrey. Locally common in many parts of Ireland where it replaces Noctule.

DESCRIPTION See Field Identification Characters. Dorsal surface dark brown, with tips of fur often paler; basal half of pelage very dark brown, almost black. Underside slightly paler, sometimes with greyish tint.

MEASUREMENTS H.&b. 60 mm (up to 63 mm); forearm 41 mm (up to 45 mm); wing-span 290 to 320 mm. Weight 14 to 20 g (Moffat, 1900). Female usually larger than male.

HABITAT Buildings and hollow trees.

GENERAL HABITS Voice a short, high-pitched squeak of metallic timbre when in solitary flight; often changes to strident screech when two bats meet, suggesting possible territorial rivalry. Very noisy in summer colonies. Emerges early at, or just after, sunset and flies for about an hour. Returns to roost and makes second flight of about similar length ending before sunrise (Moffat, 1900). Hibernates from October to mid-April, sometimes to first week in May. Changes roosting-place rather frequently. Lives in colonies and singly. Flight medium to high (10 to 50 ft), with shallow dives.

BREEDING Probably similar to Noctule (see p. 245). Segregation of sexes appears to occur during lactation.

FOOD Beetles, moths and flies, eaten during flight.

RELATIONS WITH MAN Quickly becomes tame. Male captured 24 Feb 1955, survived 372 days (M.Blackmore, unpubl.).

Noctule *Nyctalus noctula* (Schreber)

DISTRIBUTION Ranges over most of Europe, east through Asia to Japan; also Burma and Malaya. Less than a dozen subspecies. Common in most of England and Wales. Recorded in Scotland, where apparently uncommon, as far north as Morayshire.

DESCRIPTION See Field Identification Characters. Dorsal surface has long golden-brown fur (brightest in adult males) with silky sheen; underside very slightly paler and duller. Basal portion of fur on both sides scarcely lighter than tips (cf. Leisler's Bat). Female larger than male. Immature darker than adult.

MEASUREMENTS H.&b. 75 mm (up to 82 mm); forearm 51 mm (up to 54 mm); wing-span 353 to 387 mm. Weight varies considerably from 16 to 39 g (B.-H.&H.).

HABITAT Buildings and trees; rarely in rock-crevices.

GENERAL HABITS Voice, a shrill metallic squeak heard when bat is hunting; also a strident screech when excited. Emerges very early, often before sunset, but time variable. Flies for about 60–90 minutes and returns to roost until about one hour before sunrise when second flight is made. Although this is normal pattern, some may leave roost at any hour of night in summer,

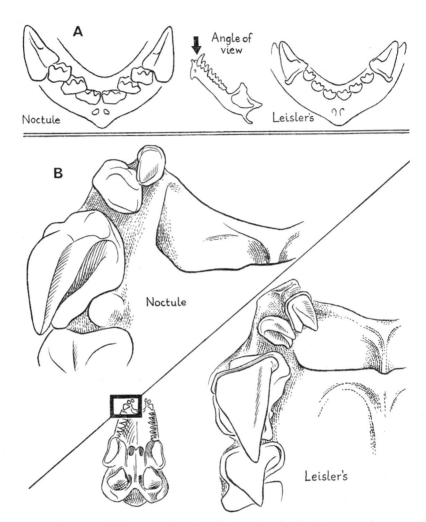

FIG. 21. Diagram showing diagnostic details between the incisors, upper and lower, of the Noctule (*Nyctalus noctula*) and Leisler's Bat (*N. leisleri*). (*a*) Lower incisors seen from the viewpoint indicated; (*b*) upper incisors in an enlargement of the area indicated in the small sketch of the skull (see text).

which suggests more than two flights made at this season; but late-night activity could be departure from one roost to another and not true feeding flight. Tree-haunting colonies move to alternative roosts at irregular and frequent intervals, especially in June and July. Observations in Germany and Holland with marked specimens show that migration occurs. Longest distance noted 750 km (Eisentraut, 1937). Hibernation from Oct until mid-March, sometimes early April, according to season. Gregarious, with colonies up to 300 recorded. Flight medium to high (15 to 80 ft). Flight well sustained with repeated steep dives.

BREEDING Copulation takes place as early as July and August in Germany (Grosser, 1903); and until Oct in Great Britain. Copulation also reported rarely in spring but may have been aberrant behaviour. Single young (in British Isles) born in June or July. Twins not uncommon on Continent. Ryberg (1947) records exceptional instance of triplets in Sweden and L. Bels (1952, unpubl.) quotes another in Holland. Some segregation of sexes apparent when females give birth to young, but mixed colonies are not uncommon towards end of July.

POPULATION Earl of Cranbrook (unpubl.) has studied by marking and recapture population of *c.* 100 in E. Anglia coming to feed on crickets at refuse tip. Population probably confined to surrounding few miles as little interchange between similar marked population 9 miles away. During July mainly females pregnant and lactating, including some one year old; in August influx of males coming into breeding condition and of newly flying young of year; in Sept young still coming into population, males go out of breeding condition and population begin to fall away, females vanishing first. By end Oct all are hibernating.

RELATIONS WITH MAN Easily tamed. Female taken 6 Oct 1933, survived 580 days (M.Blackmore, unpubl.).

GENUS *Pipistrellus*

Mainly Holarctic and Oriental, but occurs in all zoogeographical regions. Similar to *Eptesicus* but smaller, with bluntly oval ear, longer than broad. Teeth $\dfrac{2.1.2.3}{3.1.2.3} = 34$.

Pipistrelle *Pipistrellus pipistrellus* (Schreber)

DISTRIBUTION Range abroad over whole of temperate Europe and much of Asia. Many subspecies described. Commonest as well as smallest British species, ubiquitous over British Isles.

DESCRIPTION See Field Identification Characters. Dorsal surface medium to dark brown, often with reddish tinge; underside lighter. Pelage very variable. Immature usually darker than adult. Female slightly larger than male.

MEASUREMENTS H.&b. 42 mm (up to 52 mm); forearm 29 mm (up to 32 mm); wing-span 200 to 230 mm. Weight 3 to 6 g. Of population caught feeding at rubbish dump, Aug to Oct, mean weight of ♂ was 6.3 g (32 weighed, range 5.5 to 7.5 g), ♀ 6.8 g (90 weighed, range 5.5 to 7.5 g) (Lovett, 1961).

HABITAT Buildings, trees and rock-crevices. Usually occupies very confined space.

GENERAL HABITS Voice, a short high-pitched squeak often heard during flight. Emergence at or soon after sunset in August; progressively later towards either end of flying season (Venables, 1943). Some early emergence was noted in Feb and Nov by Venables, whose data during three seasons suggest that early emergence also occurs in mid-April, at end of May or early June, and at very end of season in November. Church (1957) found less variation in times of emergence in relation to sunset over similar period between June and Oct; but whereas his observations were made on a few scattered individuals, Venables watched large colony whose behaviour may have been influenced by communal living. Said to fly all night but many observations indicate activity intermittent and not continuous. Reports of all-night flights mostly based on observations made at roosting-places occupied by solitary specimens. These roosts vacated during night, but possible use of alternate temporary resting-places seems to have been overlooked. Hibernation normally from end Oct to early March, but frequent winter flights in all months recorded when temperature above 40° F (4.5° C.). Gregarious; colonies of several hundreds not uncommon. Flight medium to high (6 to 40 ft), often along definite beat; rapid and jerking.

BREEDING Ovulation and fertilization of stored sperm occurs in May. Gestation about 44 days, perhaps a little longer (Deanesly

& Warwick, 1939). Single young (in British Isles) born from third week June until second week July, with exceptionally late births in early August.

FOOD Mainly gnats but many larger insects taken. Hayden and Kirkby (1954), who examined dung under one roost, identified remains belonging to five orders of insects, including several forms which habitually fly in strong sunlight. Small prey eaten on wing but large insects carried to resting-place to be dismembered.

RELATIONS WITH MAN Easily tamed and has been kept in captivity for 'over two years' (B.-H.&H.).

GENUS *Barbastella*

Palaearctic and Oriental. Two closely related species recognized. Ears very broad and moderately long, joined at inner bases with deep notch on outer border. Nostrils open upwards. Teeth $\frac{2.1.2.3}{3.1.2.3} = 34$.

Barbastelle *Barbastella barbastellus* (Schreber)

DISTRIBUTION Ranges abroad through most of Europe into W. Asia, but nowhere recorded in large numbers. In British Isles confined to England and Wales, where distributed widely but rather locally in woodland areas as far north as Cumberland. Apparently uncommon but numerical status not really determined.

DESCRIPTION See Field Identification Characters. Dorsal surface very dark brown, almost black, with tips of long silky fur pale yellowish-brown giving frosted appearance. Underside slightly paler with tips of fur grey. Pelage noticeably extends on both sides to inner portion of wings and interfemoral membrane.

MEASUREMENTS H.&b. 49 mm (up to 52 mm); forearm 38 mm (up to 41 mm); wing-span 254 to 268 mm. Weight 6 to 8 g.

HABITAT Buildings, caves and trees (often behind loose bark in summer).

GENERAL HABITS Voice a deep 'buzz'; also harsh series of squeaks when disturbed in hibernation. Time of emergence rather variable, from sunset until about 30 minutes afterwards. Active until about midnight in August and Sept, then appears to spend long periods resting (not necessarily in roost). Further variable period of activity before dawn. Hibernates from mid-Oct to mid-April, but sometimes flies in mid-winter if weather mild. Usually found alone but small colonies recorded in summer. Flight low to medium (4 to 15 ft); heavy and fluttering as a rule, but bursts of speed noted when bat is moving from one hunting-ground to another. Alights head-upwards and also in manner of Rhinolophid bats. One observed on many nights in porch usually hung suspended by feet from under side of beam with body free.

BREEDING No information.

RELATIONS WITH MAN Difficult to keep in captivity in good health.

GENUS *Plecotus*

Mainly Palaearctic. One species. (The closely allied *Coryrhinus* of Nearctic Region has been referred to this genus by Simpson (1945)). Characterized by enormous ears, nearly equal to length of head and body, and joined at inner bases. Nostrils open upwards.

Teeth $\dfrac{2.1.2.3}{3.1.3.3} = 36.$

Long-eared Bat *Plecotus auritus* (L.)

DISTRIBUTION Extends over whole of temperate Europe and Asia east to Japan; Egypt and N. Africa. Less than a dozen subspecies. Common and widely distributed in British Isles.

DESCRIPTION See Field Identification Characters. Dorsal surface medium to greyish-brown; underside yellowish-brown or yellowish-white.

MEASUREMENTS H.&b. 46 mm (up to 51 mm); forearm 38 mm (up to 40 mm); wing-span 255 to 265 mm. Weight 5 to 9.5 g.

HABITAT Buildings and trees in summer. Hibernates in buildings and caves and probably trees.

GENERAL HABITS Voice, a high-pitched squeak, often heard when two or more bats flying together. Emerges after sunset and is intermittently active throughout night. Hibernates from about mid-Oct to mid-March, but often flies in mild winter weather. Probable migratory flight observed on warm day in November 1948, when group of bats in open formation alighted on ship about 45 miles N.E. of Spurn Point, having been watched approaching from direction of Scandinavia. After resting, they continued flight at dusk towards England (A.Gutteridge, *in litt.*). Gregarious in summer and autumn but often hibernates singly. Flight medium to high (8 to 40 ft). Frequent hovering among branches with body at angle of 45° and large ears erect and directed forward. When at rest ears are curled sideways and lie along flanks of body. When partly awake, bat will curl ears sideways so that they resemble ram's horns in shape.

BREEDING Copulation occurs Oct and Nov, but chiefly in April and May (Moffat, 1922). Not known whether spring coition occurs only among specimens too immature to copulate earlier, nor whether spring coition regular among any other British species. Single young born June or July.

FOOD Mainly moths and vanessid butterflies, but beetles, crane-flies and many other small insects also taken. Prey usually but not invariably taken on foliage and tree-trunks or (in case of butterflies) in hibernacula. Small insects eaten on wing and large prey taken to resting-place.

RELATIONS WITH MAN Can be tamed easily. A German specimen survived 428 days in captivity (Kummerlöwe, 1929).

Order Lagomorpha

This order, containing rabbits, hares and pikas, was for a long time combined with rodents and distinguished only as suborder Duplicidentata because of their having a small second upper incisor (there is also a third one which only appears in the milk dentition); superficially arrangement of teeth with wide diastema and incisors chisel-shaped and open-rooted suggests close relationship. But fossil evidence indicates that when all these animals come into record in early Eocene lagomorph and rodent groups were as well defined as now. Modern systematists have, therefore, separated hares and rabbits as self-contained order—Lagomorpha. Classified into two distinct families. (1) Ochotonidae, pikas, or mouse-hares, found in E. Europe, Asia and mountains of western N. America. Rat-size, with considerable skull differences from rabbits and hares and fore and hind limbs about equal in length. Only one living genus, *Ochotona*, known, though several fossil ones. Other family (2) Leporidae, spread throughout the world except Australia and New Zealand (now acquired by introduction), consists of homogeneous group, rabbits and hares, with 6 genera, and of 3 odd genera, sometimes placed in separate sub-family (Palaeolaginae) with fossil genera. Rabbits and hares specialized as vegetarian animals of medium size, which rely on acute senses of smell and hearing for detecting danger and on their long hind legs for escaping from it. Fore limbs smaller than hind, some species, e.g. the Arctic Hare, dispense with their use when hurried. Have habit of passing food twice through body. Like rodents, rabbits and hares undergo notable fluctuations in numbers, often, as in case of Snowshoe Hare (*Lepus americanus*), in regular cycles. Similar fluctuations imposed upon many predators which live on rabbits and hares. Range through a wide variety of habitats, being equally at home in tropics and Arctic.

FIELD IDENTIFICATION CHARACTERS

(1) Hares. Generally occupy open country, though Brown Hare may be found in woodland. Skull characters shown in Fig. 22. All hares distinguished by long hind legs and loping gait. Spend their resting period (daytime) in 'forms', or hollows made in ground vegetation (Mountain Hare makes shallow burrows), young born above ground, fully furred and with eyes open. Brown Hare (*Lepus europaeus*) weighs about 7 lb and has long ears black at tips. When running, carries tail tucked down so that white underside cannot be seen. Mountain Hare (*Lepus timidus*) has shorter ears, bluish tinge to pelage in summer, turns white in winter and mostly lives on high ground. Scottish subspecies (*L. t. scoticus*), found on moorland in Scotland and northern England and Wales, though indigenous only in the Scottish Highlands; Irish subspecies (*L. t. hibernicus*), much browner and change to winter white pelage much less complete. Brown Hare absent from Ireland (except small areas where introduced) and Mountain Hare occupies both high and low ground.

(2) Rabbit (*Oryctolagus cuniculus*). Occupies broken-up country,

especially with hedgerows, spinneys and coppices which give shelter, but also flourishes in rocky coastal areas, dunes and islands and the lower slopes of moorland. Pelage generally greyer than that of hares, ears shorter and lacking black tips and hind legs shorter. Tail usually carried upturned when the animal is

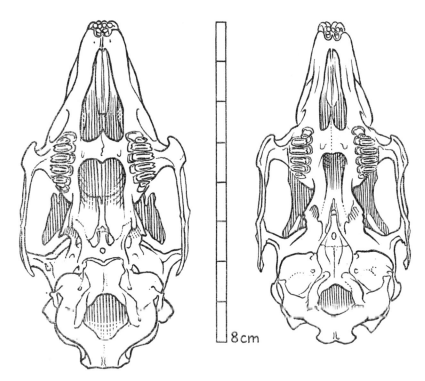

8 cm

FIG. 22. Palatal view of skulls of Brown Hare (*Lepus europaeus*), left, and of Rabbit (*Oryctolagus cuniculus*), right, showing diagnostic differences in proportions of palate (see text).

running, showing white underside. Occupies burrows and warrens, though may also live on surface like hares, young born blind and naked below ground. Iris of eye dark compared with yellowish iris of hares. Our species only one in genus, introduced into England and is same species spread by introduction over many parts of world. Has also given rise to many domestic breeds of rabbit.

s

FAMILY LEPORIDAE

Only family of this order apart from pikas (Ochotonidae). Apart from 3 aberrant genera, *Pentalagus* from Asia, *Pronolagus* from Africa and *Romerolagus* from N. America, family consists entirely of what we know as 'rabbits and hares', including American cottontails, jack rabbits, snowshoe hares, the Asiatic Bristly Rabbit and the Oriental Short-eared Rabbit.

GENUS *Oryctolagus*

Monospecific. Confined originally to Mediterranean area; has spread naturally and by introductions over much of Europe and other parts of world (spectacularly in Australia and New Zealand). Only section of Leporidae which has 'gone to ground' in a big way, though in rocky country and in woodland will live above ground like hares. Skull distinguished from that of *Lepus* by bony palate being longer in relation to posterior nares and by persistence through life of interparietal bone (Fig. 24). Teeth $\dfrac{2.0.3.3}{1.0.2.3}$

*Rabbit *Oryctolagus cuniculus* (L.)

DISTRIBUTION Europe, north to S. Sweden, east to Poland and Crete, south and west to N. Africa and Atlantic Islands. Six subspecies described (E.&M.-S.); British form (*O. c. cuniculus*) much the most widely distributed, being introduced into Australia, New Zealand, U.S.A., Chile and elsewhere. In British Isles most abundant in west, spread to Scottish Highlands in 19th century.

DESCRIPTION Sexes alike but female (doe) smaller with narrower head. Mainly buff sprinkled with black, nape reddish, underparts whitish; tail black above, white below; no black tip to ears. Much colour variation, from light sandy to black.

MEASUREMENTS Adult h.&b. up to 400 mm (16 in.). Weight at birth 30 to 40 g; at 3 to 6 weeks *c.* 300 g; adult 1,400 to 2,000 g (Stephens, 1952).

HABITAT Abundant in grassland, cultivated fields and woodlands, but also thrives on sand-dune and salt marsh, mountains, moorland or cliffs. Usually lives in warrens, which may be short tunnels or complicated burrow systems (Thompson & Worden, 1956), but also in scrub, rocky crevices or hedgebanks. Warrens not constructed to any plan, may be formed by haphazard accumulation of small burrows; characterized by blind tunnels, chambers and bolt-holes. Rats, Cats, Stoats, Foxes or Badgers may singly or severally co-habit with Rabbits in communal burrow system.

GENERAL HABITS Mainly crepuscular and nocturnal but, if undisturbed, also diurnal. Usually silent, but may scream when frightened, e.g. by Stoat; sometimes thump ground with hind feet. Fore limb unspecialized, but Rabbit digs adequately and sprints and dodges rapidly; can swim, but climbs indifferently. Makes well-marked runways, where the 'jumps' are utilized in snaring (trapping in the open now illegal). Faeces and urine often deposited in mounds at communal 'latrines'. Although may travel a mile in search of food, no clear evidence of migration in British Isles, although Rabbits often thought to move away from an area where myxomatosis is becoming established. Social, develop hierarchy in warren (Southern, 1940, 1948; Myers & Mykytowycz, 1958; Mykytowycz, 1958; Lockley, 1961).

BREEDING Mainly Jan to June, but sporadically at all times of year. Gestation 28 days; litter size 3 to 7, increasing through season. May be heavy intra-uterine mortality of over 60%, whole litters being absorbed (Brambell, 1942; Brambell & Mills, 1948). Ovulation provoked by coitus, preceded by courtship chasing and enurination (Southern, 1948; Rowley & Mollison, 1955). Nests may be made in warren, but frequently doe digs special breeding stop or short blind burrow 1 to 3 ft long; makes nest of hay or straw, lined with fur plucked from her body; temperature and humidity high, nest is also breeding place of rabbit flea *Spilopsyllus cuniculi* (Mead-Briggs & Rudge, 1960). After visits to suckle young, doe seals breeding stop. Lactation about three weeks. Doe pregnant again within twelve hours of parturition. Sex ratio equal pre-natally and in first weeks of life. Subsequently, although proportion of does believed to increase with age, sex ratio varies according to method of capture, females being more numerous in burrows and males more frequently caught in snares or by dogs. Growth continues to about nine months, but sexual maturity reached at 3 to 4 months.

POPULATION Before arrival of myxomatosis in 1953, annual crop estimated to be 60–100 million in Great Britain (Thompson &

Worden, 1956). Density of 15 to 20 rabbits per acre was considered very heavy, whereas 1 or 2 per acre was quite usual. Life expectation little over a year; numbers fluctuate with breeding activity, food supply and diseases, maximum May–June when mainly young individuals, lowest in winter when mainly adults.

FOOD Eat wide range of herbage, selecting more nutritious spp.; greatly attracted by agricultural crops, damaging cereals, roots, pastures, horticultural crops and young trees. Can eat 1 lb or more of fresh green food daily. Marked biotic effect on natural vegetation; can convert ling heath to grassland (Farrow, 1925) and by close cropping favour dwarf plant forms. By feeding close to burrows produce zonation of vegetation and may precipitate erosion. Are responsible for short turf of downland which, in absence of intensive grazing, turns to scrub. By disturbing soil encourage annual weeds and plants which they avoid (Tansley, 1949). Utilization of food assisted by reingestion, or refection, in which soft faecal pellets (mainly from caecum, where microbial digestion occurs) are swallowed (Morot, 1882; Madsen, 1939; Taylor, 1940; Southern, 1942).

PREDATORS Fox, Stoat, Buzzard, hawks, Raven, crows, Great Black-backed Gull, Wild Cat, farm and feral cats and dogs, eat adult Rabbits; Weasel, some owls, and Badger take young ones. Abundance of Rabbit before myxomatosis ensured its importance as prey species. Interesting that after myxomatosis Fox easily turned to other prey (Lever, 1959).

RELATIONS WITH MAN Introduced by Normans for food and sport, Rabbit is now major pest of agriculture and forestry. Damage to winter wheat estimated at $6\frac{1}{2}\%$, or 1.6 cwt grain per acre (Church, Jacob & Thompson, 1953; Church, Westmacott & Jacob, 1956); pasture damage also striking (Phillips, 1953; Thompson & Worden, 1956). Subject of legislation for nearly 600 years, first under game laws but latterly under Agriculture and Pests Acts; now dealt with by Rabbit Clearance Societies. Numbers controlled by cyanide gassing, dogs, shooting, ferreting, snaring, long-netting, dazzling, rabbit-proof fencing, repellents and trapping. Trapping for meat and skins once a considerable industry, but gin trap (banned in 1958) seldom achieved control, because of commercial interest (Phillips, 1955; Hume, 1958). Poison baits used for Rabbit control in Australasia, but illegal in

British Isles. Populations greatly reduced by myxomatosis in 1954–55 but show signs of recovery (Thompson & Worden, 1956; Andrewes, Thompson & Mansi, 1959). Domestic varieties much used for scientific research, fancy breeds are shown and a domestic carcass industry is thriving.

GENUS *Lepus*

An extremely widespread genus with many species, extending from tropics to Arctic of Old and New Worlds. In Europe the only genus of hares present and contains three species, two found in British Isles (see below) and African Cape Hare (*Lepus capensis*) which reaches north to Spain and Portugal. Other species in Asia, Africa and America, but majority of other genera are in New World. Snowshoe Rabbit (*L. americanus*) has notable cycles of abundance and scarcity with about a 10-year periodicity.

Brown Hare *Lepus europaeus* Pallas

DISTRIBUTION Genus has given great trouble to systematists and latest view advanced by E.&M.-S. is that *L. europaeus* and *L. capensis* roughly replace each other from north to south over whole of Old World but with broad zone of overlap, so broad that *L. europaeus* now held to reach right down to S. Africa. Otherwise range of *L. europaeus* covers Europe down to Mediterranean, eastwards into western Asia and south-eastwards to Asia Minor and Persia. Has been introduced into Scandinavia, Finland, Australia, New Zealand, Chile and region of Great Lakes in N. America. Game bag records show that until end of 19th cent. Brown Hare was generally distributed throughout British Isles except on higher mountains and in towns. During last fifty years or more has been restriction of range not only in rural areas that have become urban but in several that have remained rural. Survey carried out in 1955 showed that Brown Hares were extremely rare in Cornwall, Pembroke and a large part of the Weald. However, increase in Cornwall reported by 1960 (N.W. Moore, unpubl.). Introduced into Ireland, Isle of Man and number of Scottish islands, including Orkney (but not Hoy which has Blue Hare) and Shetland, though in latter they appear to have died out (Venables & Venables, 1955), said to have been indigenous in Jersey but to have vanished recently (Baal, 1942). British subspecies is *L. e. occidentalis*.

Fig. 23. Brown Hare (*Lepus europaeus*), top left; Mountain Hare (*L. timidus*), top right, in summer pelage; and (below) Rabbit (*Oryctolagus cuniculus*).

DESCRIPTION See Field Identification Characters. Pelage typical 'agouti' colour, but with more prominent black-tipped hairs on back than in Rabbit, giving coarser appearance. Underside white, cheeks, insides of limbs and feet yellowish or ruddy. Moult (Hewson, 1963) into dense, reddish winter coat takes place in late summer or early autumn; often contains grey patches, especially on hind quarters. Spring moult starts mid-Feb and goes on to June–July, i.e. almost beginning of autumn moult. Both moults start along back, proceed down flanks and limbs and finish on head and tail. Long legs, long black-tipped ears, tail, which is black on top and straw-coloured iris of eye distinguish species. Colour varieties not uncommon.

MEASUREMENTS B.-H.&H. give for 9 adult ♂♂ and 10 adult ♀♀ from Norfolk: h.&b. 544 mm (range 520 to 595 mm); tail with hairs 106 mm (range 85 to 120 mm); hind foot with claws 149 mm (range 147 to 152 mm); ear to notch 99 mm (range 95 to 105 mm). Weight 3.5 kg (7 lb 10 oz) (range 3.2 to 3.9 kg (7 to 8½ lb)).

HABITAT Any open ground up to c. 2,000 ft, less in Scotland where Blue Hare comes down to 1,000 ft, moorland, arable farmland, rough pasture especially downland, aerodromes, marshes, frequent in woodland. Needs some long vegetation for its 'form', but sometimes lies up in full view. Highest densities occur in plain country especially eastern counties and 'low' uplands, e.g. chalk and limestone country.

GENERAL HABITS Voice shrill, penetrating scream when hurt or terrified: both sexes make low grunts and doe has a 'guttural' pipe to young. Alleged alarm 'call' by grinding teeth. Droppings larger than those of Rabbit and slightly flattened. Surprising how so large and, often, conspicuous an animal can thrive in densely occupied land. Relies for escape on squatting in 'forms' during day, on speed and endurance when chased, and especially in knowledge of home range, which is traversed by well-used 'pads' passing through hedges and walls by customary gaps or 'smeuses' (used to be well known to poachers). Active feeding times dawn and dusk and probably through night: said to travel long distances for feeding (B.-H.&H. cite one which was tracked for 30 miles in a night), but evidence unsatisfactory. Forms changed at intervals, to denser cover during heat or rain. Intimately known home range perhaps 1–2 miles diameter but precise information lacking.

Coursed hares usually cling to this area with great adroitness; when driven out of this area may then run straight for 5 miles or more. Long hind limbs make hares least efficient going downhill and usually descend diagonally across contours. Swim well. Migration from low-lying to higher land recorded in several districts of England (N.W.Moore, unpubl.).

BREEDING Courtship and aggressive behaviour spectacular and proverbial, but no systematic account. 'Boxing', chasing, leaping (including enurination (Boback, 1954)) and aggregating in companies (hares otherwise solitary) mark onset of breeding. Breeding season in British Isles not precisely known but variable with usual peak May to July. Kolosov (1941) found season prolonged in Caucasus, 57% of females being pregnant in Jan–Feb, 100% in May and 15% between Sept and December. Ovulation follows stimulus of copulation (Stieve, 1952). Gestation 42 to 44 days and superfoetation regarded as normal by some authors, e.g. Hediger (1948), Stieve (1952). Others maintain it is exceptional and unimportant from population point of view, e.g. Rieck (1956). Considerable intra-uterine losses of embryos, especially in autumn (25% in Kolosov's figures) and these degenerating embryos easily distinguished by small size. Embryo rate in British Isles not precisely known, but some evidence from captivity (B.-H.&H.) suggests peak in mid-season, of 3 to 4, falling away before and after. This partially confirmed by Kolosov's Caucasus material, which showed mean of 1.5 in winter, 3.4 in spring and 3.0 in summer. Number of litters per year given as 4 in Germany by Rieck, 3 for hare in its first breeding season. No breeding in year of birth, young hares taking *c.* 8 months to reach sexual maturity. Young, which are born fully haired and with eyes open, deposited in forms, large litters being perhaps distributed between more than one (*Photograph 30*).

POPULATION Two types of information about hare populations; general population trends over many years from series of game-bag records and population estimates from estate owners and their keepers. From first type we learn (a) that in British Isles tendency has been for hare populations to decrease significantly since Ground Game Act of 1880 (B.-H.&H.), whereas for Denmark Andersen (1957) has shown a gradual increase since about 1900. However, (b) selected game-bag series published by Middleton

(1934) show continuously fluctuating population with peaks at irregular intervals and no general trend, which agrees with general impression of alternating periods of abundance and scarcity (the latter often accompanied by coccidiosis). Other type of information concerns density: counts on 2,000 acres by Rothschild & Marsh (1956) indicate a population mounting in 2 years, after elimination of rabbits by myxomatosis, to 1 per 10 acres. Again Rothschild (1958) gives estimate, for French estate similarly situated, of 1 per 2.5 acres. Little doubt that peak densities can reach this figure in England. This contrasts with density of introduced population in Great Lakes region of 1 per 25 acres (Reynolds, 1955). Similarly in Finland Siivonen (1956) shows that large numbers die in winters with deep snow.

FOOD No systematic observations. Odd records are for ground fungi (Kumerloeve, 1956) and voles (Gersdorf, 1958). Taste for agricultural crops, especially turnips, well known, and much damage done by barking trees. As with Rabbit, all food passed twice through body, soft faeces for reingestion appearing during daytime (Watson & Taylor, 1955, from New Zealand data).

PREDATORS Again very little information. Foxes and, in Scotland, Eagles and Wild Cats may take some adults, but main predation by these and by Stoats and large raptorial birds probably on leverets.

RELATIONS WITH MAN Almost as important as Fox as an object of the chase. Capable of considerable damage to agriculture and forestry, especially in hard weather and when at peak numbers. Has often been reared and kept in captivity and, given space, will breed.

Blue Hare (Mountain Hare) *Lepus timidus* L.

DISTRIBUTION Extends over whole of northern Palaearctic Region with outlying populations in Alps, introduced in Faeroes: probably related to Snowshoe Rabbit or Varying Hare (*L. americanus*). Sixteen subspecies described, 2 of which, *L. t. scoticus* and *L. t. hibernicus* occur in British Isles. Scottish race originally confined to Highlands now introduced into Lowlands, Hebrides, Orkney (Hoy only) and Shetland, also northern Pennines, Peak district and N. Wales (but now rare in last). Irish race occupies low, as well as high ground in absence of Brown Hare, which, however, has been introduced a number of times and appears to thrive, at least temporarily, in competition with Blue Hare. Irish race sturdier and heavier than Scottish, but not now considered worthy of specific status.

DESCRIPTION A stockier animal than Brown Hare with much shorter ears, and tail showing much white on top. In summer and autumn pelage dusky (not warm) brown and tips of fur give grey or 'blue' appearance. Three annual moults (Hewson, 1958), from white to brown in spring, from brown to brown in autumn and from brown to white in winter (*Photograph 31*). Last variable, some animals retaining much of autumn brown coloration, and in Irish form some individuals show no whitening and majority never attain complete white coat. Mountain hares introduced from Norway into Faeroes in 1820's turned white at first in winter, but had lost this capacity about 1860–70. Irish race has summer and autumn coats more russet than Scottish race, and, especially when hair is worn, may appear almost foxy red. Yellowish variety not uncommon in both races.

MEASUREMENTS (B.-H.&H.) Scottish race. H.&b. 502 mm (45 meas., range 457 to 545 mm) (females tended to be about 20 mm longer than males); tail (to end of vertebrae) 60 mm (range 43 to 80 mm); hind foot (with claws) 142 mm (range 127 to 155 mm); ear (to notch) 70 mm (range 63 to 80 mm). Weight 2.7 kg (5 lb 10 oz) (29 weighed, range 2.3 to 3.2 kg (5 to 7 lb)). Males averaged *c*. 170 g (6 oz) more than females. R.Hewson (unpubl.) gives 2.7 kg for 191 ♂♂ and 2.8 kg for 171 ♀♀. Irish race. H.&b. 545 mm (27 meas., range 521 to 559 mm); tail (to end of vertebrae) 74 mm (range 65 to 82 mm); hind foot (with claws) 156 mm (range 149 to 168 mm); ear (to notch) 75 mm (range 69 to 81 mm). Weight 3.2 kg (7 lb) (range 2.7 to 3.6 kg (6 to 8 lb)). Males averaged *c*. 198 g (7 oz) less than females.

HABITAT In Scotland usually open moorland and rocky slopes from 1,000 to 4,000 ft but thinly above 2,500 ft (Hewson, 1958). In hard winters may descend to woodlands and coast (B.-H.&H.), and same tendency to seek cover described for Finland where it prefers boggy willow/birch forest during winter (Koskimies, 1957). In Ireland all relatively open habitats occupied and in mountains they resort especially to rock crannies for shelter.

GENERAL HABITS Voice, scream similar to that of Brown Hare; otherwise little information, though Collett (quoted in B.-H.&H.) mentions a pairing 'shriek' and a hissing sound. Höglund (1957) refers to intermittent, feeble, neighing sound during copulation. Hewson noted a low-pitched growl when handling hares. Rhythm of activity, as Brown Hare, concentrated at dusk and dawn, and probably through night. Daytime forms often higher up than feeding grounds and may be shifted according to weather: frequently digs shallow burrows, but usually sits just outside them. Moves from shelter to feeding grounds by well-used paths. Home range restricted, individuals hardly ever crossing a valley. Recapture of marked animals (R.Hewson, unpubl.) was most frequent 1–100 yds away from point of release, but records of up to 1,000 yds. Said of Irish Hare that it is a quicker animal than the Brown at doubling and dodging when hard pressed during coursing.

BREEDING B.-H.&H. state for Irish hare that usual litter size is 3 with occasionally two. Concentrations occur in the mating season, but also sometimes in the winter. This herding noted for other Arctic species. Following information on breeding contributed mainly by R.Hewson from unpublished work. Males fecund by end Jan, breeding starts Feb, reaches full strength March and tails off July. Gestation c. 50 days (Höglund, 1957). Post-partum oestrus (Flux, unpubl. thesis, 1962). Litter rate, 3 per year maximum. Young never breed until year after birth, then start late and have small litters (mean corpora lutea 2.3 for adults, 1.4 for first-year hares, see Flux, 1962). Embryo rate: 1.1 in March, 2.3 in June and 1.7 in August. These figures are for large embryos and probably represent actual litter size as absorption is unlikely when embryos past mid-term. The average number of small embryos per litter throughout season was 2.2, of large embryos 1.8, the difference being due to absorption. Flux (unpubl. thesis, 1962) observed heavy losses, 34% of litters disappearing completely.

POPULATION In Scotland Mountain Hares are densest in C. Highlands up to Moray Firth. Hewson (1954) estimated c. 50 to 60 per 1,000 acres in 1951 when hares were not abundant: in Lowlands comparable figure was c. 10 per 1,000 acres and north of Great Glen 1 to 2 per 1,000 acres. However, numbers fluctuate greatly, more so than in Brown Hare (Middleton, 1934), peak population may be ten times size of low population and Flux gives 200 per 1,000 acres as average for Aberdeenshire. High numbers recorded around 1895, 1910, 1930 and 1948. Yearly bags can be as many as 550 per 1,000 acres (Inverness-shire). Possible, though evidence needed, that Irish hares do not fluctuate as violently as Scottish. Recent work by R.Hewson (unpubl.) shows that the percentage of young males (determined from condition of testes) in autumn is about 42 to 50. Sex ratio is about equal, so about half the population dies each year when it is stationary.

FOOD (Hewson, 1958, 1962.) In winter about 90% ling (*Calluna vulgaris*) and 10% cotton grass (*Eriophorum* spp.). From April to end Oct about 48% ling, 17% cotton grass and 25% grasses, the remaining 10% being made up of *Carex* spp. and unidentified plants. Grazes heavily on ling burnt within previous 2–3 years, on deer's hair grass (*Scirpus caespitosus*) during flowering season, and heath rush (*Juncus squarrosus*) in autumn. During snow cover soft rush (*Juncus effusus*), gorse (*Ulex europaeus*) are important food plants. Also said (B.-H.&H.) to eat lichens and conifer cones. In winter shallow snow is scraped away with fore paws to get at vegetation. Refection occurs during day.

PREDATORS Mainly Golden Eagles, Foxes, Wild Cats, Stoats, Buzzards.

RELATIONS WITH MAN In Scotland Mountain Hare regarded almost as pest since it is a distraction during grouse shooting and deer stalking. In severe weather will eat bark and twigs. Irish race is coursed and numbers are imported into England for this purpose. This race has been kept and bred in captivity.

Order Rodentia

Most abundant order of all mammals. Classification contains a bewildering proliferation of creatures, mouse and rat size, most of which live secretive and nocturnal lives. Ecological and economic importance vast, though often unsuspected. It may be judged from the more obvious depredations of House Mouse and of Black and Norway Rats, which have attached themselves to man.

Some rodents, such as squirrels, beavers and porcupines, reach medium size, but largest of all, S. American Capybara (*Hydrochoerus*), only about size of sheep. On the other hand, there are dozens of genera about mouse-size and smaller, down to tiny Harvest Mouse (*Micromys*) which weighs only 5 to 8 g. ´

Most striking morphological character of rodents is specialization of teeth and jaw muscles (see Fig. 24). Teeth much reduced in number and cheek teeth with folded grinding surfaces widely separated from gnawing incisors, which are deeply sunk in jaw and have permanently open roots. Rodents, therefore, live mainly on plant life, not disdaining the tougher and more woody types, but also eat animal food.

There follows the classification of major groups of this complex order as given in Simpson (1945).

SUBORDER SCIUROMORPHA

Three suborders clearly defined. This one contains squirrels, marmots and beavers, subdivided as follows.

Superfamily Aplodontoidea. Primitive, containing only 1 family Aplodontidae and 1 genus *Aplodonta*, the Mountain 'Beaver' of N. America.

Superfamily Sciuroidea. Squirrels, containing many forms and many suggested subdivisions. Only one family, Sciuridae, very large and widely distributed, including squirrels, ground squirrels, marmots, chipmunks and flying squirrels.

Superfamily Geomyoidea. New World group containing families Geomyidae, pocket gophers, and Heteromyidae, pocket mice, kangaroo mice and rats and spiny pocket mice.

Superfamily Castoroidea. Contains only one recent family, Castoridae and one genus *Castor*, the Beavers.

Superfamily Anomaluroidea. Group of doubtful affinities systematically. Contains family Anomaluridae, African scaly-tailed squirrels and Pedetidae, the African Spring Haas.

SUBORDER MYOMORPHA

Mainly rat and mouse-like forms. A great assemblage, subdivided as follows.

Superfamily Muroidea. Contains following families from all over world: Cricetidae, New World mice (rice rats, cotton rats, deer,

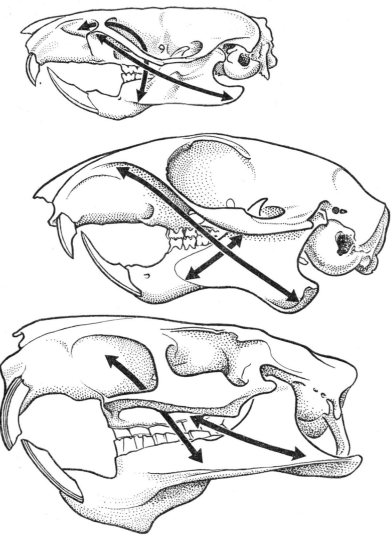

FIG. 24. Skulls representing the three sub-orders of rodents—above, Brown Rat (*Rattus norvegicus*), Myomorpha; middle, Grey Squirrel (*Sciurus carolinensis*), Sciuromorpha; and, lower, Coypu (*Myocastor coypus*), Hystricomorpha. The arrows indicate (following Romer) the positions of the specialized masseter muscles, which produce the back-and-forth and rotatory movements characteristic of the order. The lateral (overlying) masseter muscle runs simply from the back of the lower jaw to the skull in front of the orbit in some sciuromorphs and in myomorphs; the medial masseter is primitive in the sciuromorphs but has become specialized in the myomorphs, its origin pushing through the infra-orbital canal as indicated. In the hystricomorphs the medial masseter again penetrates through a foramen to the front of the orbit but the lateral masseter is much shorter than in the other two sub-orders.

mice, etc.), Old World hamsters, Malagasy rats, lemmings, voles, gerbils, mole rats and bamboo rats; Muridae, true mice and rats, mainly Old World and Australasian, some now introduced all over the world.

Superfamily Gliroidea. Dormouse-like forms, comprising families Gliridae, Palaearctic and African dormice; Platacanthomyidae, Asiatic spiny dormice; and Seleviniidae, with one Russian genus only.

Superfamily Dipodoidea. Contains the families Zapodidae, jumping mice, and Dipodidae, jerboas. Distributed over Holarctic Region and Africa.

SUBORDER HYSTRICOMORPHA

Contains mainly the porcupines and the rather aberrant groups of rodents, like Chinchilla and Agouti, from S. America. Subdivided as follows.

Superfamily Hystricoidea. Only one family, Hystricidae, Old World porcupines.

Superfamily Erethizontoidea. Only one family, Erethizontidae, New World porcupines.

Superfamily Cavioidea. Recent families Caviidae, S. American guinea pigs; Hydrochoeridae, the largest rodent, the Capybara; Dinomyidae, the S. American pacas; and Dasyproctidae, the agoutis.

Superfamily Chinchilloidea. One family only containing the S. American chinchillas and vizcachas.

Superfamily Octodontoidea. Contains 7 families: Capromyidae, including S. American Coypu or Nutria, now established ferally in British Isles; Octodontidae with sundry S. American forms like the Degu; Ctenomyidae, a S. American group with one species, the Tucu Tucu; Abrocomidae, with one form, S. American rat chinchilla; Echimyidae, a larger family, S. American again and W. Indian, the spiny rats; Thryonomyidae, with one recent genus, the African Cane Rat; and Petromyidae, with again one genus, the African Rock Rat.

In addition there are sundry groups which are difficult to classify; the Bathyergidae, the African mole rats and naked rats and the Ctenodactylidae, the African gundis.

Of the 28 families listed above, 4 are native to Britain and 1 is introduced.

FIELD IDENTIFICATION CHARACTERS

(1) Squirrels. Arboreal with characteristic bushy tail. Tooth characters as in Fig. 26. Red Squirrel (*Sciurus vulgaris*), red colour, ear tufts (sometimes absent in summer) and smaller size distinguish from introduced Grey Squirrel (*S. carolinensis*), but note that at some seasons Grey Squirrel has varying amount of reddish colour mixed with the grey.

(2) Voles. Like mice and rats in appearance, but with blunter muzzles, shorter, furred ears and tails. Cheek teeth with characteristic triangular pattern on grinding surfaces (Figs. 28 & 29). Bank Vole (*Clethrionomys glareolus*), mouse-size, coat chestnut above, silvery to creamy-grey below, tail about half length of head and body; teeth acquire roots as animal grows, triangles with slightly rounded corners. Orkney Vole (*Microtus arvalis orcadensis*), confined to Orkneys, only vole present there; much like Short-tailed Vole but larger (nearly twice as long) and deep brown in colour. Short-tailed Vole (*M. agrestis*), mouse-size, coat brown above, grey below, tail one-quarter to one-third length of body; teeth permanently open-rooted, triangles with sharp corners. Water Vole (*Arvicola amphibius*), rat-size, coat brown to black above, brownish-grey below, teeth and tail vole-like.

(3) Mice. Distinguished from voles by pointed muzzles, larger ears and long, relatively hairless tails. Cheek teeth tuberculate. Wood Mouse (*Apodemus sylvaticus*), slightly larger than House Mouse, coat brown above mixed with yellow which intensifies along flanks, white below. Eyes and ears large and prominent, tail equal in length to head and body. Yellow-brown chest-spot of varying size almost always present. Yellow-necked Mouse (*A. flavicollis*), a quarter as large again as Wood Mouse, chest spot extends up to flank line forming broad collar. South half of England only. Harvest Mouse (*Micromys minutus*), smaller than House Mouse, brown colour tends to foxy-red, especially on haunches, white below. Tail long and prehensile. Rare except in S. and E. England. House Mouse (*Mus musculus*), coat grey to grey-brown above, grey to silver-grey below.

(4) Rats. Characters as for mice, but size larger. Black rat (*Rattus rattus*), more lightly built than Brown Rat. Coat variable in colour, less shaggy than Brown Rat, tail about as long as head and body. Only in some ports and one island. Brown Rat (*R. norvegicus*), a

heavy, coarse-furred animal, brownish all over, paler on under-parts, tail thick, scaly and shorter than head and body.

(5) Dormice. Muzzle much shorter than in mice, ears fairly prominent, long bushy tail, arboreal. Cheek teeth with character-istic transverse ridges on grinding surfaces. Dormouse (*Muscardinus avellanarius*), mouse-size, bright foxy coat, white below. Fat (Edible) Dormouse (*Glis glis*), nearly squirrel-size, coat grey, white below. Introduced, confined to Home Counties.

(6) Coypu (*Myocastor coypus*), cat-size, long, dark-brown coat (the nutria of commerce), aquatic. Introduced, practically confined to E. Anglia.

FAMILY CASTORIDAE

GENUS *Castor*

Only recent genus in family, distributed over Holarctic Region. Three species described for New World, one for Old.

†Beaver *Castor fiber* L.

Survives, or until fairly recently survived, in parts of Norway, Sweden, Germany, France, Poland, Russia, Siberia and northern Mongolia. Distribution within historic times much wider, includ-ing also Switzerland, Spain and Holland, as well as British Isles, though not apparently Ireland.

Skeletal remains recovered from various superficial deposits in this country. In Wales, Beavers are recorded as surviving in one area (the river Teify in Cardiganshire) towards end of 12th cent; later records of survival probably only copied from this. In Scotland evidence suggests possible survival of Beaver to later date. As with Wolf, memory of Beaver perpetuated in a number of place-names in England, Scotland and Wales.

FAMILY SCIURIDAE

Six tribes recognized are Sciurini (Eurasian and Nearctic tree squirrels), Tamiasciurini (American Red Squirrel), Funambulini (African tree squirrels and allied Asiatic genera), Callosciurini (Oriental tree squirrels), Xerini (African ground squirrels), Marmotini (Holarctic ground squirrels). Moore (1959) adds Ratufini (Indo-Malayan giant squirrels) and Protoxerini (African

T

giant and sun squirrels) to make 8 tribes. Twelve genera of flying squirrels and 30 of tree and ground squirrels recognized. Tribe Sciurini has five genera.

GENUS *Sciurus*

Genus is Nearctic, Neotropical and Palaearctic with 9 subgenera, 34 species and some 190 subspecies (one found solely in British Isles, two or more introduced).

Red Squirrel is type species with 42 named forms, seven of which may prove to be synonyms (E.&M.-S.). There are two colour types, one predominantly red, other blackish-brown. Dark squirrels found more often in southern, mountainous part of European range, but overlap occurs.

Neosciurus subgenus comprises 50 named forms, including Grey Squirrel. Skull shape, colour, size and less conspicuous ear-tufts in winter distinguish from Red Squirrel. Subgenus found throughout eastern states of N. America, in E. Canada, Mexico, Honduras, Guatemala, Nicaragua and Costa Rica.

Red Squirrel (Brown Squirrel) *Sciurus vulgaris* L.

DISTRIBUTION Found throughout wooded parts of Eurasia from tree-line south to Mediterranean coast, from Ireland in west to Japan in east, not in Caucasus, Syria, Persia or Asia Minor. Present in Eire, Northern Ireland, Wales and Scotland, absent I. of Man, in England rare or absent in much of midland and south-eastern region, but present E. Anglia and in northern and western counties; occurs I. of Wight, Anglesey, I. of Arran (Shorten, 1957a). In Channel Islands recorded for Jersey only. Occurrence on other islands needs investigation. British race, *S. vulgaris leucourus*, not found elsewhere. Red Squirrels from Continent (distinguished mainly by size and colouring) released in British Isles: *S. v. vulgaris* from Scandinavia to Perthshire in 1793 (Harvie-Brown, 1880–81); *S. v. russus* or *fuscoater* to Epping in 1910 (Shorten, 1954a); probably others. Distribution of native Red Squirrel has fluctuated: approached extinction in Scotland during late 18th and early 19th cent, then reintroduced and spread (Harvie-Brown, 1880–81); uncertain if present in Ireland before introductions 1815–80 (B.-H.&H.; Barrington, 1880). After period of abundance became scarce throughout range 1900–24; recovery poor or none in areas occupied by American Grey Squirrel.

DESCRIPTION See Field Identification Characters. British race without dark phase. Summer coat rufous with dark mid-dorsal stripe; winter coat brownish-grey becoming ash-grey by time of spring moult; underparts white. Hairs of tail and ear-tufts shed once a year: new growth in autumn is black, becoming brown, rufous and cream in turn. Sexes alike. Juvenile colouring as adult; young moult into appropriate seasonal coat after weaning. Albinos rare.

MEASUREMENTS Recent data from East Anglia (M.Shorten & F.A.Courtier, unpubl.) give following: h.&b. 219 mm (8.7 in.) (50 meas., range 210 to 225 mm (8.3 to 8.9 in.)), tail 182 mm (7.2 in.) (50 meas., range 170 to 195 mm (6.7 to 7.7 in.)); weight ♂ 300 g (10.6 oz) (58 weighed, range 260 to 435 g (9.2 to 15.4 oz)), ♀ (non-pregnant) 296 g (10.5 oz) (70 weighed, range 260 to 345 g (9.2 to 12.2 oz)). Averages vary between localities and years.

HABITAT Found typically in coniferous woodland, also in mixed woods; where numerous, may overflow into more sparsely wooded deciduous areas but favours shelter and seclusion. Rarely found where Grey Squirrel established for ten or more years, but has also disappeared or become scarce where no Grey Squirrels present. Reasons for apparent replacement unknown, likely to be complex.

GENERAL HABITS Voice a rasping chatter, sometimes followed by hoarse call or whine. Young make shrill piping cry. Great agility and speed when climbing and jumping in trees; more hesitant on ground. Runways, like those made by Rabbits, may be found where squirrels cross grassy spaces going from one tree butt to another. Tree trunks may show roughened, chipped bark where regularly climbed; also sets of three parallel scratches from claws. Droppings scattered, vary in appearance with food but roughly similar to those of rats. Little known about social organization, home range, migration or dispersal. Diurnal, with activity peaks in early morning and before dusk; minor peak at mid-day. Wind, deep snow, ice inhibit activity. No true hibernation. Most feeding is done in trees; food collected from ground usually carried up before being eaten. Typical nest (drey) spherical, compact, of twigs and bark lined with moss, grass, leaves, shredded bark, etc.; placed where branches join trunk, less often out on limb or in crown of tree.

BREEDING Variable, depending on weather and preceding food conditions. Two main seasons: Jan to April and late May to August in south; said to be only one in Scotland (B.-H.&H.). Gestation *c.* 46 days, litter size 1 to 6, average 3. Young weaned at 7–10 weeks. No post-partum oestrus. Females appear to undergo anoestrus while moulting after young weaned in April to May and again from Oct to late Dec (needs confirmation). Sex ratio variable; 80 males : 100 females in sample of 330; 127 others cage-trapped had ratio 165 : 100 (M.Shorten & F.A.Courtier, unpubl.). At birth young weigh *c.* 12 g (less than 0.5 oz) and are blind, toothless, with closed ears and no hair other than whiskers. Hair develops after first week; lower incisors erupt at 3 weeks; during next fortnight eyes and ears open at weight of *c.* 50 g (1.8 oz). First dentition almost complete at 10 weeks; milk premolars cast at 16 weeks, soon after moult of juvenile coat at weight of *c.* 200 g (7.1 oz), h.&b. *c.* 190 mm (7.5 in.), tail 160 mm (6.3 in.). Next moult when *c.* 7 months old, 230 g (8.1 oz), h.&b. 210 mm (8.3 in.), tail 170 mm (6.7 in.). Sexual maturity probably reached between 6 and 11 months of age (M.Shorten, unpubl.).

POPULATION Very little information on densities in different environments, population turnover, distribution and causes of mortality and factors of natural regulation. Fluctuations said to follow 7-year cycle, alternatively pine seed fluctuations. Needs more investigation.

FOOD Casual information only. Seeds of conifers (especially Scots pine) important; acorns, beech mast, sweet chestnuts, hazel nuts and other tree seeds; buds, shoots, pollen, berries, fungi, bulbs, roots; insects and occasionally eggs and young of birds. Water sought in dry weather. Chalk and bone sometimes gnawed and earth eaten. Scales gnawed from cones (except for tip) in search for pine seed; hazel nuts opened with nick cut from side of point, then split lengthways into equal halves. Massive food storage in holes and nests not often observed but, where food abundant, items buried singly or in small groups. Relocation appears to be by scent rather than by memory (See chapter 2).

PREDATORS Probably little important predation. Stoat, Buzzard, Golden Eagle, Pine Marten and Wildcat may kill some. Grey Squirrel has been seen to attack and kill.

RELATIONS WITH MAN May cause serious damage in conifer plantations by stripping bark from upper main stem of Scots pine, less often from European larch, Norway spruce, lodgepole pine (Shorten, 1957b). Tops may die or be weakened, blown out. Control by shooting and trapping where necessary. Become tame in captivity, especially if taken young; a group may have to be kept for several years before breeding starts. A large, outdoor cage or well-ventilated room, provided with raised nest-boxes and

FIG. 25. Grey Squirrel (*Sciurus carolinensis*), left, and Red Squirrel (*S. vulgaris*), right, showing difference in size and proportions.

firmly fixed branches is needed; squirrels should *not* be kept in a small cage. Survival under laboratory or zoo conditions apparently not as good as that of Grey Squirrel (Chalmers-Mitchell, 1911; M.Shorten & F.A.Courtier, unpubl.) though life span up to $10\frac{1}{2}$ years recorded.

*American Grey Squirrel *Sciurus carolinensis* Gm.

DISTRIBUTION Typically in dense hardwood forests of eastern Canada and United States, from Ontario and New Brunswick down to Florida. Five races recognized; forms intermediate between *S. carolinensis leucotis* (Northern Grey Squirrel) and *S. carolinensis carolinensis* (Southern Grey Squirrel) introduced into

British Isles 1876 to 1929 and into S. Africa about 1905. Spread from *c*. 30 centres in British Isles over some 39,000 sq miles in 80 years. Now found in most English and Welsh counties but never reported from Cumberland, I. of Wight, Anglesey, I. of Man nor from Channel Islands. Only isolated or sporadic records from Northumberland, Westmorland, Caernarvon and Norfolk. Eire and Northern Ireland record it in 10 counties, Scotland in 8 (Shorten, 1954a, 1957a).

DESCRIPTION See Field Identification Characters. Winter coat grey with yellow-brown mid-dorsal stripe; paler and longer than summer coat, with white hairs behind ears and brown ear-tufts. Summer coat shorter and more brownish, bright rufous streak

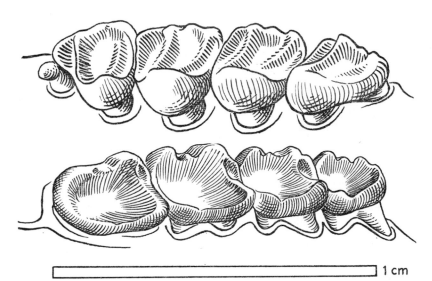

FIG. 26. Cheek teeth of Grey Squirrel (*Sciurus carolinensis*). Above —left upper jaw (anterior to left); below—left lower jaw (anterior to right).

along flanks and on paws. Tail fringed with white in winter, narrower and with less white in summer. Underparts white. Skull longer than that of Red Squirrel, braincase longer and shallower, rostrum longer and narrower, post-orbital process shorter and stouter. Sexes alike, though females perhaps have more pointed muzzles. Body hair moulted April and Sept, moult lasting 5 to 6 weeks. Hairs of tail and ears replaced once a year. Some young are more reddish-brown than adults. Albinos found in Kent, Surrey, Sussex, Scottish midlands. Melanics found in Bedfordshire, Cambridgeshire, Hertfordshire and Buckinghamshire. Erythristic forms occur sporadically.

MEASUREMENTS Average adult: h.&b. 259 mm (10.3 in.) (100 meas., range 230 to 280 mm (9.1 to 11.1 in.)), tail 215 mm (8.5 in.) (100 meas., range 200 to 240 mm (7.9 to 9.5 in.)), weight 510 to 570 g (18.1 to 20 oz), up to 750 g (26.5 oz); varies with food abundance, adults may gain or lose 150 g (5.3 oz).

HABITAT Hardwood or mixed woodland, from extensive forest to garden trees. Typically mixed woodland with some mature trees, 25% or more oak. Will nest and breed in coniferous plantations if seed-bearing hardwoods near by. Said to favour lower altitudes than does Red Squirrel (Middleton, 1931).

GENERAL HABITS Voice as Red Squirrel. Can travel on ground at 18 m.p.h. in bounds of 3 to 5 ft; can leap 12 ft from tree to tree. Swims well, using hind feet only. Seen to climb with young in mouth, held by loose skin. Can climb vertical, rough-cast walls and travel along horizontal wires. Bolder on ground than Red Squirrel; no runways seen. Scattered droppings, rat-like, variable. No evidence of territory, though females with young may drive other squirrels from nest-tree; groups of males, non-breeding females and juveniles may share nests; feeding sometimes communal but, if in close proximity, social dominance observed (Flyger, unpubl. thesis, 1955). Home range varies with food conditions; that of females less than that of males. Emigrations have been features of populations in America (Schorger, 1949); rare, minor instances in British Isles (Shorten, 1954a). Diurnal, activity peaks early morning, before dusk and minor peak at midday. Food sought at all levels in woodland, also in hedgerows and open fields. Typical nest (drey) of twigs with leaves attached, domed with side entrance, lined with grass, leaves, etc., set in large forks 30 to 40 ft up; leafy summer platforms built out on limbs. Crowns of trees, bushes and holes in trees sometimes used for nesting; wide variety of tree species. Main building season July onwards. Young of spring litters disperse May to July; summer litters, Oct; possibly less dispersal in autumn.

BREEDING Two seasons per year; time varies with weather and preceding food conditions, but typically mating occurs late Dec to Jan, and again late May to June. Gestation about 44 days, lactation 7 to 10 weeks. Females in anoestrus late Sept to late Dec with rare exceptions; some males potent every month (Allanson, 1933) but majority sexually quiescent in Sept (Kirkpatrick & Hoffman, 1960). Litter size 1 to 7, average 3; spring litters and those from juveniles average smaller than those of summer and from adult females. Unknown proportion of adult females bear two litters per year. Juveniles bear one litter in first breeding year. Failure to breed may follow mast failure. Sex ratio varies with age group; males predominate in young stages but among adults 72 to 87 males : 100 females general. At birth young weigh 13 to 17 g (*c.* 5 oz) and measure *c.* 102 mm (4 in.) total length; at 4 months weigh *c.* 375 g (13 oz) and measure *c.* 420 mm (16.5 in.); at 6 months weigh *c.* 500 g (17.7 oz) but do not reach full adult length until 8 months or older. Sexual maturity at 6 to 11 months.

POPULATION Mean density 0.5 to 5 per acre in favourable woodland habitat, varying with season and year. Breeding increase most noticeable in June, though less observations for autumn, when food abundance makes trapping more difficult. Rough index to density is number of occupied nests; but groups may share one nest and some individuals use several nests. Counting squirrels seen on walks or from fixed positions gives very low estimate. Trapping, marking, releasing, then retrapping affords best index. Average number of young per female per year 4. Mortality estimated to be 10% per year in America (Flyger, unpubl. thesis, 1955) so that two-thirds of autumn population are young of the year (Allen, 1954). In British Isles young of summer and following spring formed 60% of a population of 222 in May (Shorten & Courtier, 1955). Life span probably 5 to 6 years; in captivity up to 20 years. Little known of causes and distribution of mortality. Population declines often associated with mast failure and severe winter. In America there have been indications of a 5-year cycle (Schorger, 1949).

FOOD Wide variety listed through casual observations. Acorns most important; hazel nuts, sweet chestnuts, beech mast, seeds of pine, larch, elm, maple and sycamore; bulbs, roots, shoots, buds, catkins, fruit, fungi, grain, insects, occasionally eggs and flesh (I.Linn, unpubl., records a squirrel which stalked and caught House Sparrows); bones gnawed, earth eaten; water and sappy bark sought in summer. Surplus food buried or hidden (*Photograph 32*); scoops 1 to 2 in. deep are dug and items buried singly or in small groups, relocated by scent. Adults in captivity atc 64 to 83 g (2.3 to 2.9 oz) of hickory nuts or acorns daily, lactating females eating most (Uhlig, mimeo rep., 1955).

PREDATORS Occasionally taken by Stoats, dogs; rarely by Foxes, hawks, owls. More killed by man.

RELATIONS WITH MAN Whereas in America Grey Squirrel is prized game animal, in British Isles regarded as forest pest, having developed habit of damaging young hardwood trees by stripping bark from main stems, sometimes killing tree. Also may damage standing, stooked or stacked corn; may take fruit and vegetables. Illegal to import or keep Grey Squirrel as a pet, exhibit or for scientific study without licence from Ministry of Agriculture.

FAMILY CRICETIDAE

A vast family subdivided variously and containing most of hamsters, lemmings, voles, gerbils and New World mice. E.&M.-S. classify into 5 sub-families and 9 tribes. Sub-families are: Cricetinae, New World mice, Palaearctic hamsters and Asiatic mole mice (59 genera); Nesomyinae, Malagasy rats (7 genera); Lophiomyinae, African Crested Hamster (1 genus); Microtinae, lemmings and voles (21 genera); and Gerbillinae, Asiatic and African gerbils (10 genera). The Microtinae especially exhibit population fluctuations, sometimes amounting to plagues, and these may be strikingly cyclic, an approximate three-year periodicity being common, especially in the Arctic.

GENUS *Clethrionomys* (*Evotomys*)

Holarctic, extending down to southern U.S.A., to S. Europe, except Iberian and Balkan peninsulas. Absent from Iceland, Ireland. Prefers cooler regions and in southern parts of range lives in mountains. One exception *C. smithii* in Shikoku and Kiushiu. Fairly primitive group of voles, generally characterized by russet pelage: probably connects mice with *Microtus* group, since cheek teeth develop roots during life. Thirty-two species named, but probably many should be reduced to subspecies. All British forms best regarded, until more systematic work done, as subspecies of *C. glareolus* (Steven, 1953). The Palaearctic *C. glareolus* probably conspecific with Nearctic *C. gapperi*. Supported by cytological evidence (Matthey, 1956).

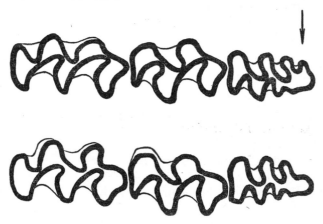

FIG. 27. Diagrams of surface patterns of cheek teeth of Bank Vole (*Clethrionomys glareolus*), showing simple (below) and complex (above) types. These show, in each case, the right upper tooth row with the anterior end to the left and the lingual side uppermost. The extra fold, which constitutes the full complex condition, is indicated by the arrow.

Bank Vole *Clethrionomys glareolus* Schr.

DISTRIBUTION Mainly in central band of Palaearctic, reaching up to Arctic and down to Mediterranean coast of Europe and N. Africa except for Balkan and Iberian peninsulas. About 20 races, probably will be reduced when revised on adequate material. In British Isles local form (*C. g. britannicus*) (of doubtful validity (see Corbet, 1964)) spread throughout, except Ireland, I. of Man, Lundy, Scillies, Orkney and Shetland, Outer Hebrides and most of Inner Hebrides. Four island races recognized, viz. *C. g. skomerensis* (Skomer I., Pembrokeshire), *C. g. alstoni* (Mull), *C. g. erica* (Raasay) and *C. g. caesarius* (Jersey).

DESCRIPTION See Field Identification Characters. Back fairly constant, belly varies from clear, silvery grey to buff, juveniles much greyer. Pale, sandy mutant not uncommon. General pattern of geographical variation as follows (Corbet, 1964). Increase in size from south to north of British Isles with moderate discontinuity between Scottish Lowlands and Highlands and large discontinuity between mainland and island races (see Crowcroft & Godfrey (1960) for Jersey race). Presence of fourth inner ridge of enamel on upper third molar ('complex' condition, Fig. 27) also geographically variable. S. England has c. 16% complex type, N. England and Scotland 33 to 41%, the island races c. 80% except Mull which is low like England (Delany & Bishop (1960) suggest Mull voles not separable from mainland form). All island races darker in colour except that on Skomer which is lighter. Cross readily with mainland form. Moult can be found in most months of year with peaks in spring and autumn, less distinct than in Wood Mouse but more distinct than in Short-tailed Vole (Stein, 1960b).

MEASUREMENTS Variable: late summer generation overwinters at about 90 mm (h.&b.), and increases with onset of breeding in next spring to 100 to 110 mm; first generation may grow to full size in same year and breed (Bureau of Animal Population, Oxford, unpubl. records); in hard winters larger animals survive best (Stein, 1956). Tail variable (40 to 60 mm). Weight subject to even more variation than length, according to generation and conditions, wintering population divided into group c. 16 g and another 20 to 22 g, summer weights may reach 30 g or more. Island races larger: 8 spring-caught C. g. skomerensis measured 109 mm (range 105 to 115 mm) and weighed 31 g (range 25 to 37 g). Crowcroft & Godfrey (1960) contrast spring-caught collections from E. Anglia and Jersey. E. Anglia, h.&b. ♂ 98.9 mm (44 meas., range 94 to 106 mm), ♀ 100.7 mm (28 meas., range 94 to 106 mm); Jersey, ♂ 114.0 mm (40 meas., range 108 to 121 mm), ♀ 112.4 mm (34 meas., range 107 to 119 mm). Cheek teeth have rounded angles on grinding surface (cf. Short-tailed Vole with sharper angles) and develop double roots during life (see Fig. 28). Zimmermann (1937) first showed age distribution of wild population could be worked out from molar root development. Later work (V.P.W.Lowe, unpubl.) shows generations can be distinguished by stages of growth, but complicated by faster root development in spring and early summer (see also Zejda, 1961). Sexes similar: young animals sometimes difficult to sex from external genitalia.

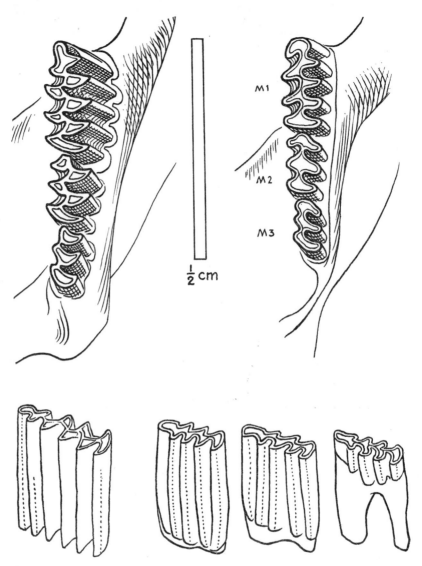

FIG. 28. Above. Left lower jaws of Short-tailed Vole (*Microtus agrestis*), left, and Bank Vole (*Clethrionomys glareolus*), right, showing longer m_1 of former (with 5 triangles on the lingual side compared with 4 in the Bank Vole) and sharper angles to the prisms. Below. Right lower m_1 of Short-tailed Vole (extreme left), showing parallel sides indicating continuous growth with wide-open pulp cavities beneath. The three drawings on the right show the same tooth in the Bank Vole at different ages. The roots develop progressively as shown from left to right.

HABITAT Most abundant in deciduous woodland and scrub; also along banks and hedges, usually in thick cover, in which it moves easily above the ground. Not infrequent on open ground with high herb layer or cover of banks and walls (e.g. Scotland and Norway (Linn, 1954, and unpubl.)). Extends up to 2,600 ft on scree in Scotland.

GENERAL HABITS Voice not so noisy as *Microtus*, but has similar chattering and squeaking. Runs rather than jumps. Agile climber. Markedly diurnal in thick cover: some results (Brown, 1956a) suggest mainly diurnal, but others (Miller, 1955; Osterman, 1956) say active throughout 24 hrs with more nocturnal activity in summer. Home range *c*. 45.5 m (*c*. 50 yds) diameter (Evans, 1942; Brown, 1956b), but some males move much further. As well as foraging above ground, are active burrowers, making runway system centred on nest at 2 to 10 cm depth (von Wrangel, 1939).

BREEDING Length of season and breeding success vary greatly: usual extent mid-April to Sept, but in some years to December. Usually late-born young remain non-parous through winter (Brambell & Rowlands, 1936). Female oestrous cycle *c*. 3 days; embryo rate rises and falls through season, mean for England 4.4. Gestation 17.5–18 days (said to be prolonged to 21 during lactation but see under *Microtus*) (von Wrangel, 1939). Number of litters during season uncertain, but could be 4 to 5. Sex ratio *c*. 50%. Breeding nests may be below or above ground (in tree stumps, etc.) made of bark, grass and moss lined with finer material (von Wrangel, 1939). Young *c*. 2 g at birth, weaned about 2½ weeks, may reach sexual maturity in 4 to 5 weeks.

POPULATION Over Britain numbers more stable than those of Short-tailed Vole, but outbreaks known in Norway (Wildhagen, 1952) and in Germany (Stein, 1956) where, at high densities, heavier animals known to survive winter better. Densities probably between 5 and 25 per acre (sometimes considerably more). Normally overwintering population (mostly young of previous year which have never bred) grows quickly in spring and produces first generation, which in its turn may become swiftly mature and produce second summer generation. This one grows slowly without reaching sexual maturity. These last again form the bulk of the overwinterers. Can be some variations on this theme, especially when breeding occurs in winter (Newson, unpubl. thesis, 1960,

1963). Length of life, therefore, highly variable and average figures mean little. (Leslie, Chitty & Chitty (1953) give valuable details of small population studied in Wales.)

FOOD On whole, more vegetable than animal food with much higher proportion of green plants than Wood Mouse, also prefers fleshy parts of, e.g. hawthorn, whereas Wood Mouse prefers the hard centre. Insects (adults and larvae) *c.* one-third of diet. Also eats fungi and other Bank Voles (records from wild animals) (Turček, 1953; Miller, 1954).

PREDATORS Taken by most birds and beasts of prey, but only in small numbers by species that hunt open ground: Tawny Owls and Weasels probably most important (Southern, 1954).

RELATIONS WITH MAN Has been known a long time on Continent as occasional forestry pest, not only eating seeds and seedlings, but barking small trees, especially larch and elder, up to 16 ft (von Wrangel, 1939). Similar records in Britain in winter between 1958 and 1960 (Keeler, 1961). Easily takes to captivity and breeds freely, though some individuals remain very wild. Skomer Bank Vole remarkable for its docility. Usual diet in captivity, hay, oats, etc., slows down development of molar roots.

GENUS *Microtus*

Holarctic, widespread and abundant genus. The 'typical vole' with permanently open-rooted teeth, more specialized than Bank Vole for living in grassland. From Arctic down to S. Mexico, to Kamchatka, Japan (Kiushiu), Mediterranean coast of Europe and Libya. European Common Vole (*M. arvalis*) has spectacular 'plagues' and much work has been done upon it. Many species and subspecies named, about equally divided between Palaearctic and Nearctic: critical study will probably reduce this number.

Guernsey Vole *Microtus arvalis sarnius* Miller

DISTRIBUTION Confined to Island of Guernsey (not present on Herm). Other races of *M. arvalis* are the common voles of Europe, but species absent from British Isles, except in Guernsey and Orkney.

DESCRIPTION Closely resembles Short-tailed Vole but less buff on underparts. Dentition differs from it mainly in absence of small postero-internal loop of second upper molar (Fig. 29).

MEASUREMENTS H.&b. 100 mm (29 meas., range 83 to 120 mm); tail 30 to 45 mm; weight up to 45 g.

HABITAT Bishop & Delany (1963a) found it mainly in rough grass areas; missing from farmland.

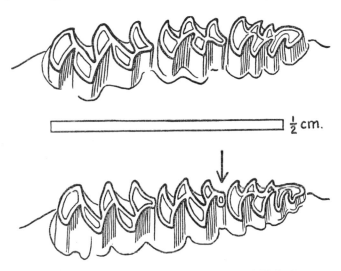

Fig. 29. Right upper cheek teeth of Short-tailed Vole (*Microtus agrestis*), below, and Orkney Vole (*M. arvalis orcadensis*), above, showing the extra postero-internal loop of enamel on m₂ which is one distinguishing feature of the Short-tailed Vole. This character has encouraged the placing of both Orkney and Guernsey Voles as subspecies of the European Vole (*M. arvalis*).

GENERAL HABITS In 1961 Bishop & Delany (1963b) record early breeding with mating taking place in Feb and young of the year difficult to distinguish by August. Eight pregnant females had mean litter size 3.3, range 2 to 5.

Orkney Vole *Microtus arvalis orcadensis* Millais

DISTRIBUTION Orkneys only: present on all larger islands except Hoy and Shapinsay (Hewson, 1948). Pelage variation between islands, the three southern ones (Mainland, S. Ronaldshay,

Rousay) deep brown, the two northern ones (Sanday, Westray) paler. Fairly distinct from *M. agrestis* (no posterior loop on second upper molar), and closely allied to Continental *M. arvalis* with which it crosses readily (Zimmermann, 1959a). Stein (1958) places both *orcadensis* and *sarnius* as subspecies of *arvalis*. Evidence of chromosomes (Matthey, 1956) supports this.

DESCRIPTION See Field Identification Characters. Large animal with stronger skull than *M. agrestis*.

MEASUREMENTS Ad. h.&b. 114 mm (38 meas., range 100 to 124 mm); tail 38 mm (38 meas., range 32 to 44 mm); weight 34 to 63 g (38 weighed). Males averaged *c.* 10 g more than females (B.-H.&H.).

HABITAT Throughout pasture and arable land and up to at least 700 ft on heather, but thinning out here. Runway systems rather conspicuous, especially in heather (Hewson, 1948), and these link up underground burrows.

GENERAL HABITS Certainly diurnal, probably nocturnal also.

BREEDING Nests may be above or below ground, April to September. Litter rate, mean 4.0 (5 rec. B.-H.&H.), but much larger figures from captive animals give mean of 2.7 (508 rec., Leslie *et al.*, 1955).

POPULATION Often quite dense, especially on lower ground, but does not appear to fluctuate in numbers like *M. agrestis*. Mean expectation of life in laboratory about 1.6 years, longer than Short-tailed Vole in similar conditions. Since litter rate also different from Short-tailed Vole, population turnover slower, which may partly account for greater stability of numbers (Leslie *et al.*, 1955).

FOOD Little information: fond of roots of *Juncus squarrosus* (B.-H.&H.).

PREDATORS Abundantly preyed on by resident Hen Harriers, Short-eared Owls and others.

RELATIONS WITH MAN Easily takes to captivity (see Chitty, 1957).

Short-tailed Vole *Microtus agrestis* (L.)

DISTRIBUTION Throughout N. and C. Palaearctic (*M. pennsylvanicus* of N. America probably closely related, though chromosomes differ (Matthey, 1956)), tending more to north and *M. arvalis* to south, but broad overlap, where habitat distinction, *M. arvalis* preferring cultivated areas. Fourteen subspecies outside British Isles. In British Isles absent from Ireland, I. of Man, Lundy, Scillies, Shetland, Lewis, Barra (but present on other large outer Hebridean islands, N. and S. Uist, Benbecula), many smaller islands of Inner Hebrides (S. Rona, Raasay, Rhum, Colonsay), Orkney (replaced by *M. arvalis orcadensis*), Channel Islands (replaced in Guernsey by *M. arvalis sarnius*). Following subspecies arrangement for British Isles probably needs critical revision: *M. a. hirtus* (England and Scottish Lowlands), *M. a. neglectus* (Scottish Highlands), *M. a. exsul* (Outer Hebrides, most of Inner Hebrides and N.W. Highlands), *M. a. mial* (Eigg), *M. a. luch* (Muck), *M. a. macgillivrayi* (Islay), and *M. a. fiona* (Gigha).

Following is trend of variation as analysed by Corbet (unpubl. thesis, 1960). South to north increase in size with main discontinuity between Scottish Lowlands and Highlands. No discontinuity between Highlands and Islands.

A fourth inner ridge on the first upper molar occurs with increasing frequency from south to north with large discontinuity at the Great Glen, and considerable one between Highlands and Islands. Mull exceptional in having frequency like S. England, also shorter tail than any others (1 less vertebra).

DESCRIPTION See Field Identification Characters. Back colour variable from ochraceous to deep brown, always without ruddy hue of Bank Vole. Underside buffish to pure grey. Albinos and partial albinos occur rarely, melanic very rare, buff and sandy forms not uncommon (a sandy form with pink eyes found wild (I.Linn, unpubl.); also bred in Bureau of Animal Population at Oxford for some years). Moult can be found at all months of the year with ill-defined peaks in spring and autumn (Stein, 1960).

MEASUREMENTS Even more variable than in Bank Vole because they change also with stage of population cycle. Head and body roughly from 90 to 115 mm, tail 31 to 46 mm. More information about weights in Chitty (1952): as with Bank Vole most over-

U

wintering animals are late-born young which stay around 20 g and do not breed in first year: next spring they increase to a mean roughly between 25 and 30 g (though some reach 40 g and over). Mean weights of this spring breeding population vary with stage of cycle of abundance: at high densities mean weight may be 5 to 6 g greater than in low years. Zimmermann (1955) and Stein (1957) have shown for *M. arvalis* that jaw and skull lengths also are greater in peak years. Large males have pronounced musky smell. Northern subspecies tend to be larger at all stages of cycle. Cheek-teeth open-rooted throughout life and distinguished from Bank Vole by sharp angles on grinding surface and by having one more triangle (Fig. 28). Noisier than Bank Vole, angry outbursts of chattering diagnostic. Not a climber.

HABITAT Mainly rough grassland, where it makes network of runways at ground level or shallowly underground. Young forestry plantations with lush growth of grass after exclusion of rabbits, provide ideal breeding ground and plagues sometimes cause great loss of young trees. Also in marginal habitats—grass leys, scrub and woodland (thinly), wet and marshy ground, dunes, scree and moorland up to 2,500 ft in Ross-shire (Hewson, 1953), and to 4,000 ft in Cairngorms (I.Linn, unpubl.). Runway systems persist long after population has 'crashed', but bright green droppings and heaps of cut grass stems show recent use.

GENERAL HABITS Davis (1933) showed, in captivity, 24-hour activity with intensification at night. Brown (1956a) confirmed this in field by trapping. Home range small; trapping (Brown, 1956b) showed most animals moved less than 30 yd (27 m) and estimates range as 1,162 sq yd (975 sq m). Godfrey's (1954) more critical work with Geiger counter gave 235 sq yd (198 sq m). Sometimes appear to be suspicious of live traps on first encounter (Chitty & Kempson, 1949; Linn, 1954; E.Shillito, unpubl. thesis, 1960).

BREEDING Season roughly March to Sept (sometimes to Dec) and sequence of generations much as in Bank Vole, but more variability. Baker & Ranson (1932 a & b, 1933) suggest daylength controls breeding, but great complexity imposed by state of population cycle. Normally polyoestrous with 3- to 4-day cycle, continuing during lactation (H.Chitty, 1957). Embryo rate variable, usually between 3 and 6. Gestation 21 days (Ranson,

1934), not prolonged by lactation. Weaning 14 to 18 days. Sex ratio approximately equal. Nests usually made of grass and placed at root level or below ground. Young weigh just over 2 g at birth, females become sexually mature at 3 weeks (c. 12 g), mate at 6 weeks. In related Continental Vole (M. arvalis) growth more rapid in spring-born than in summer- and autumn-born young, which also stop at relatively low overwintering weight. Growth may similarly be checked in spring-born young if population is crowded (van Wijngaarden, 1960).

POPULATION Much research done upon cyclic fluctuations in numbers (periodicity 3 to 4 years) of this species by Chitty (1952, 1958), Leslie, Chitty & Chitty (1953) and of M. arvalis by e.g. Stein (1957) and van Wijngaarden (1957). Pattern of generation sequence much as in Bank Vole, but much greater variation in that some generations may practically fail to breed or die off when young. In British Isles most spectacular increases on hill grasslands enclosed for plantations and at high peaks damage may occur on wide scale to young trees and grass: densities can range from negligible to hundreds per acre: on Continent M. arvalis may reach higher densities and is more damaging because it occurs in agricultural ground. These cyclical changes often profoundly influence breeding and concentration of predators (see, e.g. Lockie, 1955). Plagues of this kind may be synchronous over large areas, but often are not and recent work by Chitty and others suggests crashes due to a lowering of viability resulting from crowding (see also Elton (1942) for a general survey of plagues). Figures for expectation of life mean little under the circumstances, but in laboratory conditions Short-tailed Voles will live on average about 71 weeks.

FOOD Staple food is grass, particularly the bases of stems. Godfrey (1953) showed by analysing faeces that voles living on limestone grassland mainly ate about five species of grasses, tor grass (Brachypodium pinnatum) being the commonest. N.Charles (pers. comm.) finds that the main food in Scotland is the blades and stems of the softer, more succulent grasses but, when these are less plentiful, particularly during winter, they will turn to coarser ground species and to bulbs, roots, crops and bark.

PREDATORS Practically all birds and beasts of prey eat Short-tailed Voles, but predominantly those that quarter open country, such as Kestrel, Buzzard, Short-eared Owl, Barn Owl and harriers. Among mammals Fox has a characteristic pouncing method of catching voles in grass and feeds widely on them, now Rabbits are reduced (Lever, 1959). During plagues concentration of predators build up (see e.g., Lockie, 1955), though doubtful if they can have much effect on numbers (Chitty, 1938).

RELATIONS WITH MAN At high densities will cause considerable damage to grassland and young trees: do not, however, climb and bark saplings high up.

Accommodates itself easily to captivity (Chitty, 1957) and stocks have been maintained at Bureau of Animal Population, Oxford, for many years. Mean expectation of life in captivity is 71 weeks (Leslie *et al.*, 1955).

GENUS *Arvicola*

Genus distributed all over Palaearctic Region and probably allied to Nearctic *Aulacomys*. Nearest relative *Microtus*, only differing in being larger, having flank musk-glands, longer tail and slight differences in teeth.

Opinions differ as to number of species in genus: one to four are suggested. Certainly four distinguishable forms in Western Europe: *amphibius* in British Isles, *sapidus* in Spain and S. and W. France, *scherman* in C. Europe and *terrestris* in N. and E. Europe, penetrating to Holland. *Sapidus* is well separated, on chromosome number (2n = 40) (Matthey, 1956) and shape of penis (de Balsac & Guislain, 1935) from other three (2n = 36); overlaps with range of *scherman*, but keeps ecologically distinct. Other three all vary in size, in degree of terrestrial habit and in degree to which incisors project forwards. Perhaps best to keep all four species at the moment, recognizing *sapidus* as far the most distinct, until more known about situation in E. Europe and Asia, where distinctions between *terrestris* and *scherman* said to break down. However, R.A.Davis (unpubl.) suggests *terrestris* and *amphibius* are also difficult to separate.

Water Vole (Water Rat) *Arvicola amphibius* L.

DISTRIBUTION Species, as at present understood, confined to England, Wales and Scotland. Those in Scottish Highlands separated as *A. a. reta*, being slightly smaller and darker and having high frequency of melanic specimens. *A. a. brigantium* also described from Yorkshire, having forwardly directed incisors. Discovery of population with similar teeth near Edinburgh (de Balsac & Guislain, 1935) suggests British population may be heterogeneous with smaller, pro-odont forms, reminiscent of the Pleistocene *A. abbotti*, as relics in the middle of a form derived from *A. terrestris*, which invaded before Continent was cut off. Melanic specimens occur rarely throughout range of *A. amphibius*,

FIG. 30. Water Vole (*Arvicola amphibius*) showing characteristic hunched-up attitude with shaggy fur, rather flat face and (for a vole) long, hairy tail.

and, in higher frequencies, in Cambridgeshire and Norfolk. Species known to occur on I. of Wight and Anglesey, otherwise absent from islands.

DESCRIPTION See Field Identification Characters. A large vole with dark brown pelage and relatively long tail, perhaps confusable in water with Brown Rat, though swims and dives more expertly (*Photographs 36 & 37*). Out of water, furred tail, short ears and chubby face, and habit of sitting up and holding food with forelimbs distinguish it (Fig. 30).

MEASUREMENTS B.-H.&H. give following: h.&b. ♂ 201 mm (23 meas., range 185 to 219 mm), ♀ 187 mm (22 meas., range 170 to

220 mm); tail ♂ 124 mm (23 meas., 106 to 136 mm), ♀ 116.5 mm (22 meas., 92 to 144 mm). Weights of sexually mature animals, ♂ 263 g (4 only), ♀ 232 g (5 only). Perry (1943) gives mean weights of over-wintering animals as 120 to 180 g, of spring animals 200 to 300 g, with males slightly heavier.

HABITAT In lowland country mainly along banks of ponds, canals and slow-running rivers where water level does not vary much. In Highlands ascends the burns up to about 2,000 ft. In Europe some forms, e.g. *A. scherman,* are smaller and terrestrial, burrowing like moles, and this character has been used to separate the forms. However, there are some areas in England where *A. amphibius* does this, e.g. Read's Island in the Humber (Southern & Crowcroft, 1956), and Caistor, Lincs. (R.A.Davis, unpubl.).

GENERAL HABITS Van Wijngaarden (1954) gives activity rhythm (from catches) as beginning about 4 a.m., continuing fairly active to 4 p.m., then rising to a peak at 9 p.m., declining quickly with little activity at night. However, C.H.B.Worrall (unpubl.) reports main activity at dusk and little during day. Resident animals have home range not more than 200 yds long and males fight intruders fiercely, especially in spring, preparing with an upright, aggressive posture and much chattering. Homing experiments (P.Best, unpubl.) show unfailing return up to 300 yd up or down stream and 200 yd away from water; some returns from as far as 1 mile downstream. Home range marked by secretion of flank glands, which is smeared on to hind feet and stamped into the ground (Frank, 1956). Tunnels distinguished from those of Mole by being upright oval instead of horizontal oval. Also hills made by burrowing flatter than those of Mole and mixed with grass (Mehl, 1939). Trackways sometimes very visible in vegetation.

BREEDING Nests made of rushes and grass (not shredded as Short-tailed Vole) either in burrows, or above ground in reed-beds, etc. Males fecund Feb, females in March, first pregnancies early April. Early young mature and breed themselves at length of *c.* 15 cm (130 g). Embryo rate 5.7, corpora lutea 6.4 (England, 18 records), 4.5 (Holland) after estimated pre-natal mortality of *c.* 30%. Rate increases with size of female, also rises and falls during season. Litter rate, *c.* 4.4 per annum (Holland). In first part of season, conception at post-partum oestrus usual, but not so frequent later on. Breeding ceases in October. Young at birth *c.* 4.5 to 5 cm h.&b. (*c.* 7.5 to 10 g), grow fast to 15 cm (130 g), then gradually to *c.* 200 g. (Data for England from Perry (1943); for Holland from van Wijngaarden (1954)). Sex ratio equal but males predominate in trapped samples.

POPULATION Overwintering animals mainly late-born young which have not bred. Also some late breeders, which can be distinguished from condition of internal genitalia, not from weight. All increase in weight in spring: young begin to appear in May with peak in July–August. Considerable population fluctuations, but much greater on Continent.

FOOD Occasionally takes animal food, as evidenced by remains of fresh-water mussels (*Anodonta*) and water snails (*Limnaea*) at feeding platforms. Otherwise all vegetable with marked preference for flote-grass (*Glyceria*), reed (*Phragmites*) and reed-grass (*Phalaris*). Dean (1947) notes how strip of grass along bank is kept mown and producing young growth. Some large food plants are 'felled', e.g. *Cicuta*, others pulled down, e.g. *Glyceria*. Seeds may be stored.

PREDATORS Many birds and mammals, also Pike (*Esox lucius*). Dean (1947) notes how, at time of abundance, pair of Tawny Owls and two fledged chicks settled at colony and plundered it. Appears to hold its own with Brown Rat.

RELATIONS WITH MAN In British Isles rarely damages crops, and burrows rarely frequent enough to undermine river banks, though known to bark trees and to eat twigs of, e.g. willow. Damage much more serious on Continent owing to burrowing habits, which enable it to feed on root crops, stores of, e.g. potatoes, and so on. Further east carries bacillus of *Tularaemia*.

GENUS *Ondatra*

Native to Canada and U.S.A. Highly specialized for aquatic life. Three species named.

*†**Musk Rat** Ondatra zibethica* (L.)

This is far most widespread of species, 13 subspecies having been distinguished. Largest of sub-family Microtini (h.&b. up to 320 mm), has long, almost naked tail laterally compressed. Makes 'houses' of aquatic vegetation and burrows extensively in river banks. Fur (musquash of commerce) soft and thick. Species has been introduced into Europe, U.S.S.R. and Japan in fur farms and escapes have built up large and widespread populations, which do great damage to river banks, etc. Imported about 1929 into British Isles, it established itself at two main colonies in Shropshire and mid-Scotland and three smaller ones in Surrey, Sussex and Ireland. Intensive trapping had exterminated all these colonies by 1937. Information about the course of the campaign and about measurements, weights, breeding, food and general habits is given in Warwick (1934, 1940).

FAMILY MURIDAE

Large family, confined to Old World (except for introductions), Palaearctic, Ethiopean, Oriental and Australasian regions. Largest sub-family, Murinae, with 68 genera, including the now widely spread *Rattus* and *Mus*. Other sub-families are Dendromurinae, African tree mice with 6 genera; Otomyinae from Africa with 2 genera; Phloeomyinae, from Asia, E. Indies and Philippines with 6 genera; Rhynchomyinae, Philippine 'shrew' rat with 1 genus; and Hydromyinae, New Guinea, Philippine and Australian water rats with 8 genera.

GENUS *Apodemus*

Genus Palaearctic with some six species (two in British Isles). On the whole, colours more saturated in western parts of range with tendency for increase in size at higher latitudes and altitudes. Outstandingly nocturnal and occurs over wide range of habitats. Zimmermann (1962) has recently reviewed groupings within the genus.

Distribution of Wood and Yellow-necked Mice intriguing, but more information wanted. Wide geographical overlap in Europe and British Isles with indications of habitat segregation in some places (e.g. Scandinavia and some parts of Germany, see Curry-Lindahl, 1959; Heinrich, 1951; Felten, 1952; Zimmermann, 1936). In England, Yellow-necked Mice tend to occur in small patches among general Wood Mouse populations (Thurlow, 1938). Some authors consider them conspecific (see, e.g., Dalimier, 1952) but scarcity of intermediates makes this doubtful.

FIG. 31. The four species of mice found in the British Isles—
above, Yellow-necked Mouse (*Apodemus flavicollis*); middle, Wood
Mouse (*A. sylvaticus*); lower, House Mouse (*Mus musculus*) with
the Harvest Mouse (*Micromys minutus*) clinging to a stalk of wheat.

Wood Mouse (Long-tailed Field Mouse) *Apodemus sylvaticus* (L.)

DISTRIBUTION Species extends abroad to Iceland in north, C. Asia, N. India and Persia in east and N. Africa in south. Size and saturation of colour increase from N.E. to S.W. in Europe (Ursin, 1956). Common all over British Isles except on high ground (though recorded once at 4,000 ft (Corbet, 1960)). Known to be present on following islands: Skomer, Bardsey, I. of Man, most west Scottish islands (incl. St Kilda) (see Delany, 1961), Orkney, Shetland (incl. Fair Isle and Foula). Absent from Lundy, Lunga, N. Rona and I. of May, in Scillies present St Mary's and Tresco only (I. Linn, unpubl.). Present on all Channel Islands (Bishop, unpubl. thesis, 1962). British Isles have type subspecies (*A. s. sylvaticus*), centred on W. Europe. Many subspecies described, among which are British forms *A. s. hebridensis* (Hebrides), *A. s. hirtensis* (St Kilda), and *A. s. fridariensis* (Shetland).

DESCRIPTION See Field Identification Characters. Juveniles with much greyer coats can be mistaken for House Mice. Adult pelage variable, some with much brighter yellow on flanks. Size of yellow chest-spot variable (may even be absent), sometimes produced into streak down middle of breast. Various mutants, including silver-grey and melanic, known. Moult mainly spring and autumn, but some spread (Stein, 1960).

MEASUREMENTS (B.-H.&H.). H.&b. ♂ 87.6 mm (20 meas., range 81 to 92 mm), ♀ 87.7 mm (20 meas., range 83 to 94 mm); tail ♂ 87 mm (20 meas., range 76 to 100 mm), ♀ 85.4 mm (20 meas., range 78 to 93 mm). Weight ♂ 19.6 g (20 meas., range 14 to 25 g), ♀ 20.9 g (20 meas., range 17 to 29 g, embryos included). Larger specimens, especially overwintered animals, are not uncommon, up to 100 mm and 37 g. Island races tend to be larger. Boyd (1959) records largest male caught on St Kilda 54.2 g and largest female 48.5 g. These large races have been assigned to the Yellow-necked Mouse by E.&M.-S. but recent investigations suggest this is wrong (Cranbrook, 1957; Bishop, unpubl. thesis, 1962).

HABITAT Characteristic small rodent of woodland, living in runways in and below litter. Occupies areas with less ground cover than Bank Vole. Also in hedgerows and fields, gardens, sometimes grass and heather, especially where no Short-tailed Voles present (e.g. Hebrides), but rarely on high moors and scree, except where stone walls and buildings afford cover. Will occupy houses and buildings, especially where no House Mice present.

GENERAL HABITS Voice a high squeaking, rarely heard. Locomotion rapid, either scurrying or leaping, quite different from voles. Uses a complex system of underground runways but forages more diffusely above ground, frequenting bare areas more readily than voles. Droppings larger than those of House Mouse, rather rounded in section, may be pale but darken rapidly. Social organization loosely based on family unit but one mouse's home range may be widely overlapped by neighbouring ones. Home range generally small (c. 1,000 sq yd (840 sq m)) but good deal of movement in spring and summer, especially by males (J.Kikkawa, unpubl.). Homing sure from 400 yd; from 725 yd half of mice return (Hacker & Pearson, 1951). Activity almost entirely nocturnal with dusk and dawn peaks in winter, single peak in summer (Miller, 1955). Most active on dark nights; inhibited even by moonlight (J.Kikkawa, unpubl.). Nests below ground, usually constructed from finely shredded grasses. Used normally for resting places as well as for breeding. Platforms above ground, such as old birds' nests, often used for feeding places and littered with, e.g. shells of haws and droppings. Food stored in winter below ground and Longworth traps may be found with entrances stuffed with soil and sticks.

BREEDING Males become fecund in March and pregnancies occur in April, reaching peak in July–August, declining by Oct (Baker, 1930). In some seasons breeding may continue to Dec, or even throughout winter (Newson, unpubl. thesis, 1960). Gestation 25 to 26 days. Embryo rate starts at mean of 5, rises at height of breeding season to nearly 6, then declines to below 5. Corpora lutea counts show that early in season some eggs fail to be fertilized, later less eggs are ovulated (Baker, 1930). Number of litters per season unknown but females may be pregnant at 12 g and conception at post-partum oestrus regular (Lowe, 1957). Late-born young do not come into breeding condition until following spring. Young weaned at c. 21 days (Lowe, 1957). Sex ratio probably about equal but live traps often catch more males, especially in summer. Young first leave nest at 15 to 16 days (c. 6 g). In summer males fecund at 15 g; females pregnant at slightly higher weight.

POPULATION Mean density in woodland varies from *c.* 5 to 40 per acre according to season and year. Breeding increase most notable in July–August, perhaps through poor survival of early litters. Peak population Sept–Oct, sometimes later, then decline to lowest numbers in March–April, but in some years this course of events breaks down. Mean expectation of life from weaning *c.* 6 months. Numbers fluctuate from year to year but not so violently as those of Short-tailed Vole. A check on age can be made from degree of wear of molar teeth (Bishop & Delany, 1962).

FOOD Much casual information, showing main items grain, seedlings, buds, fruits, nuts, snails, etc.—not fond of coarse material such as bark, roots and grain husks. Study in woodland shows seeds in 84% of stomachs, adult insects in 30%, larvae in 48% and spiders in 6% (Miller, 1954). Recent study in Czechoslovakia (Holišóvá, 1960) shows seeds occur in 78% of stomachs, berries in 8%, buds in 3%, green plant material in 28%, roots in 7%, fungi in 5% and animal food in 59%. Variation according to season, seeds predominating in latter half of year, animal food and green plant material in earlier half; according to sex, males eating more insects and less green food than females; and according to age, young mice eating less insects and more buds and fungi than adults. Sometimes predominantly animal food is taken (Kikkawa, 1959). Hazel nuts typically opened with slightly irregular hole gnawed in blunt end; snail shells by biting through shell away from the spire. Grain manipulated with fore paws and typical coarse dust of 'kibblings' left behind, as with House Mice but not with voles.

PREDATORS Many mammals and birds eat Wood Mice but most important probably owls, especially Tawny Owl (in woodland Wood Mice have been shown to compose up to 30% of its prey (Southern, 1954)) and small carnivores.

RELATIONS WITH MAN Wood Mice sometimes come into houses but more usually found in outhouses and sheds, especially where apples stored. Occasionally will graze down sprouting winter wheat seriously (Roebuck, 1951) and will raid newly planted peas. They can be kept in captivity and will sometimes settle down to breed but never become really tame and always demand some skill in handling. If one is picked up by any part of the tail other than the base, the skin sloughs off and the exposed portion eventually drops off.

Yellow-necked Mouse *Apodemus flavicollis* (Melchior)

DISTRIBUTION Abroad distributed entirely within the range of Wood Mouse except in N. Europe (Curry-Lindahl, 1959) but absent from large areas. Yellow collar fades away towards S. and E. Europe (Ursin, 1956). In British Isles probably more widespread than appears from records. Most counties have only one or two, at most six, records, but in Hereford and Suffolk, where more diligent search made, Yellow-necked Mouse has been found many times. Confined mainly to south England, being recorded for most counties south of and including Suffolk, Cambridgeshire, Bedfordshire, Northampton, Derby, Cheshire and Shropshire. Still no records for Stafford, Warwickshire, Buckinghamshire, Oxfordshire, I. of Wight, Devon and Cornwall. Northwards only known in Lincoln and doubtfully in Northumberland. In Wales recorded in Brecon, Cardigan, Carmarthen, Denbigh, Radnor, Merioneth and Montgomery (Matheson, 1963b). Not in Scotland, Ireland nor I. of Man. British race is *A. f. wintoni*.

DESCRIPTION Larger than Wood Mouse and tail usually longer than head and body (Saint-Girons, 1957). Colour brighter than Wood Mouse, more rufous above and whiter below; chest-spot always spreading sideways to form bright yellowish-buff collar between forelegs, sometimes extending back down the belly as well. Forms intermediate between Yellow-necked and Wood Mice rarely found. Sexes alike. Juvenile pelage less bright, greyer so that study specimens difficult to distinguish from young Wood Mice unless reliable measurements recorded; but collar usually present, even if suffused with dark grey.

MEASUREMENTS (B.-H.&H.). H.&b. ♂ 105 mm (22 meas., range 94 to 124 mm), ♀ 101.6 mm (10 meas., range 85 to 115 mm); tail ♂ 110.8 mm (22 meas., range 94 to 124 mm), ♀ 106.6 mm (10 meas., range 98 to 115 mm). Weight 33.7 g (6 weighed, range 32 to 35.5 g).

All measurements significantly larger than for Wood Mouse (Larina, 1958); upper incisors proportionately deeper from back to front, which may distinguish remains in owl pellets and give clue to systematic relationships within the group (Cranbrook, 1957).

HABITAT In British Isles much as Wood Mouse—woods, hedges, shrubberies, gardens, allotments, etc., not infrequently apple stores, potting sheds, houses, even churches and beehives. Trapping results show it occurs in pockets throughout populations of Wood Mice. Recorded up to 500 ft.

Continental authors, e.g. Zimmermann (1936), Grodzinski (1959), mostly indicate habitat divergence between two species but this not found in British Isles. Yellow-necked Mouse more truly woodland animal; Wood Mouse occupies fields and scrub. Parallel difference in food indicated by Heinrich (1951). Some authors, e.g. Collett (1911–12) in Norway, note that Yellow-necked Mouse replaces Wood Mouse at higher altitudes.

GENERAL HABITS Apart from above, little known about Yellow-necked Mouse but habits probably much the same as those of Wood Mouse. Two species will live amicably in captivity, though there are records of the larger one attacking the smaller. Zimmermann (1957) has tried to hybridize them in captivity but failed.

BREEDING Presumably as Wood Mouse, though Stein (1950c) noted longer breeding season (viz. Feb to Oct) than in Wood Mouse. Mean embryo rate 5 (13 records).

GENUS *Micromys*

Restricted almost entirely to central band of Palaearctic Region, down to Mediterranean in west, to north Burma in east. Monospecific.

Harvest Mouse *Micromys minutus* (Pallas)

DISTRIBUTION Broad distribution as genus. Many subspecies described, showing tendency for tail length to increase towards S.E. of range. In British Isles most abundant in S. and E., thinning out towards Midlands and north, though odd records as far as Aberdeenshire (Adams, 1913).

DESCRIPTION See Field Identification Characters. Pelage greyer in younger animals; russet appearing first on haunches, then over whole back. Eastern races slower to acquire russet colour (B.-H.& H.; Kubik, 1953). Sexes similar. No mutant types known.

MEASUREMENTS Figures for two samples collected from corn ricks Jan to March (Southwick, 1956; Rowe, 1958) are notably similar. Rowe gives following: h.&b. ♂ 57.0 mm (72 meas., range 50 to 63 mm), ♀ 57.1 mm (47 meas., range 50 to 69 mm); tail ♂ 53.1 mm (72 meas., range 46 to 62 mm), ♀ 53.3 mm (47 meas., range 48 to 66 mm); weight ♂ 6.1 g (72 meas., range 4.2 to 8.2 g), ♀ 6.1 g (47 meas., range 4.4 to 10.2 g).

HABITAT In summer, cornfields and surrounding hedgerows; dykes and reed-beds; long grass, even out into open fields and salt marshes. In winter tends to live more in burrows just below ground level and in corn ricks, but does not breed there, as House Mouse does. Recorded in woodland in Poland (Kubik, 1953).

GENERAL HABITS Voice, faint squeaks; M.Knight (unpubl.) records bird-like chirruping during courtship. Active throughout 24 hours, more diurnal than other species of mice. Shelter during non-active periods in nests or burrows. Nests very characteristically woven of grasses in shape of ball and built above ground. Nothing known of home range.

BREEDING Little known. Nest building described in B.-H.&H. Gestation 21 days (Harting, 1895). Litter rates between 5 and 9 recorded, but very few. O.Hook (pers. comm.) reports between 7 and 25 Sept 1 nest with four young, 2 with five and 2 with six. Growth of young: 8 days, eyes open, 11–12 days, excursions from nest, 15 days, independent at weight of 5.5 g. Reach adult weight in 24 days (Kästle, 1953). Breeding said to begin late April in Poland (Kubik, 1953). Rowe (1958) found 48% males in ricks fecund by March.

POPULATION Rough population analysis by tooth wear suggests average life in wild is 16 to 18 months and no second autumn moult (Kubik, 1953). Most variable in numbers even in neighbouring localities (Southwick, 1956) and from year to year. Numbers in Britain probably declined, except perhaps in east and south, during last 100 years, but 1955 saw considerable revival (Southwick, 1956). Usually live to about 2 years in captivity.

FOOD Grain, fruits, green vegetable matter, insects. No systematically collected data exist.

PREDATORS Practically no data from British Isles. Uttendörfer (1939) states that in Germany Tawny Owl takes most, but even that is not many.

RELATIONS WITH MAN Favourite animals for keeping in captivity, needing little food or attention and being devoid of smell. See Southern (1957) and, for breeding in captivity, Pitt (1945).

GENUS *Mus*

Restricted originally to Palaearctic, Oriental and Ethiopian Regions. Five groups of species in Oriental and Ethiopian Regions and one (*M. musculus*) originating in Asia, now world-wide. Nearest related genus *Rattus*.

House Mouse Mus musculus (L.)

DISTRIBUTION Originally mainly Palaearctic, now world-wide. Species tends to be divided into shorter-tailed, light-bellied forms living wild, especially in the Asian steppes, perhaps original home, and longer-tailed, grey-bellied forms living commensally with man (see review by Schwarz & Schwarz, 1943). Many subspecies described, but systematics tangled owing to transport by man. Common all over British Isles, especially as commensal in buildings and around farms. This species, though often referred to locally as 'field mouse', is the one which populates corn ricks so abundantly. Known to live and breed in fields and hedgerows of arable country (Southern & Laurie, 1946) but not known how far this population supported from mice inhabiting ricks. Known from many outlying islands. *M. m. faeroensis* (Faeroes) and *M. m. muralis* (St Kilda) are fairly distinct variants; latter now extinct.

DESCRIPTION See Field Identification Characters. Eyes and ears not so prominent as in Wood Mouse. Tail does not 'skin'. Sexes similar. Mutants: albino, pied, sandy, hairless not uncommonly found. Distinctive musky smell. Genetics of domestic strains dealt with by Grüneberg (1943). Teeth like Wood Mouse, but smaller and simpler; largest upper molar with three roots distinguishes skull from that of Wood Mouse, which has four (Fig. 32). Examples from outlying islands tend to be larger and this applies especially to *M. m. faeroensis* and *M. m. muralis*.

MEASUREMENTS Crowcroft & Rowe (1961) show wide range of variability between mice of same age, living in confined colonies. B.-H.&H. H.&b. ♂ 79 mm (20 meas., range 72 to 84 mm), ♀ 77.6 mm (20 meas., range 70 to 92 mm); tail ♂ 77.6 mm (20 meas., range 70 to 83 mm), ♀ 77.5 mm (20 meas., range 70 to 84 mm); weight ♂ 15.6 g (20 weighed, range 13 to 21 g), ♀ 16.5 g (8 with embryos) (20 weighed, range 10 to 30 g). Evans & Vevers (1938) give following figures for Faeroes, away from towns: h.&b. ♂ 87.7 mm (7 meas., range 81 to 98 mm), ♀ 91.8 mm (13

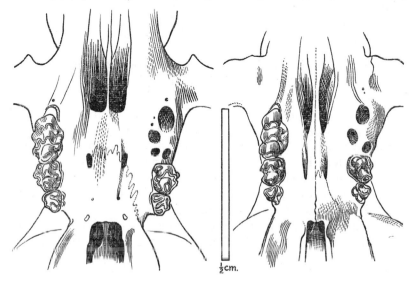

FIG. 32. Palatal view of skulls of Wood Mouse (*Apodemus sylvaticus*), left, and House Mouse (*Mus musculus*), right, showing upper cheek teeth. From both skulls the left m_1 has been removed revealing four root sockets, or alveoli, in the Wood Mouse and three in the House Mouse.

meas., range 84 to 102 mm); tail ♂ 82 mm (6 meas., range 74 to 92 mm), ♀ 83.9 mm (13 meas., range 74 to 91 mm); weight ♂ 22.4 g (12 weighed, range 16 to 32 g), ♀ 27.7 g (5 with embryos) (21 weighed, range 19 to 41.5 g).

HABITAT Open fields, chiefly in arable country, walls and hedgerows; corn (especially wheat and oat) ricks, farm premises, town buildings; recorded from coal mine. Tend to move into cover during winter.

x

GENERAL HABITS Voice, a high squeak, frequently heard. So-called 'singing' mice due to inflammation of lungs. Mainly nocturnal, but not completely so, as Wood Mouse. Considerable individual variation in daytime activity (Chitty & Southern, 1954), also according to state of hunger. Foraging range normally small (*c.* 50 sq ft), and can be shared with many mice. Captive colonies of wild mice (Crowcroft, 1955) show that, at moderate densities, males will live with one or more females in territories which they defend vigorously. At high densities dominance relationships established whereby surplus lives in subordinate state without territory or breeding. Faeces similar to those of Wood Mouse, but smaller.

BREEDING Continuous in most habitats throughout the year, but much reduced in winter in field-living populations. Breeding rates in different habitats fully studied by Laurie (1946a); range from 10.2 litters per female per year in ricks to 5.5 in urban premises. Nests made from any available material, grass to silk stockings, shredded up. Ricks often have communal nests with two or more litters. Litter size 5.6. Data on breeding of domestic variety extensive, see especially Snell (1941). Oestrous cycle 4 to 6 days, copulation leaves vaginal plug which persists for 18 to 24 hours. Gestation 19 to 20 days. Fertilization occurs at post-partum oestrus and implantation is then delayed 2 to 16 days. Young weaned at 18 days. Females fecund at 7.5 g, males at 10 g.

POPULATION Density in ricks can be very high, up to 15 per cu m. In houses great abundance usually due to plenty of food and lack of disturbance. Mean length of life in laboratory *c.* 90 weeks; in wild very much less. Mass increase to plague proportions recorded, especially in areas to which they have been introduced (Australia, U.S.A.) (see Southern & Chitty, 1954; Elton, 1942). Snap-trap samples usually biased in favour of heavier animals. Crowcroft & Rowe (1957, 1958) and others cited in their papers, have studied population growth of confined colonies and its limitation.

FOOD Little known about food of field populations; review of types of grain and other urban foods, and quantities eaten in Chitty & Southern (1954). Mean consumption of grain *c.* 3.5 g per day. Can exist on very little water.

PREDATORS Many mammals and birds in the wild, especially the Barn Owl; in town and on farms, domestic cats.

RELATIONS WITH MAN A long-standing pest. Estimates of damage caused to grain stacks (up to 16%) given in Chitty & Southern (1954). For details of keeping in captivity see Snell (1941), and Philip (1957).

GENUS *Rattus*

A vast genus, containing more than 550 named forms, distributed all over the Old World. Some species most successful colonizers and commensals of man, and their distribution now cosmopolitan. Only genus of mammals, other than bats and *Mus*, which has reached remote oceanic islands early in historic times.

*Black Rat *Rattus rattus* L.

DISTRIBUTION Originally distributed in Indo-Malayan region, extending into southern China; was carried from Middle Ages onwards all round world, but has gradually given way to Brown Rat and persists in British Isles only in ports, where thought to be maintained by immigration (Matheson, 1939), though numbers now declining (Bentley, 1959). Still found away from buildings on Lundy and on all Channel Islands (Baal, 1949).

Seventy-four subspecies recognized, though many doubtful and some nearly related species may eventually be included in *R. rattus*; systematics still fluid. In most parts of range three forms discernible, classified as subspecies, but probably only colour phases: *R. r. rattus*, black above, grey beneath, the true 'Black Rat'; *R. r. frugivorus*, agouti above and white below; and *R. r. alexandrinus* agouti above, like *R. r. frugivorus*, but greyish below because white hairs have slatey bases. Mixed populations show segregation of types with *R. r. frugivorus* genetically dominant to *R. r. alexandrinus* and *R. r. rattus* dominant to both (Feldman, 1926) though there is another, much less common, recessive form of black. Some geographical separation, however, of these forms: on the whole, white-bellied *R. r. frugivorus* is predominant wild-living rat (India (E.&M.-S.), Cyprus (Watson, 1950), New Zealand (Watson, 1959), New Caledonia (Nicholson & Warner, 1953)); the black form is commensal (India (E.&M.-S.); Port of

London (Watson, 1950)); and the grey-bellied form has its head-quarters in the Middle East. Authors disagree about proportions in British Isles but may fluctuate.

DESCRIPTION See Field Identification Characters. A more slender animal than Brown Rat, with long tail, large ears and finer pelage. Skull lighter and has supra-orbital ridges which curve out, giving pear-shaped outline to cranium: in Brown Rat, these ridges are parallel (Fig. 33). Albinos recorded, and white-spotting, especially on forehead and chest, not infrequent.

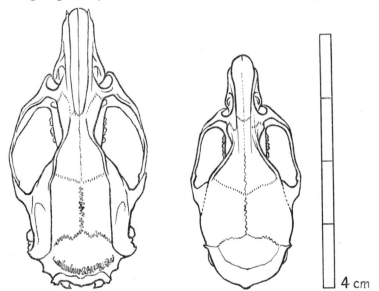

4 cm

FIG. 33. Cranial view of skulls of (left) Brown Rat (*Rattus norvegicus*) and (right) Black Rat (*R. rattus*). Apart from the smaller size and more slender build of the latter, the flask-shaped outline of the cranium is diagnostic.

MEASUREMENTS As with many small rodents, growth continues after sexual maturity. B.-H.&H. give following for British 'full-grown' rats: h.&b. ♂ 191 mm (17 meas., range 165 to 228 mm), ♀ 174 mm (18 meas., range 143 to 198 mm); tail ♂ 219 mm (17 meas., range 188 to 252 mm), ♀ 203 mm (17 meas., range 140 to 232 mm). Weights variable, but full-grown usually *c.* 200 g.

HABITAT A climbing species which, in country areas outside British Isles, is often arboreal. In urban areas inhabits top stories of buildings, travelling along power lines, etc., while Brown Rat inhabits ground level. On Lundy reported mainly on sea-shore, though occurs on higher ground (I.Linn, unpubl.). The most common species on ships and port populations probably maintained by these immigrants.

GENERAL HABITS Used to be widespread in towns and farmland, living in roofs and walls of houses, as it still does in sea-ports. Nests in rafters and behind partitions and travels along wires and beams, leaving a diagnostic, crescentic smear from oil in the fur where it passes under cross-beams (*Photograph 35*). Progressively driven out since beginning of 18th century by Brown Rat, which is known to kill them in mixed captive colonies (Barnett, 1958). Activity mainly nocturnal. Presence often traced by damage, but faeces characteristic, *c.* 10 mm long × 2 to 3 mm wide and curved, compared with fatter and more solid droppings of Brown Rat (17 × 6 mm). Range of movement rarely more than 100 yd. Females more sedentary than males (Watson, 1951).

BREEDING Sex ratio varies, often biased to males in young and old age-groups (Watson, 1951). Sexual maturity at 3 to 4 months (*c.* 90 g) (Leslie, Perry & Watson, 1945). Breeding season variable: usually some breeding throughout year with either one (summer) or two (summer and autumn) peaks (Davis, 1953). Breeding more continuous in protected habitats. Embryo rate in British Isles *c.* 7, elsewhere 5 to 10, varying with size of mother. Litter rate *c.* 3 to 5 per year. Gestation period 21 days (Kenneth & Ritchie, 1953).

POPULATION Densities vary greatly with environment. Watson (1951) found 2 to 5 per acre on scrubland in Cyprus. Turnover is fast, annual mortality being of the order of 91 to 97% (Davis, 1953).

FOOD A tremendous variety of foods is eaten, which it is almost impossible to particularize.

PREDATORS In urban areas, mainly domestic cats. In country districts many birds and beasts of prey.

RELATIONS WITH MAN Can be first-class pest by eating and fouling fruits, seeds and cereals: also, where it lives arboreally, by stripping bark off trees. In tropics especially can act as reservoir for bubonic plague.

*Brown Rat (Norway Rat) *Rattus norvegicus* Berkenhout

DISTRIBUTION The *R. norvegicus* group is much less diffuse than the *R. rattus* group, to which it is nevertheless closely related. Only five subspecies described, four from China and Siberia, whence world-wide stocks must have been derived, and one from Celebes, but group closely related to Chinese *R. n. caraco* and to others in Oriental region. Present distribution astonishing in its versatility, reaching in Antarctic to S. Georgia (Olstad, 1930) and, in the Arctic, to Spitsbergen (Løvenskiold, 1954), the Aleutians (Schiller, 1952) and Alaska (Schiller, 1956), though in last place it suffers badly from frostbite in winter. Reached British Isles in the early 18th century and ousted Black Rat firmly. Process still continues in U.S.A., where between 1946 and 1951 replaced the other over 1,000 sq miles of south-west Georgia (Ecke, 1954).

Over present vast geographical range characters remain remarkably stable. There is sparse occurrence of albinism, partial and total, but best-known variation is melanic. Normally these are only about 1 or 2% (Watson, 1944; Becker, 1952), but in rapidly expanding populations may rise to 20% (Smith, 1958).

DESCRIPTION See Field Identification Characters. Heavy body and relatively short tail, together with shaggy appearance of fur in adults, distinguish Brown from Black Rat (Fig. 34).

MEASUREMENTS (B.-H.&H.). H.&b. ♂ 233 mm (19 meas., range 203 to 267 mm), ♀ 240 mm (7 meas., range 216 to 267 mm); tail ♂ 196 mm (14 meas., range 165 to 229 mm), ♀ 186 mm (7 meas., range 178 to 203 mm).Weight variable, can be up to 500 g and more, so about 2½ times weight of Black Rat.

HABITAT Largely connected with man in town buildings and yards, rubbish tips, sewers, especially farm buildings and corn ricks, but spreading out from these in summer along banks and walls, through fields and into woodland, especially where there are rabbit warrens. May be numerous along river banks and marshy coasts, being good swimmer and often mistaken for Water Vole, or 'Water Rat' (*Photographs 36 & 37*). Especially abundant along hedge-banks in E. Anglia, often in connection with sugar-beet crops. Always living on and under the ground, being active burrower.

GENERAL HABITS Range of movement within a settled environment *c.* 100 ft (Davis, Emlen & Stokes, 1948), though often much greater; shelter wherever possible a burrow or burrow system which may be extensive and complicated (Pisano & Storer, 1948). Runways obvious and diagnostic, winding through vegetation, or zig-zagging up sides of ricks. Shows intimate knowledge of environment and reacts suspiciously to any change which may

FIG. 34. Black Rat (*Rattus rattus*), above, contrasted with Brown Rat (*R. norvegicus*), below. Note the larger, thinner ears of the Black Rat, the relatively longer and slimmer tail and the less shaggy pelage.

inhibit exploratory drive (*Photograph 38*), constantly used by other small mammals, for 48 hours or so (Shorten, 1954b). Activity basically nocturnal with peak at dusk, then pause, then building up to another peak *c.* 3 a.m. and continuing until dawn (Chitty, 1954). Day feeding results from hunger, disturbance or conditioning. Mass movements often reported and movements on smaller scale occur when environment is disturbed or destroyed, e.g. corn ricks, though there is an exodus from these anyway in spring. Droppings easily recognized, being spindle-shaped and quite large (*c.* 17 mm long). Can be aggressive and full-grown female in defence of young can be formidable opponent of dog, or even man.

BREEDING Sex ratio about 50%: Leslie, Venables & Venables (1952), from whom most of following taken, found slightly more males in very large sample. Breeding may be nearly continuous

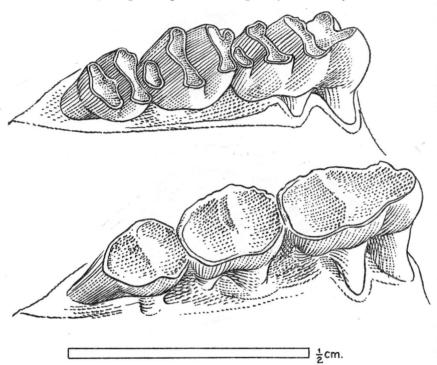

FIG. 35. Left lower cheek teeth of Brown Rat (*Rattus norvegicus*), showing (above) unworn condition and (below) the well-worn teeth of an older animal. The largest tooth is the anterior one.

in constant environment like corn rick and these authors found *c.* 30% females pregnant throughout year. In other environments either one or two peaks during year. Embryo rates vary with weight of mother, being *c.* 6 at 150 g and *c.* 11 at 500 g; generally higher in corn ricks than in other environments. Litters per year also variable, from 3 to 5 according to conditions. Gestation *c.* 24 days, females become mature at *c.* 115 g (*c.* 80 days old). Nests bulky and made of any material handy, sometimes above ground. Young ready to leave it in about 3 weeks.

POPULATION Densities vary greatly with habitat: corn ricks are recorded with 500 or more, though more usual figure <100. Populations quickly adapt themselves to variation in food and cover, levelling off though intra-specific competition and starvation at steady value, while environmental resources remain constant (Davis, 1953). Various census methods devised including measurement of bait taken (Chitty, 1954), since a population can be drawn to feed almost exclusively on bait provided. Population indexes are counts of droppings, runways, burrows, etc. When population reaches saturation, high mortality of young in nest and just after emergence, reckoned by Davis (1953) to be at the rate of 99% per annum. Mortality of adults is *c.* 91 to 97% per annum. This fast turnover enables population to recover rapidly after control measures.

FOOD Where cereals plentiful, will live almost entirely upon these, but can manage on incredible variety of foods; rats living along shore or in frozen meat stores must live almost entirely on animal food. Country-living rats probably eat wide range of invertebrates and whatever vertebrates they can catch or scavenge. A year's study of food, based on faeces and food remains, carried out by Drummond (1960) on island off E. coast showed rice grass (*Spartina*) was commonest food, though insects and crustaceans eaten in summer. Nests in ricks and food stores sometimes surrounded by corpses of House Mice, which are eaten by neatly everting the skin. Amount of food eaten per day determined by Leslie & Ranson (1954) based on wheat, as 10 to 40 g according to weight; water intake (Chitty, 1954) varied similarly from 17 to 35 ml.

PREDATORS Young rats are fair game for most predatory animals, but even Stoat may have difficulty in tackling full-grown one. Established populations less vulnerable to predators than rats on the move and Elton (1953) showed that farmyard cats can prevent reinvasion, but cannot reduce established infestation. After myxomatosis had killed off rabbits, rats occurred in 13% of Fox stomachs examined by Lever *et al.* (1957).

RELATIONS WITH MAN Brown Rats basically commensal with man and probably one of the most damaging pests he has to contend with. Figures from survey of corn ricks in 1943 (Elton & Laurie, 1954) suggest that from Jan to March in England and Wales rats were eating about 10 tons of grain a day. In addition to what is eaten, a vast amount of damage is done by spoiling and gnawing. Brown Rats also carry the disease organisms of food poisoning (*Salmonella*), leptospiral jaundice and trichinosis. On other side great value must be mentioned of domesticated strains of Brown Rat in medical and other research. Directions for care and maintenance as laboratory animals and as pets given by Porter (1957).

FAMILY GLIRIDAE

Fairly distinct and relatively small group with two sub-families, Glirinae, Palaearctic dormice with 6 genera, and Graphiurinae, African dormice with 1 genus.

GENUS *Glis*

Genus monospecific. Largest of European dormice; on continent may be confused with smaller, more numerous Garden Dormouse (*Eliomys*), but lacks head markings of latter.

Edible Dormouse (Fat or Squirrel-tailed Dormouse) Glis glis (L.)

DISTRIBUTION Distributed in C. Europe, south to N. Spain and Mediterranean islands, east to Persia and N.W. Turkestan, north to c. 200 miles short of Channel and N. Sea coasts and to S. shores of Baltic. Introduced into Tring Park, Herts in 1902, has spread slowly, now occupying triangle bounded by Beaconsfield, Aylesbury and Luton (Thompson, 1953).

DESCRIPTION Much larger than native Dormouse (Fig. 36), having long bushy tail, flattened dorso-ventrally with 'parting' on underside. Distinguished from Grey Squirrel by smaller size and nocturnal habits. Pelage grey-brown, dark stripes on outsides of legs, dark ring round eye, pupil dark and horizontal.

MEASUREMENTS Av. adult: h.&b. 175 mm, tail about the same; weight 150 to 200 g.

HABITAT Deciduous woodland, but known in Britain mainly from specimens found in houses, which they invade in autumn prior to hibernation. Often drowned in water cisterns.

GENERAL HABITS Voice, squeaks and a snuffling 'woofle-woofle'. Usually nocturnal, very agile climber, may be noisy when in lofts or walls of houses. Shelters during day in tree-holes, etc. Hibernates in Europe from Oct to April, usually in burrows in ground

FIG. 36. Relative sizes of (above) the Common Dormouse (*Muscardinus avellanarius*) and (below) the introduced Fat Dormouse (*Glis glis*).

or in tree-holes, thatch or lofts. May lose 35–50% weight in this period (Vietinghoff-Riesch, 1952). Normally sedentary, having home range *c*. 100 m (110 yd) in diameter, autumn dispersal up to three-quarters of a mile.

BREEDING In tree-holes and will use nest-boxes. In Europe (Vietinghoff-Riesch, 1952) wakes in April, pairs come into nest-boxes and start breeding mid-June. Breeding ends August; probably one litter only. Number varies from 2 to 7; yearly mean litter size may vary from 2.0 to 6.4.

POPULATION Density fluctuates widely in Europe, from 0.1 to 2 per acre. Mark-recapture study by Vietinghoff-Riesch (1955) shows population composed of 73% 1- to 2-year-old animals, 18% 3-year, 4% 4-year, 3% 5-year and 2% older. Sex ratio about 50% except in years of population decline when females predominate. Said not to breed until 2 years old.

FOOD All kinds of fruit and nuts, insects, bark of willow and plum trees. Not known to store food.

PREDATORS Especially dogs, cats, rats, Stoats, Weasels, owls. Vietinghoff-Riesch (1952) mentions particularly Tawny Owl in his study area in Germany.

RELATIONS WITH MAN In classical times Edible Dormice were favourite food of Romans, who fattened them specially for the table. Can be serious pests to fruit crops in Europe when numbers high, but not likely to be troublesome in present restricted (*c.* 100 sq miles) range in England.

GENUS *Muscardinus*

Genus monospecific, four other genera in sub-family.

Dormouse *Muscardinus avellanarius* (L.)

DISTRIBUTION From France to Urals and Asia Minor. In British Isles used to be fairly abundant in south, less so in west and north of England and rare or absent in Midlands, East Anglia. Absent from Scotland and Ireland. Has certainly declined in numbers during last 50 years from status of common pet, so its general biology little studied. Five subspecies described showing tendency for southern European forms to be brighter in colour.

DESCRIPTION See Field Identification Characters. More bushy tail than any other British mouse-size animal; careful handling essential to prevent skin stripping off tail. Young greyer than adults and among adults variation between greyish and clear red. Moult into winter pelage occurs October, spring moult not studied. Form with white tip to tail not infrequent; albinos recorded, but rare. Skull easy to identify from unusual transverse ridges on molar teeth (Fig. 37). Four digits on front feet, four and vestigial stump of digit 1 on hind feet.

MEASUREMENTS H.&b. 70 to 86 mm (7 in B.-H.&H.), tail 55 to 68 mm. In Poland Sidorowicz (1959) gives following measurements for h.&b. in summer population: juveniles 65 mm (7 meas., range 57 to 74 mm), subadults 68.6 mm (6 meas., range 65 to 74 mm), adults 75.1 mm (11 meas., range 69 to 80 mm). Weight variable, 23 to 43 g according to time of year, being heaviest before hibernation (Rabus, 1881).

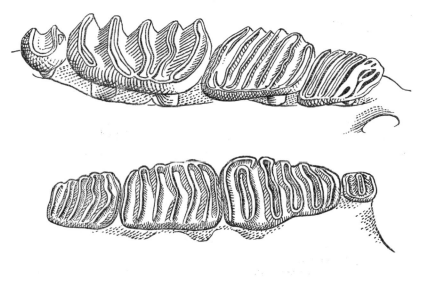

$\frac{1}{2}$cm

FIG. 37. Cheek teeth of Common Dormouse (*Muscardinus avellanarius*). Above—upper left tooth row viewed from lingual aspect, anterior to left; below—lower left tooth row viewed from lingual aspect, anterior to right.

HABITAT Most authors agree Dormice prefer secondary growth of woodland and scrub, especially where there are trees with edible seed crops, e.g. beech, hazel, sweet chestnut. Forages above ground, and summer nests for sleeping and breeding may be quite high. Winter hibernation nests more often at or below ground level.

GENERAL HABITS Silent animal. Strictly nocturnal except occasional young animal. Shelter nests built of grass or of honeysuckle bark (E.Hurrell, 1962). Often betrayed by stripped honeysuckle stems. Three to five may be built in a season (Wachtendorf, 1951). Sometimes slightly colonial with number of occupied nests close together (B.-H.&H.). These nests rarely contain more than one Dormouse. Hibernation in this and related genera widely studied, see, e.g., Eisentraut (1930).

BREEDING On Continent two main peaks of breeding, one late June to early July, the other late July to early August, sometimes extending into September and Sidorowicz (1959) records blind young on 10 October. Wachtendorf (1951) believes later litters born to animals of previous year. Gestation 22 to 24 days. Embryo rates not known. Number of young in litter usually about 4 (B.-H.&H.). Figures for S. Germany give mean of 3.7 (51 litters, range 2 to 7) and for Poland 3.55 (33 litters). Wachtendorf (1951) believes only one litter per year but Sidorowicz (1959) states for Poland minimum of two. Earlier litters larger than later ones. Nursery nests larger than shelter nests. Young furred in 13 days, eyes open at 18 days, forage out of nest at 30 and independent at 40 days (Wachtendorf, 1951). B.-H.&H. suggest shorter time. Young start with grey pelage and moult at c. 18 days into one like adults, but paler, which is kept until following year. They do not become sexually mature in year of birth and hibernate during first winter at little over half adult weight (H.G.Hurrell, unpubl.). Hibernation nests built any time from October. Dormice mostly hibernate singly, but more than one young may sometimes hibernate together. Male driven from nursery nest by female and occupies non-breeding nest near by (M.Knight, unpubl.). Sidorowicz (1959) suggests that growth and maturation of gonads may take place during hiberation.

POPULATION Life span about 4 years (B.-H.&H.); recorded to 6 years in captivity. Population in British Isles fairly sparsely distributed; even in Devon, where relatively common, only 3 out of 1,500 'mice' caught on anemone farm (E.Hurrell, 1962); same probably holds for Continent, judging from relative paucity in owl pellets (Uttendörfer, 1939). Exception noted in Czechoslovakia where Kindler (1946) states very common after good mast years and damages young trees seriously. Sidorowicz (1959) notes different proportions of young to adults in autumn of two seasons, viz. 1957 51 to 41, 1958 19 to 36. Examination of Russian material (Lozan, 1961) shows that tooth ridges very sharp up to first hibernation, a year later are flattened and show bands of dentine and by third year ridges more or less worn away. Very few survive beyond this age.

FOOD Largely vegetarian, living on tree fruits, beech, hazel, chestnut; also seeds of conifers, shoots and bark of trees. Fattens itself on tree crops for hibernation. Faeces like those of mice, but often with ridged, not smooth, surface; often found as accumulating deposits at certain places in bushes above ground. Has been said method of opening hazel nut diagnostic, though samples from Dormouse and Wood Mouse very difficult to distinguish; however, hole usually neater in case of Dormouse and kernel extracted with tip of tongue (M.Knight, pers. comm.).

PREDATORS Little known. Probably not infrequently dug out of hibernacula by crows, Magpies, etc., as several reports of them being dropped by such birds. Badgers and Foxes probably do same.

RELATIONS WITH MAN Easily kept in captivity, but sometimes difficult to bring through hibernation. Animals found hibernating should not be woken up too suddenly, though it is not unusual for hibernating sleep to be broken on occasional warm days.

FAMILY CAPROMYIDAE

One of the many odd S. American groups included in the hystricomorph rodents (see classification given under order).

GENUS *Myocastor*
Monospecific.

*Coypu (Nutria) *Myocastor coypus* Molina

DISTRIBUTION S. American species now feral in N. America, Europe (incl. U.S.S.R.), and probably elsewhere on smaller scale, e.g. Kenya; established in E. Anglia, especially in Broads. Introduced into British Isles about 1930 for fur-farming and escaped soon after. In 1946 only few localities in E. Anglia and odd ones in south-east England (Laurie, 1946b). Now widely distributed in Norfolk, well established parts of E. Suffolk and occurs sporadically up to 20 miles from occupied areas. Elsewhere isolated colonies may persist, since there is still small one near Slough, Bucks. For distribution map see Davis (1960, 1963).

DESCRIPTION Superficially rat-like, though belonging to porcupine group. Has a massive head, large, orange-yellow incisors, short, round, hairy ears with tuft of black hair in centre. Body broad, back humped, heavy pelage with underfur not easily wetted, typically dark brown but may be blackish or gingery. Belly fur greyish and soft, forms 'nutria' of commerce after removal of guard hairs. Coat thinner in spring and summer. Front legs short with strong claws, hind legs longer and feet strongly webbed. Under-surface of feet black and hairless. Tail thick, round, bristly, somewhat scaly, rat-like. Mammae 4+4 along the sides of the back, the first at height of fore-leg 'elbow', last at height of femur. Eye pupils vertical.

MEASUREMENTS Adults: h.&b. 43.5 cm (13 meas., range 35.7 to 58.0 cm), tail 27.3 cm (13 meas., range 22.4 to 34.3 cm); weight 3.2 kg (14 meas., range 1.4 to 6.4 kg) (data from Laurie, 1946b). Newly born young average 200 g, a litter of 9 from Norfolk ranging from 169 to 220 g (R.A.Davis, unpubl.). During trapping of c. 60 animals in Norfolk most frequent weight groups were: winter months, 2.3 and 5.5 kg, May–June, 4.5 kg, June–July, 5 kg, Aug–Sept 5.9 kg (J.D.Norris, unpubl.). Coypus probably take about 16–18 months to reach maximum weight. A captive female grew from 1.8 kg to nearly 7.7 kg in 62 weeks (R.A.Davis, unpubl.).

HABITAT Reed-beds, river banks and marshes in the Broads and along rivers leading into them.

GENERAL HABITS Voice, low grunts, louder 'mooing' or humming noises even when swimming; hisses when menaced and has harsh, cat-like scream when distressed. Also grinds teeth and clicks incisors violently when captured; pieces of tooth sometimes fly off. Droppings large and spindle-shaped, often with parallel ridges along sides, about 2.5 to 5.0 cm long. Activity mainly at dusk and dawn but during night as well; during day only if frosty. Moves slowly on land with crouching gait but can move rapidly in short hops and bounds. Runways continuous through vegetation, often circling back quickly into water again; may form steps on steep banks. Nests made of piled-up marsh plants above ground level. Burrows usually short refuges but occasionally longer, e.g. holes in dyke-banks may extend from water-level up to ground level. Appears rather ferocious because of large size and prominent incisors; can inflict fierce bites on dogs and incautious trappers but normally docile animal. Can be handled safely by tail, unless small (under 2 kg) and correspondingly more agile.

BREEDING Apparently throughout year. Fecund at *c.* 1.8 to 2.2 kg (5 months old) (Maurice, 1931; Laurie, 1946b), but observations in America (Anon, 1957) suggest 8 months with litters small and infrequent until 15 months. Oestrous cycle variable, perhaps 17-28 days (more information wanted) gestation 100 to 130 days, older females taking longer time (? due to conception at post-partum oestrus, which is known). Embryos, av. 5, range 2 to 9. Litters, *c.* 2 per year. Young born furred and with eyes open, move around in few hours and take solid food after day. Suckled in water from dorso-lateral mammae, weaning *c.* 7 to 8 weeks. Large litters reported may be due to amalgamation of family groups.

POPULATION No accurate figures, but spreading in Broads and sometimes numerous. Can become dense enough locally to be serious pest to agriculture at distances up to one mile from water. Average life in captivity *c.* 10 years (Maurice, 1931), probably at least 5 in wild with an animal that matures so slowly, though mortality may be heavy during first year of life (J.D.Norris, unpubl.).

FOOD Many water and marsh plants with special preference for parts just above roots. Preferred species are reed (*Phragmites*), reed-mace (*Typha*), various sedges (*Carex* spp.), flote grass (*Glyceria*), and the summer growth of water parsnip (*Sium*), Canadian waterweed (*Elodea*), water milfoil (*Myriophyllum*) and arrowhead (*Sagittaria*). Occasionally eats mussels (*Anodonta*).

PREDATORS Weasel, Otter, Brown Rat, owls and hawks (mostly on young).

RELATIONS WITH MAN In the Broads waterways are opened up by removal of vegetation. Not entirely beneficial because, if abundant, they flatten and remove much cover, altering habitat for other animals, and damage reeds which are harvested for thatching. Not yet serious threat to river banks by burrowing, like

Y

Musk Rat. Damage mainly to agricultural crops, especially sugar-beet, kale, cereals in green stage and occasionally potatoes. Pasture may also suffer and Coypus may be seen in evening sitting in lines grazing like Rabbits. Official campaign now (1962) undertaken to reduce numbers.

Takes easily to captivity and thrives on fur-farms with diet of soaked grain, grass cuttings and vegetable scraps. Market for skins variable, now only about 10–15s. per skin.

Order Cetacea

Group including whales, porpoises and dolphins. Despite fish-like general form they are mammals with all fundamental character-istics of class, conforming to same general pattern of nervous, vascular, respiratory, muscular, alimentary and reproductive systems. In cetaceans morphological and physiological modifica-tions found in relation to needs of aquatic environment. Cetaceans entirely aquatic, being born, feeding, reproducing, sleeping and dying in the water; accidental death by stranding on beaches directly or indirectly result of displacement from natural environ-ment.

Externally, anatomical accommodation to aquatic existence including obliteration of neck region, head passing without break in contour into trunk; nostrils (*blowhole*) displaced backwards to position remote from end of snout (except Sperm Whale); fore limbs (*flippers*) fin-like, with fingers enclosed in common integu-ment; absence of ear pinnae; external openings of ear tubes tiny, situated on each side of head between eye and flipper insertion; frequent occurrence of fleshy fin on back; absence of hind limbs; continuation of trunk posteriorly into tapering massive tail expanding terminally into two horizontal fleshy lobes (*flukes*); absence of external evidence of mammary glands, with conceal-ment of teats in slits; absence of hairy covering to body, a few scattered isolated hairs on head and along jaw of adult baleen whales and in toothed cetaceans similarly disposed but only found in young; texture of skin extremely smooth.

Thick layer of fat (*blubber*) enveloping body except for flippers, flukes and dorsal fin, acting as insulator in maintenance of body heat and as food reserve. Sweat and sebaceous glands absent on skin. Blood supply of peripheral regions of appendages so arranged that heat loss diminished by absorption of heat from warmer arterial blood flowing towards surface by cooled venous blood returning to heart.

Muscles of trunk greatly modified especially those going tailwards for the provision of power required to move flukes, the main propulsive organs of cetaceans. In pelvic region absence of hind limbs associated with profound modifications of muscular arrangements but even reduced pelvic bones still forming attachment for important muscles. In flipper, muscles which in terrestrial mammals function in moving forearm and fingers diminished or atrophied concomitantly with loss of independent movement of these parts. Labial muscles involved in blowhole closure and shifted from snout tip leaving lips immobile.

Cetacean brain large, highly convoluted cerebral hemispheres and disproportionately large cerebellum. With loss of sense of smell diminution or disappearance of olfactory nerves. With increased dependence on hearing greatly enlarged auditory nerves, and highly elaborated modifications of the whole auditory system for reception of waterborne sounds. Eyes functional in most cetaceans but some River Dolphins blind. Taste and tactile senses believed to be normal.

Respiration by a succession of emergences at water surface during which blowhole exposed, air forced out from lungs and fresh supply inhaled; the succession of brief surface appearances usually followed by period of much longer and deeper submergence (*sounding*). Internal termination of nose passages prolonged to surround extended reverse-funnel-shaped upper end of windpipe, so that continuous tube extending from blowhole to lungs; latter with extensive cartilaginous strengthening of ramifying tubes (*bronchi* and *bronchioles*) conducting air to ultimate thin membranous sacs (*alveoli*).

Skeleton greatly modified; skull large, up to one-third total body length; snout elongated as beak and of varying width. Extensive overlapping of forehead bones by snout bones, above former in toothed cetaceans, below in baleen whales. Nasal orifices remote from snout tip, nasal bones reduced and barely or not overhanging orifices. Back of skull expansive. Bony palate posteriorly extended at expense of soft palate, base of cranium generally greatly modified and bones contorted and excavated.

Bones of trunk and tail of simpler pattern than in terrestrial mammals, articular processes reduced, articulations less intimate. Neck vertebrae greatly compressed and in some forms completely fused together, rib-bearing vertebrae with backward sloping spines of increasing size rising from them. Ribs in baleen whales very loosely connected with vertebrae dorsally and breastbone ventrally, these articulations more normal in first four or five ribs of toothed cetaceans. Lumbar vertebrae passing into those of tail without intervening region of fixed vertebrae (*sacrum*). Note that no skeletal support either for back fin or lobes of flukes. No collarbone.

Bones of flippers including those normally found in mammalian fore limbs, but flattened in conformance with paddle-like form of these members, arm bones shortened, forearm and hand bones disproportionately elongated; finger bone elements not limited to three, may be up to thirteen. Hind limb skeleton very greatly reduced, in toothed cetaceans a pair of pelvic bones remotely situated from back bone; in some baleen whales, in addition to these, thigh and shin bone vestiges present.

The whales are classified under three suborders as follows.

(1) Archaeoceti (Zeuglodonts), an entirely fossil group. (2) Mysticeti, Baleen or Whalebone Whales, which have no teeth (except vestigial ones which disappear before birth) but, instead, baleen, a system of triangular horny plates suspended in two series one on each side of the upper jaw. The plates are set in the palate at right angles to the long axis of the head by the shortest side of the triangular outline. The labial edge of each plate is smooth, the lingual frayed out into a fringe of bristles. The frayed inner edges together act as a sieve to strain from the water the planktonic animals on which these whales feed. They are mostly large (10 to 30 m), have a double blowhole and symmetrical skull. The Mysticeti are divided into three familes, two of which occur in British waters. (3) Odontoceti, Toothed Whales, varying in size from the Sperm Whale down to dolphins, and characterized by possessing teeth, a single blowhole, an asymmetrical skull and long, narrow flippers. Abundant and widely distributed, being divided into six families, of which five have been recorded round our coast.

FIELD IDENTIFICATION CHARACTERS

The key below, from Fraser & Parker (1953), is reproduced by kind permission of the Trustees of the British Museum (Natural History).

1. Whalebone present on palate. Teeth absent. Lower jaw very wide, its halves arched outwards ... ... WHALEBONE WHALES 2
Whalebone absent. Teeth present, though sometimes concealed beneath the gum. Lower jaw narrow, at least in front ... ...
TOOTHED WHALES 7

WHALEBONE WHALES

2. Lower surface of throat not grooved. No back fin. Mouth and upper border of lower lip much arched. Whalebone blades long, up to 6–9 feet ... ... ATLANTIC RIGHT WHALE
Lower surface of throat with numerous parallel grooves 3
3. Flippers extremely long, nearly one-third the length of the animal, sometimes white externally, with a scalloped lower margin ... ...
HUMPBACK
Flippers much less than one-third the total length, not scalloped below ... ... RORQUALS 4
4. Whalebone, yellowish white or slate-coloured, or both 5
Whalebone, black or nearly black 6
5. Size, up to 70 feet. Whalebone, yellow and slate-coloured, except at the front of the right side, where it is white; its hairy fringes, white or yellowish. Tail-flukes white below ... COMMON FIN WHALE
Size, up to 30 feet. Whalebone and its hairy fringes, all white or yellowish. A white region on outer side of flipper LESSER RORQUAL
6. Size, up to 85 feet. Whalebone very black, with coarse black hairs ...
BLUE WHALE
Size, up to 50 feet. Whalebone mostly dark, with very fine, white, curling, silky hairs. Tail-flukes not white below ... SEI WHALE

TOOTHED WHALES

7. Size, that of a large whale. Head square in side view. Lower jaw very narrow, with many large teeth, several inches long. Upper jaw toothless or with a few irregular teeth, smaller than in lower jaw ...
SPERM WHALE
Not exceeding about 30 feet in length, and often much smaller ... 8
8. Back fin absent 9
Back fin present 10
9. Head short, with prominent 'forehead'. Colour greyish, with black spots or mottlings. Either without visible teeth (females), or with a tusk-like tooth, several feet long, spirally twisted, projecting forwards from the front of the upper jaw (males), exceptionally with two spiral tusks ... ... NARWHAL
Colour, white all over (greyish-brown in young individuals), 8–10 pairs of teeth in each jaw ... ... WHITE WHALE

10. Teeth confined to the lower jaw, or apparently absent   11
   Teeth in both jaws   15

11. Back fin large, near middle of body. Teeth 2–7 pairs, at front end of
   lower jaw ...   .   RISSO'S DOLPHIN
   Back fin considerably behind middle of body. Front end of jaws
   narrow. Two grooves on throat... (Whales of the 'Bottle-nosed' type)   12

12. Size large, up to 25–30 feet. Distance from tip of snout to blowhole
   one-fifth to one-seventh the total length. 'Forehead' very prominent.
   Teeth (one to two pairs) at tip of lower jaw, usually concealed   ...
   BOTTLE-NOSED WHALE
   Distance from tip of snout to blowhole less than one-seventh the total
   length   13

13. Size large, up to 26 feet. Distance from tip of snout to blowhole one-
   tenth to one-eighth the total length. 'Forehead' not specially prominent. Teeth one pair at tip of lower jaw, massive in males (diameter
   1 inch), concealed in females   ...   .   CUVIER'S WHALE
   Size smaller, not exceeding 20 feet. Beak long   14

14. Length about 15 feet. Colour mostly black, usually with white marks.
   One pair of teeth at middle of length of lower jaw, conspicuous and
   triangular in males, concealed in females   ...   SOWERBY'S WHALE
   Size rather larger. Colour not satisfactorily known. One pair of teeth
   at tip of lower jaw, conspicuous and flattened sideways in males,
   concealed in females   ...   .   TRUE'S BEAKED WHALE‡

15. Size large, 15–30 feet in adults. Teeth 8–13 pairs in each jaw   ...   16
   Seldom exceeding 12 feet, usually less than 9 feet. Teeth not more
   than ½ inch in diameter, more than 15 pairs   18

16. 'Forehead' greatly swollen, overhanging the tip of the very short beak.
   Flippers narrow, about one-fifth of the total length. Colour black,
   with only a small amount of white on lower surface. Teeth, 8–12 pairs
   in each jaw, less than ½ inch in diameter   ...   PILOT WHALE
   'Forehead' not prominent. Teeth, 10–13 pairs in each jaw, at least
   ¾ inch in diameter   17

17. Colour conspicuously black and white (or yellow). Flippers broad, not
   pointed. Teeth about 1 inch in diameter   ...   ...   KILLER
   Colour black all over. Flippers narrow and pointed. Teeth as in the
   Killer   ...   .   FALSE KILLER

18. Size up to 5½ feet. Teeth about 21–24 pairs in each jaw, flattened
   sideways, with spade-shaped crowns. Beak not distinguishable   ...
   COMMON PORPOISE
   Size larger, teeth conical, the crowns not flattened sideways. Beak
   distinct   19

19. Length up to 12 feet. Beak about 3 inches long in middle line. Teeth
   large, 20–25 pairs in each jaw; diameter, ⅜–½ inch   ...   .
   BOTTLE-NOSED DOLPHIN
   Teeth not exceeding ¼ inch in diameter   20

20. Beak about 2 inches long in middle line. Length, 9–10 feet   21
Beak up to 6 inches in middle line. Teeth, 40–50 pairs in each jaw,
about $\frac{1}{10}$ inch in diameter. Length up to 7 feet   22

21. Upper lip white. Dark colour of flippers continuous with that of body,
their lower margin not much curved. Teeth, about 25 pairs in each
jaw; diameter, $\frac{1}{4}$ inch   ...   .   WHITE-BEAKED DOLPHIN
Upper lip black. Flippers, with strongly curved lower margin, arising
from white part of body, usually connected with dark part by a narrow
dark streak. A conspicuous white region on each side, behind the
back-fin. Teeth, 30–40 pairs in each jaw; diameter, $\frac{3}{16}$ inch   ...
WHITE-SIDED DOLPHIN

22. A well-marked, narrow dark band of pigment extending from the eye
along the flank and curving down to the vent, with a subsidiary branch
in the region of the flipper insertion   ...   EUPHROSYNE DOLPHIN
This band wanting, but an arrangement of yellowish, white and dark
bands on the sides of the body ...   .   COMMON DOLPHIN

‡ In addition to Sowerby's Whale and True's Beaked Whale, the two species
of *Mesoplodon* mentioned in bracket 14, it is probable that a third species (*M. europaeus*), perhaps reaching 20 feet in length, will be recorded as British. Its external appearance is not well known.

SUBORDER MYSTICETI

FAMILY BALAENIDAE

Right whales, found in all oceans. Distinguished from only other British family, Balaenopteridae (rorquals and humpbacks), by following characters.

	BALAENIDAE	BALAENOPTERIDAE
Throat	No grooving	Grooving on skin extending to chest
Dorsal fin	None (except in Pigmy Right Whale)	More or less developed
Flippers	Broad and rounded	Long and narrow
Upper jaw	Narrow, greatly arched	Broad, triangular, flattened
Lower jaw	Scoop-like, with large fleshy eminence on each side fitting into arch of upper jaw	Without such fleshy eminences, basin-like
Baleen	Very long, narrow, flexible	Short, broad in proportion to length, less flexible

The family found in all oceans. Three genera, of which only one, *Balaena*, occurs round British Isles, *B. glacialis* being Atlantic in distribution.

GENUS *Balaena*

Species below, only one recorded in British Isles. Other species occur in Arctic, Pacific and Southern Oceans.

Biscayan Whale (N. Atlantic Right Whale) *Balaena glacialis* Bonnaterre

DISTRIBUTION Formerly abundant in N. Atlantic–Bay of Biscay, Newfoundland, Norway and southern parts of Arctic seas, now much rarer. No British strandings since 1913 when systematic recording started. Sixty-seven landed at Scottish whaling stations Outer Hebrides between 1908 and 1914.

DESCRIPTION A horny excrescence near tip of upper jaw—the 'bonnet'. This and mouth region generally infested with worms, whale-lice and barnacles. Blowhole a pair of slightly divergent slits on top of head. Head one-quarter of total length. Other features as for family. General body colour black, occasionally irregular white patches on belly.

MEASUREMENTS Length up to 18.5 m (*c.* 60 ft), weight estimated *c.* 40,000 to 50,000 kg (40 to 50 tons). Baleen blades 1.8 to 2.7 m (6 to 9 ft) long; black with fringes of same colour.

GENERAL HABITS Little known. Regular migration to Spain, Portugal, N. Africa in winter and in summer to higher latitudes, passing westwards of the Hebrides. Calves born about mid-summer.

FOOD Small swarming crustaceans, probably mainly *Meganyctiphanes norvegica* and other related forms. Method of feeding by scoop-like action of lower jaw, closing of mouth, raising of powerful tongue to force water out of mouth leaving the food residue on sieve-like fringes of baleen plates (compare feeding in rorquals).

RELATIONS WITH MAN Relatively uncommon now and protected from commercial exploitation.

FAMILY BALAENOPTERIDAE

Rorquals and the Humpback, comprising the major section of baleen whales, with two world-wide genera both represented around Great Britain. All are, or have been, of great economic importance for their oil and meat.

GENUS *Megaptera*

Humpback Whale; one species only.

Humpback Whale *Megaptera novaeangliae* (Borowski)

DISTRIBUTION World-wide. Migrations associated with feeding and breeding, to warm waters in winter when young born and pairing takes place; then to higher latitudes in summer, this route lying west of Faeroes and Hebrides. In British Isles no records of stranding in recent years but included in catch of whales operating from Hebrides earlier in present century.

DESCRIPTION General form stout. Most conspicuous feature the narrow, very elongated, irregularly knobbed flippers one-third to one-quarter body length. Snout short, broad, with numerous small humps (associated with hair follicles). Similar humps along sides of lower jaw. Dorsal fin at commencement of hinder third of body, small, variable in general shape and set on low hump. Posterior margin of flukes with notch in middle and irregularly scalloped. Throat grooves fewer in number and more widely spaced than in rorquals. Number of grooves 20 to 36. Barnacles and whale-lice very common on body, particularly on head and flippers (*Coronula* and *Conchoderma* spp. and *Cyamus*). Back black, belly white but very variable, white area being sometimes reduced by ventral extension of pigmented regions. Under surface of flippers white, which may extend to greater or less extent on to upper surface. Flukes equally white underneath. Baleen to about 1 m (3 ft) in length, 300 to 400 plates a side. Colour nearly black, with fringes of same colour. Occasionally some anterior blades white.

MEASUREMENTS Length up to 15 m (*c.* 50 ft). Weight at 12.4 m (45.5 ft) 31,000 kg (31 tons).

GENERAL HABITS Capable of great variety of swimming movements, breaching clear of the water, rolling over and over, side swimming, 'lob tailing'. The 'blow' a short, broad jet distinctive (to whaling men) of species. In the breathing sequence a series of shallow dives followed by a much deeper one ('sounding'), commencement of which indicated by flukes appearing above surface of water.

BREEDING Parturition and copulation in winter. Gestation period about a year, lactation about 5 months.

FOOD Planktonic crustaceans (krill); small swarming fishes, exceptionally codfish and, accidentally, cormorants. Method of feeding by relaxation of muscles underlying throat grooves so that cavity on floor of mouth greatly enlarged, filling with water containing food animals, subsequent contraction of muscles to diminish cavity forcing water out of mouth between baleen blades, so straining it off from the food supply.

GENUS *Balaenoptera*

Rorquals. Whales belonging to this genus distinguished from Humpback by flipper length being much less than one-third total body length and not irregularly outlined. Hinder margin of tail smoothly outlined (but with notch in middle as in Humpback). Grooves on throat and chest more numerous, averaging 85 to 90. Four species, all widely distributed and all recorded in British waters.

Common Rorqual (Fin Whale) *Balaenoptera physalus* (L.)

DISTRIBUTION World-wide. Migratory, passing British coast on way northwards in late winter or early spring and southwards again in autumn. Not uncommon in British waters but less frequently stranded now than earlier in present century.

DESCRIPTION General form slender in relation to length. Margins of snout forming acute angle. Dorsal fin at commencement of hinder third of body, rather high, triangular, with concave hinder edge. Flippers about one-ninth body length, narrow, tapering. Throat grooves about 85 to 90 in number, ending tailwards of navel. Asymmetry of head colour diagnostic of species. External surface of right lower jaw white, that of left pigmented. Internal surface of right lower jaw pigmented, that of left unpigmented. Asymmetry of pigmentation of tongue also. General body colour grey above, white below including lower surfaces of flukes and inner surfaces of flippers (cf. Sei Whale). Largest blades of baleen *c.* 1 m (3 ft). Blades on right side of palate usually white for 2 or 3 ft from front end of series. Remaining blades right side and all on left a slatey-grey colour alternating with longitudinal yellowish bands. All baleen fringes white.

MEASUREMENTS Length up to 24.5 m (80 ft) but 18 to 21 m (60 to 70 ft) more usual, females attaining greater size than males. Calves at birth *c.* 6.7 m (22 ft). Weight at 20.8 m (68 ft 3 in.) 52,750 kg (52 tons 16 cwt).

GENERAL HABITS Inclined to congregate in schools varying in number from a few to one or two hundred. As in all rorquals 'blow' vertically upwards and prior to being dissipated shape a long, slender, inverted cone. In diving not usual for flukes to be exposed at any stage but, very exceptionally, whole body may be projected above water surface.

BREEDING Young born and copulation takes place in warmer waters during winter. Pairing season protracted—7 to 8 months, gestation *c.* 1 year, lactation 6 to 7 months.

FOOD Planktonic crustaceans (krill), Herring, Capelin. Method of feeding as in Humpback (q.v.).

Lesser Rorqual (Pike Whale) *Balaenoptera acutorostrata* Lacépède

DISTRIBUTION World-wide. Migrates between higher and lower latitudes, associated respectively with feeding and breeding. Stranding recorded on all parts of British coast except southern N. Sea and English Channel. Distribution of strandings suggests migration route to and from N. Sea by west coast and round north of Scotland.

DESCRIPTION Smallest and, in British waters, commonest of all rorquals. General form similar to Fin Whale but more robust in relation to length. As in Fin Whale, snout distinctly triangular in outline. Flippers one-eighth body length, shape as in Fin Whale. Throat grooves *c.* 50 in number, ending posteriorly in front of navel. Dorsal fin at commencement of hinder third of body, conspicuous. Flukes with median notch. Colour dark greyish-brown to black dorsally, white ventrally. Outer surface of flippers coloured as back but with white patch which at once distinguishes this species. Baleen has all blades white, with white fringes of fine texture, these characters being distinctive of species.

MEASUREMENTS Length up to 9 m (30 ft). Newborn calves *c.* 2.8 m (9 ft). Weight at 4.9 m (16 ft) 1,250 kg (1 ton 5 cwts).

GENERAL HABITS 'Blow' inconspicuous. Tail not usually breaking surface as animal dives but records existing of 'breaching', i.e. projecting body from water into air.

BREEDING Pairing Jan to May. Gestation *c.* 1 year. Lactation usually coincides with pregnancy, most mature females producing calf each year. Sexually mature at 2 years.

FOOD Diet varied, Herring and krill favoured, Cod and other gadoid fishes also taken. Gravel and stones up to the size of an egg have been found in stomachs.

Sei Whale (Rudolphi's Rorqual) *Balaenoptera borealis* Lesson

DISTRIBUTION World-wide. Migrates to high latitudes for month or so during summer. Route includes western seaboard of British Isles, where most abundant in June. Moves to warmer waters for breeding in winter. From evidence of stranding on British coast, Sei Whales not very abundant in British waters, but whaling statistics indicate a larger population.

DESCRIPTION General form less slender, but otherwise resembling Fin Whale. Margins of snout forming acute angle. Fin at commencement of hinder third of body, relatively bigger than in Blue or Fin Whale of similar length, triangular, concave hinder margin. Flippers *c.* one-eleventh total length. Posterior margin of flukes with median notch. Throat grooves fewer (40 to 60) and shorter (ending some distance in front of navel) than in Blue or Fin Whale. A few hairs on upper and lower jaws and chin. General colour, including dorsal surface of flukes and under surface of flippers, bluish-grey varying in shade, lighter grey on under surface. White area in ventral groove region, very variable in extent, not usually extending to chin or beyond limits of grooves posteriorly. Under surface of flukes pigmented, sometimes as darkly as dorsal surface. Inner surface of flippers also usually pigmented. Baleen black with very soft, fine, white fringes. Sometimes a few white blades at front end.

MEASUREMENTS Length up to 18.3 m (60 ft) but usually to about 15.25 m (50 ft). Newborn calf *c.* 4.5 m (15 ft).

GENERAL HABITS 'Blow' low and rather inconspicuous. Surfacing for respiration usually involving least possible exposure of body, but has been observed on occasion to leap clear from surface of sea. Said to be capable of great burst of speed, 30 m.p.h.

BREEDING Gestation *c.* 1 year. Lactation about 5 months. Breeds once in two years. Sexual maturity at age of *c.* 18 months, breeding occurring at end of second year after birth.

FOOD Planktonic crustaceans (krill) and the copepod *Calanus finmarchicus.*

Blue Whale (Sibbald's Rorqual) *Balaenoptera musculus* (L.)

DISTRIBUTION World-wide. Migrates to lower latitudes in winter and to higher latitudes in summer for breeding and feeding. Very infrequently stranded, but not uncommon on western seaboard of British Isles.

DESCRIPTION Largest, heaviest, existing mammal. Snout broad, flattened, with sides nearly parallel to within short distance of tip. Flippers about one-seventh body length. Dorsal fin in hinder third of body length, small for size of animal, triangular. Throat grooves 70 to 120, extending more than half-way towards tail. Tail flukes with median notch in hinder edge. Few hairs on chin, and rostrum. Colour dark bluish-grey, with no large unpigmented areas either dorsally or ventrally but with numerous and widespread splashes of white, which may form local aggregations. Under surface and tip of upper surface of flipper exceptions to remainder of body, pigmentation being absent. Baleen short, broadly inserted in palate, jet-black with similarly coloured fringes. Number of plates in each 'side' 300 to somewhat less than 400.

MEASUREMENTS Length may be as much as 30.5 m (100 ft) but usually about 6 m (20 ft) less. Females slightly larger than males of same age. Weight at 27 m (89 ft) 119,700 kg (119 tons 14 cwt).

GENERAL HABITS 'Blow' high and well-defined. Despite its great size Blue Whale rather timid, easily scared by strange noises. Tail flukes not usually exposed when 'sounding'.

BREEDING Gestation about a year. Weaning takes place 6 to 7 months after birth. Sexual maturity attained when animals are two years old.

FOOD Planktonic crustaceans (krill).

SUBORDER ODONTOCETI

FAMILY PHYSETERIDAE

Contains two genera, *Physeter*, the Sperm Whale, and *Kogia*, of which the one species *K. breviceps*, the Pygmy Sperm Whale, has not yet been recorded in British waters, though its eventual appearance is to be expected.

GENUS *Physeter*

Contains only the species below.

Sperm Whale (Cachalot) *Physeter catodon* (L.)

DISTRIBUTION Population concentrated in warmer waters, tropical and sub-tropical, but stragglers, mainly males, wander into colder waters. Undertake ill-defined migrations, sometimes in schools of many individuals. On British coasts 11 have been stranded since 1913.

DESCRIPTION Largest of all the toothed cetaceans. Head one-third total body length, with single blowhole on left side, placed near anterior limit of body. Front of head flat, rounding off to top and sides and tapering off ventrally towards anterior end of upper jaw. Lower jaw not extending to anterior limit of head, extremely narrow for most of its length, the two halves only commencing to diverge posteriorly a little distance in front of angle of gape. Teeth in lower jaw numerous and large, in upper jaw inconspicuous or concealed. Flippers rounded. Back fin ill-defined, low and succeeded by four or five smaller humps. Hinder margin of tail with median notch. On the sides surface of body irregularly corrugated. A few short furrows in throat region. General colour dark grey to black, lightening somewhat to sides. Very light grey to white area on belly, varying greatly in extent. White usually in region of jaws and on front of head, especially in old males. Twenty to 30 teeth in each side of lower jaw. Very large, their crowns, when jaws closed, fitting into sockets along each side of palate. Upper jaw teeth much smaller, variable in number, non-functional, usually situated to inner side of sockets accommodating crowns of lower jaw teeth.

MEASUREMENTS Length ♂ to about 18.5 m (60 ft), ♀ to 9 m (30 ft). Newborn calf 3.7 to 3.9 m (12 to 13 ft). Weight at 18 m (59 ft) 52,400 kg (52 tons 8 cwt).

GENERAL HABITS 'Blow' directed obliquely forwards from the blowhole. On surfacing 'hump' (or back fin) appears first, then upper surface of head. Spouts up to about forty times in 7 to 10 minutes before sounding again, at commencement of which head dropped, body arched, tail coming out of water and whale submerging almost vertically.

BREEDING Polygamous. Sex ratio 50%. No definite sexual season in male. Ill-defined pairing period, roughly spring to early summer. Gestation c. 16 months. Lactation probably c. 6 months. Sexual maturity in male c. 2 years, in female c. 15 months.

FOOD Large squids, cuttlefish, sharks and other fish.

RELATIONS WITH MAN Especially valuable to whaling industry for waxy spermaceti, contained principally in head, for blubber oil and for ambergris found in intestine.

FAMILY ZIPHIIDAE

Whales belonging to this family (Bottle-nosed or Beaked Whales) medium in size, 4.5 to 9 m (15 to 30 ft) in length, all having well-defined, more or less elongated snout and triangular dorsal fin situated at commencement of hindmost third of body length. Tail without well-defined notch in middle of hinder margin. Two throat grooves posteriorly divergent. Single crescentic blowhole, concave towards snout. Three genera are represented in the British Isles.

GENUS *Hyperoodon*

World-wide. Two species, one Southern Ocean, the other below.

Bottle-nosed Whale *Hyperoodon ampullatus* (Forster)

DISTRIBUTION Fairly common round British coasts; most abundant in Arctic Ocean. Believed to undertake migrations to high latitudes in summer, southward route including coastal waters of British Isles, where strandings commonest in late autumn and winter.

DESCRIPTION Snout 15 to 17.5 cm (6 to 7 in.) long in front of bulging forehead, latter increasingly so with age. Triangular dorsal fin not distinguishable from that of any other beaked whale.

Flippers small, tapering to rounded tip. Tip of snout to blowhole one-fifth to one-seventh body length. Colour dark grey to black generally over body, with varying amount of lighter grey or white on undersurface. Old males tend to be much lighter in forehead region. A single pair of teeth (very rarely two pairs) at tip of lower jaw. Teeth in female concealed, in male crown regularly conical, projecting from gum to lesser or greater extent. Tooth length up to 4.5 cm ($1\frac{3}{4}$ in.). Oval cross-section, diameters about 1.9×1.7 cm ($\frac{3}{4} \times \frac{1}{2}$ in.). Rows of small vestigial teeth sometimes embedded in gums of upper and lower jaws.

MEASUREMENTS Length ♂ up to 9 m (30 ft), ♀ to 7.5 m (24 ft). Newborn calf *c*. 3 m (10 ft). Weight ♀ at 6.6 m (21 ft 8 in.) 2,900 kg (2 tons 18 cwt).

GENERAL HABITS Moves about in small schools of up to a dozen. Females perhaps more numerous than males. Little really known about general habits and breeding.

FOOD Chiefly cuttlefish, also Herring.

GENUS *Ziphius*

World-wide; only the single species below.

Cuvier's Whale (Goose-beaked Whale) *Ziphius cavirostris* Cuvier

DISTRIBUTION Distribution of British strandings on west coasts of England, Scotland and Ireland suggests approach from Atlantic to British Isles. Since 1913 23 strandings have occurred.

DESCRIPTION General form rather robust. Head with snout passing without conspicuous break into forehead, the latter not noticeably prominent. Distance of snout to blowhole less than one-seventh total length. Back fin about commencement of hinder third of body length. Flippers and back fin not distinguishable from those of Bottle-nosed Whale. Mid hinder margin slightly concave but not notched as in Delphinidae. Colour inadequately known. Said to be bluish-black on back, lighter below; characteristic long narrow scars on skin. A single pair of teeth at tip of lower jaw, exposed in male, conical in shape and circular in cross-section. Length to 5.7 cm ($2\frac{1}{4}$ in.) diameter to *c*. 3.2 cm ($1\frac{1}{4}$ in.). Greatest diameter at half length, tapering to root and crown. In female teeth smaller, more slender, usually but not always entirely concealed in gums. Vestigial teeth may occur in both upper and lower jaws.

MEASUREMENTS Length up to 7.9 m (26 ft).

GENERAL HABITS Little or nothing known.

GENUS *Mesoplodon*

Distributions of species not well known; about six species from various parts of world.

Sowerby's Whale *Mesoplodon bidens* (Sowerby)

DISTRIBUTION A North Atlantic whale known from stranded specimens found on New England coast in America and Western European seaboard. Comparatively rare, 17 British strandings since 1913.

DESCRIPTION Low forehead passing into slender elongated snout. Distance from tip of snout to blowhole less than one-seventh body length. Flippers, fins and tail not distinctive of species. Colour mostly black, with some white on belly. Scratches and scars common on skin. A single pair of teeth situated about half-way between tip of lower jaw and angle of gape. In male teeth project as flattened triangular prominences, in female concealed and altogether smaller in size than in male.

MEASUREMENTS Length up to 4.9 m (16 ft).

GENERAL HABITS Almost nothing known. One stranded specimen reported as lowing like a cow.

True's Beaked Whale *Mesoplodon mirus* (True)

DISTRIBUTION One of the least known of cetaceans. Five known strandings, two on the American coast (N. Carolina and New England) and three from British waters (two Irish, one Outer Hebrides).

DESCRIPTION Body slender, compressed laterally, tail stock particularly so. Slender snout, low forehead. Nothing specifically distinctive in flippers, flukes or back fin. Teeth diagnostic of species. Situated at extreme tip of lower jaw, directed obliquely forward, a single pair projecting above gum in male, concealed

Z

in female. Teeth flattened oval in cross-section, 2.5 × 1.3 cm (1 × ½ in.).

MEASUREMENTS Length about 5.2 m (17 ft).

GENERAL HABITS Nothing known.

FAMILY MONODONTIDAE

Contains two genera only, both monospecific and together meriting distinctive superfamily rank.

GENUS *Delphinapterus*

Beluga (White Whale) *Delphinapterus leucas* (Pallas)

DISTRIBUTION An Arctic cetacean only rarely penetrating to more temperate latitudes. Very few records of occurrence in British waters, one specimen since 1913 in River Forth about 25 miles inland of bridge.

DESCRIPTION Head not produced into a beak, forehead only slightly sloping tailwards from tip of upper jaw. No back fin. Flippers broad, moderately large, rounded, not tapering in acute angle. Flukes with notch in middle of hinder margin and obliquely truncate lobes. General body shape, head small in relation to body bulk and with suggestion of definition of a neck. Body rather robust. Pure white or cream colour of adult specifically diagnostic. The grey colour of calf might lead to confusion with Narwhal but White Whale bears teeth on upper and lower jaws and so distinguished. 8 to 10 teeth in each jaw, *c.* 0.6 cm (¼ in) in diameter.

MEASUREMENTS Length usually 3.7 to 4.3 m (12 to 14 ft). Upper limit perhaps 5.5 m (18 ft).

GENERAL HABITS Gregarious to extent of small family groups. Very vocal. Although occurring in the open ocean also known to ascend rivers for considerable distances.

FOOD Cuttlefish, crustaceans, fishes.

RELATIONS WITH MAN Has been exploited commercially for 'porpoise-hide', and meat and blubber for food of animals and man. One of the first cetaceans to be kept in an aquarium, Brighton 1878.

GENUS *Monodon*

Narwhal *Monodon monoceros* (L.)

DISTRIBUTION An Arctic cetacean, very few British strandings.

DESCRIPTION No snout, high forehead, inconspicuous low ridge in normal back fin position. Flippers short and rounded. Flukes with notch in middle of hinder margin. Colour mottled grey, lighter on sides and belly. Juveniles darker and lacking mottling. Teeth remarkable for production of left incisor of male into tusk several feet long, with anticlockwise spiral. Vestiges of other teeth occur and occasionally the tusk duplicated on right side.

MEASUREMENTS Length to 4.9 m (16 ft).

GENERAL HABITS Gregarious, swift swimming. Seldom found far from polar waters. Congregating in large numbers at holes in sea ice (known to Greenlanders as savssats) keeping these open by head blows. Little known of breeding habits.

FOOD Cuttlefish, fishes and crustaceans.

FAMILY PHOCAENIDAE

True porpoises, divided into two genera, *Phocaena* and *Neomeris*.

GENUS *Phocaena*

Several species (if *Phocaenoides* included), in both hemispheres. Some forms have become isolated in freshwater lakes.

Common Porpoise (Atlantic Harbor Porpoise) *Phocaena phocoena* (L.)

DISTRIBUTION Widely distributed in coastal waters of N. Atlantic, including Baltic, White, North and Greenland Seas. Ascends rivers and frequents estuaries. Commonest British species of cetacean.

DESCRIPTION General form short, stout and robust. No beak. Low receding forehead. Back fin triangular at middle of body length. Flippers with roughly oval outline. Tail notched posteriorly. Tail stock slender. Considerable individual variation in colour. Back black, belly white, varying amount of grey on sides. Dark streak from flipper to mouth. Upper and lower jaws, chin, flippers and flukes black. Teeth, 22 to 27 upper and lower, each side. Diameter at gum 0.25 cm (1/10 in.). Spade shape diagnostic of species.

MEASUREMENTS Length 1.8 m (6 ft). Newborn calf *c.* 0.76 m (2 ft 6 in.). Weight at 1.5 m (5 ft) 59 kg (1 cwt 18 lb).

GENERAL HABITS Not highly gregarious. Not speedy and not leaping clear of water.

BREEDING Pairing in summer, gestation about a year, single calf born July onwards.

FOOD Herring, Sole, Whiting, crustaceans and cuttlefish.

FAMILY DELPHINIDAE

Contains the greater part of all cetaceans. World-wide and divided into 14 genera, 8 of which known from British waters.

GENUS *Orcinus*

Containing only one species.

Killer (Grampus) *Orcinus orca* (L.)

DISTRIBUTION Cosmopolitan species, fairly common in British waters.

DESCRIPTION Powerfully built, robust. No beak, receding forehead. Back fin in mid-body length; in females and young, moderate in height, posterior concavity in margin. In adult males dorsal fin high (to 1.8 m (6 ft)), short based, triangular. Flippers rounded, in size increased disproportionately in males. Flukes with posterior median notch, tail size increased disproportionately in old males. Black back, white belly. Lens-shaped white patch behind eye. Lobe of belly white extending on to side between dorsal fin and tail. Flippers black, flukes black above, white below. Grey saddle mark behind back fin, variable in extent, indefinite in outline. Teeth, 10 to 13, upper and lower, each side. Large, powerful, 2.5 to 5 cm (1 to 2 in.) diameter. Cross-section oval (cf. False Killer) with longer axis across jaw.

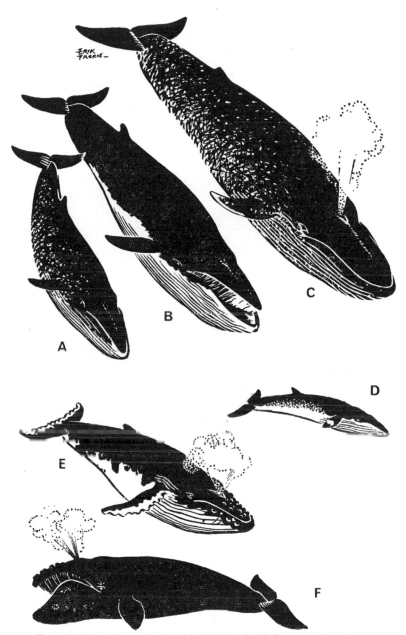

FIG. 38. Whalebone whales. (*a*) Sei Whale (*Balaenoptera borealis*), (*b*) Common Rorqual (*B. physalus*), (*c*) Blue Whale (*B. musculus*), (*d*) Lesser Rorqual (*B. acutorostrata*), (*e*) Humpback (*Megaptera novaeangliae*), and (*f*) Right Whale (*Balaena glacialis*). These drawings are not necessarily to the same scale and the text should be consulted for sizes.

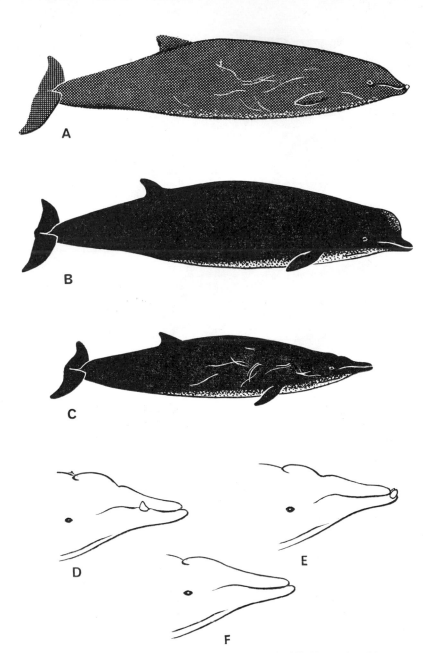

FIG. 39. Toothed whales. (*a*) Cuvier's Whale (*Ziphius cavirostris*), (*b*) Bottle-nosed Whale (*Hyperoodon ampullatus*), (*c*) Beaked Whale (*Mesoplodon* spp.) with details of head in (*d*) Sowerby's Beaked Whale ♂ (*M. bidens*), (*e*) True's Beaked Whale ♂ (*M. mirus*) and (*f*) female of both species.

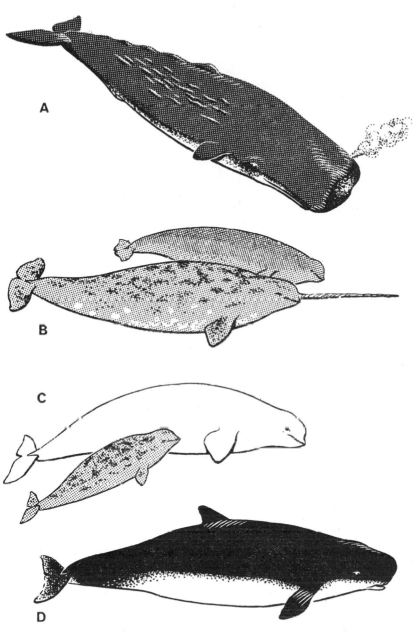

Fig. 40. Toothed whales. (*a*) Sperm Whale (*Physeter catodon*), (*b*) Narwhal (*Monodon monoceros*), (*c*) White Whale (*Delphinapterus leucas*) and (*d*) Pygmy Sperm Whale (*Kogia breviceps*).

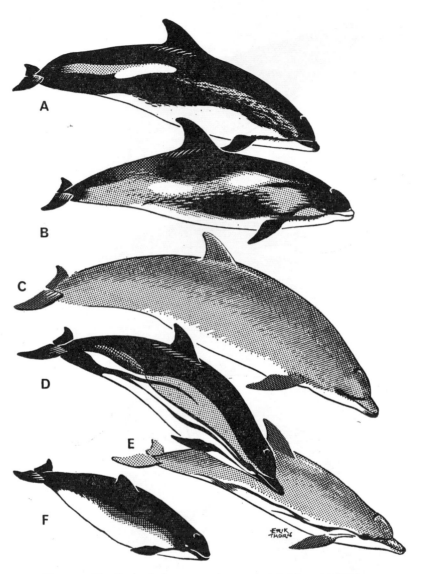

FIG. 41. Toothed whales—porpoises and dolphins. (*a*) White-sided Dolphin (*Lagenorhynchus acutus*), (*b*) White-beaked Dolphin (*L. albirostris*), (*c*) Bottle-nosed Dolphin (*Tursiops truncatus*), (*d*) Common Dolphin (*Delphinus delphis*), (*e*) Euphrosyne Dolphin (*Stenella styx*) and (*f*) Common Porpoise (*Phocaena phocoena*).

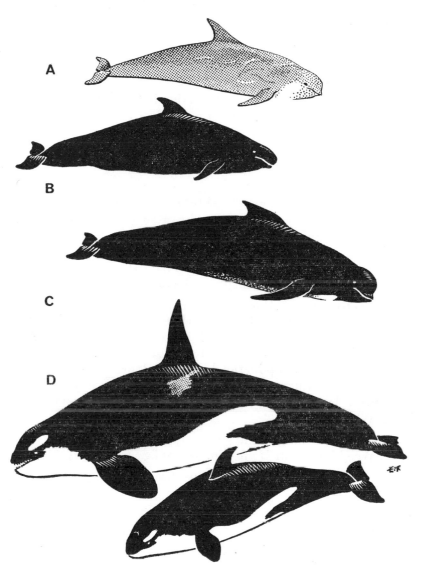

FIG. 42. Toothed whales—dolphins and killers. (a) Risso's
Dolphin (*Grampus griseus*), (b) False Killer (*Pseudorca crassidens*),
(c) Pilot Whale (*Globiocephala melaena*) and (d) Killer Whale ♂
(above) and ♀ (below) (*Orcinus orca*).

MEASUREMENTS Length ♂ to 9.2 m (30 ft), ♀ to 4.6 m (15 ft). Newborn calf *c.* 2.1 m (7 ft).

GENERAL HABITS Powerful, aggressive, preying on warm-blooded animals—seals, sea-lions, porpoises, some say whales, besides fishes (including salmon). Hunt in packs.

BREEDING Little known of reproductive habits. Young believed born at end of year. Gestation *c.* 12 months.

GENUS *Pseudorca*

Containing only one species.

False Killer *Pseudorca crassidens* (Owen)

DISTRIBUTION Cosmopolitan dolphin of sporadic occurrence in widely distant regions. Known mainly from large schools stranding, seldom encountered otherwise. Has thus stranded on three occasions on British coast; Dornoch Firth 1927, *c.* 150, South Wales 1934, *c.* 25, Forfar, Lincoln and Yorks, Norfolk, 1935, *c.* 75.

DESCRIPTION General form slender for length. No beak, rounded forehead, projecting somewhat beyond lower jaw tip. Back fin in mid-body, moderate height, concave posterior border. Flippers tapering, one-tenth body length (cf. Pilot Whale). Flukes notched at mid-posterior border. Colour black, except for scars of wounds which are white. Teeth, 9 to 11 each side, upper and lower. Diameter 2.5 cm (1 in.) circular cross-section (cf. Killer Whale).

MEASUREMENTS Length ♂ to 5.6 m (18 ft 6 in.), ♀ to 5.0 m (16 ft 6 in.). Weight at 5.3 m (17 ft 5 in.) 1,700 kg (1 ton 14 cwt).

GENERAL HABITS Highly gregarious. Breeding season extending over several months.

FOOD Chiefly cuttlefish but fish such as Cod also.

GENUS *Globicephala*

At least three species, possibly more.

Pilot Whale (Caa'ing Whale, Blackfish) *Globicephala melaena* (Traill)

DISTRIBUTION A North Atlantic species; strandings on British coast from Shetland to Cornwall. Local hunting of species in Orkney, Shetland and Faeroes; 41 British records of stranding since 1913.

DESCRIPTION Long, slender body. Head bulging, forehead gibbous above inconspicuous beak. Back fin low with long base and commencing slightly in front of middle of body length. Flippers very long (one-fifth body length, cf. False Killer), slender and tapering. Hinder margin flukes notched at middle. Colour black, except for white throat patch extending tailwards to variable length. Teeth, 8 to 10 each side, upper and lower jaws. Diameter less than 1.3 cm ($\frac{1}{2}$ in.). Tooth rows confined to front ends of jaws.

MEASUREMENTS Length over 6 m (20 ft), perhaps to 8.5 m (28 ft).

GENERAL HABITS Highly gregarious, schools of many hundreds recorded. Although some in high latitudes at all times of year, indications of general migration to northern waters after mid-summer.

BREEDING Pairing probably in warmer water, calves born following year at higher latitudes.

FOOD Cuttlefishes, including *Ommatostrephes*, *Architeuthis* and *Toderodes* spp.

RELATIONS WITH MAN Highly organized drives have been carried out for centuries in the Faeroes and still continue. The species takes well to captivity and can be trained.

GENUS *Grampus*

Contains only one species.

Risso's Dolphin *Grampus griseus* (Cuvier)

DISTRIBUTION Cosmopolitan distribution. On British coasts strandings more abundant than Blackfish (37 since 1913), chiefly on south and west coasts.

DESCRIPTION Rather stout for length. Head without beak. Forehead prominent, only slightly receding from tip of upper jaw. Dorsal fin at mid length of body, high, tip backwardly directed and posterior margin pronouncedly concave. Tail with median notch in hinder margin. Flippers rather long, broad proximally, tapering to a point, one-sixth body length. Colour in general grey, lighter on head, darker on sides. Belly may be white, fins and tail black. Upper jaw normally toothless. Lower jaw 2 to 7 each side, usually 4.

MEASUREMENTS Length to 4 m (13 ft). Weight at 3.4 m (11 ft) 343 kg (6 cwt 84 lb).

GENERAL HABITS Very little known. Occurs in small schools or singly. Distribution of strandings suggests Atlantic approach to British waters. The famous Pelorus Jack that escorted ships between the North and South Islands of New Zealand for 32 years is said to have been a Risso's Dolphin.

GENUS *Lagenorhynchus*

A widespread genus with a number of species, two of which recorded in British waters.

White-beaked Dolphin *Lagenorhynchus albirostris* (Gray)

DISTRIBUTION North Atlantic, Baltic, North Sea, Greenland, Davis Straits. In British waters commoner in North Sea than elsewhere. One of the commoner British species.

DESCRIPTION General form stoutish. Distinct beak *c.* 5 cm (2 in.) long. Forehead receding. Back fin prominent at mid-body length, tip pointing tailwards, distinct concavity of hinder margin. Tail stock with transverse width much less than depth. Flippers tapering to rounded tip, broad at insertion. Flukes notched in middle posteriorly. Colour: white beak; forehead and back to at least behind back fin very dark to black; longitudinal light areas on sides, which may approximate and meet behind back fin. Darkly pigmented region on sides behind flippers extending well on to belly, latter from throat to behind vent white. Tail stock, flukes, flippers dark. Dark streak from mouth to flipper insertion, above which a speckled region. Teeth, 22 to 25 each side upper and lower jaws, *c.* 0.6 cm ($\frac{1}{4}$ in.) diameter.

MEASUREMENTS Length *c.* 3.1 m (10 ft). Newborn calf *c.* 1.2 m (4 ft). Weight at 2.3 m (7 ft 7 in.) 216 kg (4 cwt 1 qtr); at 2.8 m (9 ft 2½ in.) 305 kg (6 cwt).

GENERAL HABITS Very gregarious, sometimes very large schools.

BREEDING Calves born usually after middle of year.

FOOD Herring, Cod, Whiting.

White-sided Dolphin *Lagenorhynchus acutus* (Gray)
DISTRIBUTION North Atlantic including Greenland, American coast to Cape Cod, N.W. European coasts including Norway where abundant, Orkney, Shetland and occasionally as far south as Yorkshire on east and Sligo on Atlantic seaboard.

DESCRIPTION General form robust. Distinct beak *c.* 5 cm (2 in.) long. Receding forehead. Prominent back fin in mid-body length, tip tailwardly projecting, concave hinder border. Tail stock even more strongly compressed and keeled than in White-beaked Dolphin. Snout, top of head and back dark, belly white, pigmentation on sides not extending so far ventrally as in White-beaked Dolphin, so that flippers inserted in unpigmented region. Narrow dark streak from mouth to flipper insertion. Flippers, flukes and chin dark. Broad, elongated light region on flanks from level of back fin to hinder end of tail stock. Teeth, 30 to 34 each side, upper and lower jaws. Diameter *c.* 0.5 cm ($\frac{3}{16}$ in.).

MEASUREMENTS Length 2.7 to 3.0 m (9 to 10 ft).

GENERAL HABITS Gregarious, large schools. Not so abundant in British waters as White-beaked Dolphin.

BREEDING Gestation about 10 months, birth in spring before mid-summer.

RELATIONS WITH MAN Takes readily to captivity and is easily trained.

GENUS *Tursiops*
A widely distributed genus with about three or four species, one of which is recorded from British waters.

Bottle-nosed Dolphin *Tursiops truncatus* (Montagu)
DISTRIBUTION Widely distributed in N. Atlantic, Mediterranean and English coastal waters, chiefly south and west. Next in

abundance to Common Porpoise and frequently seen in English Channel.

DESCRIPTION General form stoutish. Snout *c.* 7.6 cm (3 in.) long. Forehead low, receding. Back fin moderate height, tip tailwardly directed, hinder margin concave. Tail stock not pronouncedly keeled. Flukes with notched posterior edge. Flippers of moderate size tapering to rounded tip. Colour very dark grey, black or dark brown on back, throat and belly; white from lower jaw tip to behind vent, rest of ventral surface dark. Flippers and flukes dark. Teeth, 22 to 25 each side, upper and lower. Diameter 1 to 1.3 cm (⅜ to ½ in.).

MEASUREMENTS Length to 3.7 m (12 ft). Weight at 3.4 m (11 ft) 394 kg (7 cwt 84 lb).

GENERAL HABITS Congregates in schools composed of equal numbers males and females in spring, later segregation of sexes. Known occasionally to ascend rivers for considerable distances from sea.

BREEDING Spring to summer. Gestation 10 to 12 months, calves born about middle of year.

FOOD Wide variety of fishes, squids.

RELATIONS WITH MAN Aquarium specimens showing trainability and playfulness indicative of intelligence ranking between dog and chimpanzee.

GENUS *Stenella*

A genus widely distributed but systematics still very doubtful. Several species have been described.

Euphrosyne Dolphin *Stenella styx* (Gray)

DISTRIBUTION A North Atlantic species about which little known. Stranded only three times on British coasts, extreme south-west of England.

DESCRIPTION General form slender. Elongated beak (to *c.* 12.7 cm (5 in.)) well defined from forehead, which is low and receding. Back fin height moderate, concave hinder margin, tip tailwardly projecting. Tail stock without pronounced keeling, rather slender.

Flukes with notch in middle of hinder border. Flippers tapering, lower border shallowly convex, upper convex proximally, concave distally. Colour, dark back, white belly. Characteristic narrow dark bar from eye along side to vent, giving off branches, two from eye to base of flipper, another obliquely ventrally behind flipper level. Flippers and flukes darkly pigmented; former inserted in white region of side. Teeth, 43 to 50 each side, upper and lower. Diameter $c.$ 0.3 cm ($\frac{1}{8}$ in.).

MEASUREMENTS Length to 2.5 m (8 ft). Weight at 1.7 m (5 ft 5$\frac{1}{2}$ in.) 54.9 kg (1 cwt 9 lbs).

GENERAL HABITS Nothing known.

FOOD Fish (876 otoliths of *Gadus minutus* in one specimen), cuttlefish.

GENUS *Delphinus*

The most commonly recognized cetacean, entering into folk-lore of Mediterranean. Various forms have been described, but doubtful if they are specifically distinct from the more familiar one reaching British waters.

Common Dolphin *Delphinus delphis* (L.)

DISTRIBUTION Common in temperate and warm seas. In British waters more abundant in south and west, less frequently in North Sea. Ranks about equally with Bottle-nosed Dolphin in number of strandings.

DESCRIPTION General form slender. Elongated beak (to 10.7 or 12.2 cm (5 in. or 6 in.)) with groove separating it from low, receding forehead. Dorsal fin of moderate height, tailwardly directed tip, concave posterior margin. Flukes with notch at middle of hinder margin. No pronounced keeling of tail stock. Flipper; lower margin convex, upper convex proximally, concave distally. Although, when dead, back very dark to black, in life impression of brown coloration. Belly white. Complicated pattern of alternating light and dark bands on flanks, two waves of colour intersecting at level of dorsal fin being characteristic. Dark circle round eye extended into line along side of forehead. Tapering band from base of flipper to side of lower jaw. Teeth, 40 to 50 each side, upper and lower. Diameter 0.3 cm (1/10 in.).

MEASUREMENTS Length to 2.4 m (8 ft). Weight at 2.1 m (7 ft) 114 kg (2 cwts 26½lbs).

GENERAL HABITS Speedy, vigorous, sportive, frequently leaping clear of water, playing round ships' bows.

FOOD Various fishes, including Herring, Pilchard, lantern fishes, sauries, horse mackerel; cuttlefish and octopus.

General references to cetacean literature are the following: Allen (1916), Fraser (1952), Kellogg (1928), Matthews (1952), Norman & Fraser (1948) and True (1904).

There are also many references to Blue, Fin, Sei, Humpback and Sperm Whales in *Discovery Reports* (Cambridge University Press) and to all the British species in *Reports on Cetacea stranded on the British Coasts* (British Museum (Natural History)).

Order Carnivora

Very successful and important order, third most numerous in species among mammals. Primarily flesh-eaters, but many species have wide variety of diet and some, e.g. pandas, entirely vegetarian. Whole group has specialized dentition, characterized in Fissipedia by development of carnassial cutting and shearing cheek teeth (pm^4 and m_1 being modified), prominent canines and small (reduced) incisors in both jaws. Axis of articulation of jaw transverse and narrow and does not allow lateral movement. Strong muscles needed are attached to well-marked ridges on skull.

Carnivora form well-defined systematic group and their identity was clearly recognized by Linnaeus. Size range large, from Weasel up to relatively huge bears and elephant seals, but size only generally related to prey taken; Weasels will kill and carry off prey much larger than themselves, while Foxes feed frequently on quite small beetles. Sight poor and probably monochromatic (many species nocturnal), but both hearing and smell acute. Many species have scent glands (sometimes developed in an exaggerated way for defence, e.g. Skunk) used for marking ownership of territory.

Carnivores conflict with man in two ways. Many have dense and lustrous fur with which man seeks to clothe himself or his mate. This has probably depleted the numbers of some terrestrial and freshwater species, while some of fur-bearing seals almost exterminated before conservation measures taken. Carnivores, also, have misfortune to eat many things that man wants for his own table, so throughout world they are gradually being edged away from settled areas. Decline of British carnivores during last two centuries, especially during hey-day of game rearing, has been notable. There has, however, been some revival in past 30 years.

Carnivores fall clearly into three suborders, one of which, Creodonta, entirely fossil. Other two are Fissipedia, which includes all terrestrial forms, and Pinnipedia (seals and sea-lions).

E.&M.-S. regard each of suborders as full order and apply name Carnivora to Fissipedia only. Grassé also regards them as orders but retains Fissipedia, using Carnivora as super-ordinal name to include all these orders. System here used is that of Simpson. Earlier authors (and more recently Romer) used for superfamilies of Fissipedia Arctoidea (= Canoidea) and Aeluroidea (= Feloidea). Later names are to be preferred since genus *Aelurus* (panda) now placed in Canoidea.

Fissipedia divided into two well-defined groups.

Superfamily Canoidea with 4 families: Canidae (dogs, wolves, foxes, jackals; 12 genera, world-wide), Ursidae (bears; 5 genera, Europe, Asia and N. America), Procyonidae (racoons, coatis, kinkajous, pandas; 8 genera, New World and C. Asia), and Mustelidae (weasels, stoats, badgers, skunks, otters, etc.; 29 genera, world-wide).

Superfamily Feloidea with 3 families: Viverridae (genets, civets, mongooses; 36 genera, Old World, with interesting concentration and diversity of forms in Madagascar), Hyaenidae (hyaenas and aard-wolf; 3 genera, Southern Asia and Africa) and Felidae (cats, lynxes, lion, tiger, etc.; 3 genera split into 23 sub-genera, world-wide).

Classification of Pinnipedia is simpler since it contains only three families. All with thick layers of fat (blubber) below skin and with webbed hands and feet forming flippers. Otariidae (eared seals, comprising fur-seals and sea-lions; 5 genera, Pacific and Indian Oceans, Antarctic), Odobenidae (1 genus only, Walrus; Arctic) and Phocidae (true seals; 10 genera, all seas and some large inland waters).

Otariidae and Odobenidae possibly more closely related to
AA

each other than either is to Phocidae. Absence of good fossil record prohibits further analysis of relationships which could be indicated by superfamily divisions as in Fissipedia but true seal is almost as different from fur-seal as cat from dog.

FIELD IDENTIFICATION CHARACTERS

Most of British Fissipedia so distinctive that it is hardly necessary to go into detail for their identification.

(1) Fox (*Vulpes vulpes*) too well known for any mistake to arise, when actually seen. Voice almost as diagnostic, especially short, sharp bark of dog, heard frequently in winter and howl or scream of vixen. Footprints have characteristic rosette arrangement of dog family, but are smaller than those of most country-ranging breeds of domestic dog.

(2) Marten (*Martes martes*) now rare and mainly confined to Scotland, Wales and N.W. England. Both Marten and Polecat have typical elongated and short-legged form of Stoat, but are larger, Marten being about 2.5 lb in weight and measuring some 17 in. (excluding tail) compared with 0.5 lb and 10 in. for Stoat. Marten has rich brown fur with cream patch on throat and chest, long tail (*c.* 12 in.) and is often arboreal in habits, though British 'relict' populations have mainly taken to open, rocky habitats.

(3) Polecat (*Mustela putorius*), another rare species mainly found in Wales, has much shorter tail than Marten and dark pelage with buffish underfur showing through. Reddish form also found in West Wales. Muzzle and cheeks patched with yellowish-white. Feral ferrets may be mistaken for Polecats, but, of course, are often of albino variety.

(4) Stoat (*Mustela erminea*) and (5) Weasel (*M. nivalis*) can be considered together. The two species of smaller carnivores which remain widespread and abundant in British Isles in spite of persecution. Active by day and so naturalist, who is constantly afield, bound to encounter them reasonably often. There is no mistaking exaggeratedly long body and short legs, lithe movements and inquisitive upright but rounded ears, which characterize them both. Apart from difference in size (Weasel's body measures some 7 in. in contrast to the Stoat's 10 in.), Stoat's longer tail with black tip will immediately identify it. General

reddish-brown colour common to both and, in winter, Stoat much more prone to turn white (producing well-known ermine coat) than Weasel.

(6) Badger (*Meles meles*) is as distinctive in its own way as Fox, for black-and-white striped head and heavy dog-size body immediately identify it on rare occasions when it is caught out of doors in daylight. Presence of Badgers in neighbourhood readily detected by vast excavations they make with well-trodden highways leading to and from them. Footprints, also, cannot be muddled up with those of any other British mammals. At night confident, foraging Badger betrayed by way it stamps and crashes through undergrowth (careful stalk will bring observer within the range at which he can watch directly with red torch).

(7) Last of our mustelids, the Otter (*Lutra lutra*) perhaps needs as little description as any of our carnivores. Long, rather heavy body, broad muzzle, prominent vibrissae and long tapering tail identify it on land, while in its more usual environment, water, frequent clue is train of bubbles which marks its underwater course. In some parts of British Isles may be confused with feral American Mink.

(8) The Wild Cat (*Felis silvestris*) is another rarity except in Scottish Highlands. By night, its usual period of activity, best stalked by sound and these will be familiar to anybody who has listened to caterwauling of domestic cats. If rare glimpse should be caught of it by daylight, Wild Cat looks much like common striped tabby but with thicker and more distinctly ringed tail.

Only two species of Pinnipedia, both belonging to family Phocidae, regularly seen in British waters and which breed on coasts. Not easily distinguished unless one or more of following characters visible. Size distinction useless in almost all circumstances.

(9) Common Seal (Sand Seal, Harbor Seal) (*Phoca vitulina*). Mottled grey colour, spots quite small and very numerous, silhouette of nose concave giving rather puppy-like appearance (retroussé profile), top of head rounded (Fig. 43); nostrils at V angle and almost touching below (Wynne-Edwards, 1954) (Fig. 43).

(10) Grey Seal (Atlantic Seal, Great Seal) (*Halichoerus grypus*). Colour very variable and not really reliable for identification but

dark spots when visible usually larger and less numerous than in Common Seal, silhouette of nose straight (female) or convex (male) (Greek or Roman profile), top of head flattish (may be slighly domed in young) (Fig. 43). Nostrils almost parallel and not touching below (Fig. 43).

Four other species of Phocidae very occasionally seen in northern waters or hauled out on northern coasts.

(11) Ringed Seal (*Pusa* (= *Phoca*) *hispida*). Adults 4–6 ft overall length; colour brownish-black above, yellowish below, back and sides spotted with oval light spots with dark grey centres (rings).

FIG. 43. Diagnostic field characters of Common Seal (*Phoca vitulina*) and Grey Seal (*Halichoerus grypus*). Heads in profile show (top left) ♂ Grey Seal with 'Roman nose', (top centre) ♀ Grey Seal with straight nose and (bottom centre) Common Seal with 'retroussé' nose. Heads, full face, on the right: (top) Grey Seal and (below) Common Seal, show diagnostic shape of nostrils (see text). Below left, single teeth of Grey Seal (left) and Common Seal (right).

(12) Harp or Greenland Seal (*Pagophilus* (= *Phoca*) *groenlandicus*). Adults 4–5 ft overall length; colour variable but males yellowish-white with black bands along each side joining over shoulders (harp); females bluish-grey above, yellowish below, black markings indistinct or absent.

(13) Bearded Seal (*Erignathus barbatus*). Adults 7–10 ft overall

length; colour variable, dark grey above, lighter below with dark spots on back; bristles of whiskers curved at end.

(14) Hooded Seal (*Cystophora cristata*). Adults 7–8 ft overall length; males dark grey above, lighter below; females paler; scattered light spots on both; male has inflatable sac between nostrils and eyes.

A few Californian Sea-lions (*Zalophus californianus*) (Otariidae) escaped from sea-side zoos and now free in North Sea. No evidence of breeding. Appearance familiar. Prominent external ears, large fore-flippers and hind flippers capable of being turned forwards and used for walking when on land (characteristics of Otariidae).

(15) Walrus (*Odobaenus rosmarus*) (Odobaenidae). Adults 10–12 ft overall length; but juveniles only reported on British coasts. Characters as for family.

FAMILY CANIDAE

Widely distributed and abundant over whole world except Australasia, where only the doubtfully indigenous Dingo in Australia.

GENUS *Canis*

Practically world-wide, containing dogs, wolves and jackals. Ancestors of all domesticated breeds.

†Wolf *Canis lupus* L.

Formerly widely distributed in British Isles and in Europe, now extinct in this country and over most of Western Europe, though still present in parts of Spain and Portugal, Italy and Scandinavia. From Russia extends eastward right across Siberia, and southward to parts of Balkans, Asia Minor, India and China. Widely distributed in N. America.

Available evidence indicates that it became extinct in England and Wales during the 16th cent., in Scotland and in Ireland during the early 18th cent. Numerous place-names in English, Gaelic and Welsh, as well as records in early literature and legislation, testify to former abundance.

GENUS *Vulpes*

Widespread genus occurring in Palaearctic, Oriental, Ethiopian (except central tropical Africa) and Nearctic Regions (E.&M.-S.).

About 12 species. *V. vulpes*, species of British Isles, most widespread and probably conspecific with *V. fulva* of N. America (Churcher, 1959); chromosome number (2n = 38) and form are the same (Lande, 1958). Three colour phases of *V. fulva*, viz. red fox, cross fox and silver fox, last extensively ranched for skins. Colour phases also occur in *V. vulpes* (Oksala, 1954).

Red Fox (Common Fox) *Vulpes vulpes* (L.)

DISTRIBUTION Most of Palaearctic Region up to south island of Novaya Zemlya and Kolguev, down into Oriental Region as far as Indo-China and Central India; E. to Sakhalin and Kurile Islands; if conspecific with *V. fulva*, N. America down to Virginia and New Mexico. Found up to *c.* 14,000 ft in Central Asia (Novikov, 1956). Introduced into Australia 19th century. Over 30 races described in Old World. General pattern of variation is for southern races to be duller and smaller (Novikov, 1956). In British Isles C. European *V. v. crucigera* is common form, but in Scotland Scandinavian *V. v. vulpes* also present owing to introductions (Tetley, 1941; Hattingh, 1956). Missing from Orkney, Shetland and Scottish islands, except Skye.

DESCRIPTION Sexes alike and difficult to distinguish in field, though vixen usually smaller and with proportionately shorter coat. Also suggested vixen has narrower face (Hurrell, 1962). Coat yellowish to brownish-red, darker on back, underparts grey-white, some black, especially on lower limbs and backs of ears; long, bushy tail, usually with white tip. Cubs chocolate-brown with woolly fur for first month, adult coat gradually appears after emergence from earth and complete before autumn (Hurrell, loc. cit.). In Scotland thought to be two varieties, larger and paler red form and smaller, dark grey-brown one (Matthews, 1952). Colour phases are known in northern part of range. Oksala (1954) reports black mutant with a black-bellied heterozygote (becoming 'cross' with a modifier) and a form with a woolly coat lacking the guard hairs. Moults only once a year, prolonged, late spring to autumn; fur hairs grow last so coat only thickens as winter approaches. Strong scent gland under tail. Teeth $\frac{3.1.4.2}{3.1.4.3}$. Claws not retractile, 5 on forefeet and 4 on hind.

MEASUREMENTS Av. adult: h.&b. 65 cm (26 in.), tail 40 cm (16 in.); weight ♂ *c.* 15 lb (6.8 kg), ♀ 12 lb (5.5 kg). Scottish specimens thought to be larger than elsewhere in British Isles with larger skull and teeth (as in Scandinavian form); however, weights quoted by Lund (1959) for Norway lower than above.

HABITAT Most variable, from mountains to lowland farms, disused mines, scrub of all kinds, sea-cliffs.

GENERAL HABITS Most commonly heard noise is contact bark, often triple, higher and sharper than a dog. Given by both sexes, but more usually by male. Also wailing scream, generally by vixen but also by male (Hurrell, 1962). Screaming described as part of bloodless combat in American Fox (Vincent, 1958). All noises and their functions described by Tembrock (1958a).

Usual gait walk or trot, but will gallop and run for long distances, when hunted, and will adopt devices for confusing trail, e.g. taking to water, or climbing trees. Swims well.

No easily recognized trails, but tends to move along topographical features such as ridges, ditches, glades, etc. Footprints like those of dog, but often distinguishable by nails and fur between toes (Scott, 1941a). Both sexes mark home range with urine (Tembrock, 1957) and these can be distinguished by human nose. Marking becomes more frequent before breeding season.

Faeces smaller than those of Badger or most dogs. Often deposited on bare mounds or hummocks. Those containing fur and bones small, those with fruit and insects larger. Av. length *c.* 12 cm and usually with distinctive 'tail'. Bedding places can sometimes be found and Scott (1943) for American Red Fox notes that these often have combed-out tufts of hair with two holes made by canines, 0.8–0.9 in. apart.

Mainly solitary apart from breeding season, when dog hunts for family. Social hierarchy noted among individuals coming to bait in Alaska (Vincent, 1958). Family breaks up during summer, when considerable dispersal by juveniles. Errington & Berry (1937) tagged three-quarter grown American foxes and made recoveries averaging 30 miles. Various estimates of home range, but roughly agreed on *c.* 1 sq mile: probably must be considerable overlap.

Activity intensively studied by Tembrock (1958b) on captive colony. In pre-breeding and early breeding season activity

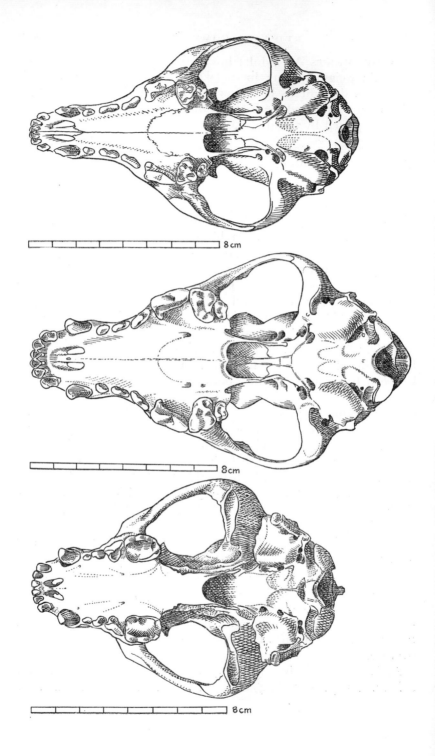

8 cm

8 cm

8 cm

showed peak of *c*. 12 hrs per day, falling by April to *c*. 7 hrs per day, at which it remained for rest of year. In autumn and early winter little daytime activity, but big peak at dusk falling through night to dawn. In Feb–March activity more evenly spread over 24 hours; over rest of year daytime activity reduced and night activity falls into three main peaks.

Prey sought mainly by stalking and pouncing; for mice there is characteristic high leap, descending fore-paws first on to prey (*Photograph 40*). Runways sometimes dug out. Mice swallowed whole, birds usually have feathers sheared off near bases, eggs have some third of shell bitten out. Cached food often betrayed by stray feathers.

May clean out several earths before deciding on one for breeding, but during dependence of young, may move three or four times to other earths. Can happen as result of very slight disturbance. Earths are often littered around with remains of prey.

Tembrock (1958a) with his captive colony showed that play was important part of fox behaviour: social play mainly derived from sexual activities, solitary play from 'maintenance' activities, feeding, grooming, etc. Social play most frequent just before breeding and in young animals (*Photograph 41*).

BREEDING Rut may begin late Dec, but peak usually late Jan and Feb. Vixens receptive for three weeks, but capable of being fertilized for three days only. Overlap of individual vixens means rut may last some five weeks. Both latitude and weather affect onset of rut (Tembrock, 1957). Dog Foxes in England fecund Dec to Feb (Creed, 1960). Large number examined in France by Bernard (1959) show large spread of pregnancies (all months but August to Oct when no data) but peak in March to April. Gestation lasts 51 to 52 days (longest 56); mean litter size 4.7 (Tembrock, 1957). Records from America give mean figures for

Fig. 44. Palatal views of skulls of Fox (*Vulpes vulpes*) (top), Dog (*Canis familiaris*) (centre) and Badger (*Meles meles*) (bottom). These are probably the three carnivores whose skulls are most frequently picked up. The skulls are distinguished as follows: that of the Badger is compressed antero-posteriorly, the snout being shorter and broader, the molars reduced in number and the articulation of the lower jaw so tight that the skull must be broken to remove the jaw; those of the Fox and Dog have a much longer snout, which is narrower and more tapering in the former than in the latter; the posterior margin of a Dog's skull is hump shaped, while in the Fox the margin is straighter and has a notch in the mid-line.

embryo rates 5.4 (95 examined, Sheldon, 1949) and 4.9 (210 examined, Switzenberg, 1960). Only one litter born per season. Tembrock (1957) gives following times for development of young; emerge from earth at 3½ weeks, stay around earth for another 4 weeks and leave it permanently at 7–8 weeks. Sheldon gives weaning 8–10 weeks, but cubs take food long before this. Apparently little known about sex ratio: Sheldon (1949) records 48% males in embryos and juveniles. Young weigh *c.* 100 g at birth, 1,130 g at 6 weeks and 3,160 g at 4½ months; reach adult size at 25 weeks and breed in winter following birth (Rowlands & Parkes, 1935).

POPULATION No precise information for British Isles. Probably at least 50,000 foxes (young and old) killed each year by hunting and shooting, a toll which does not affect population level.

In N. America numbers known to fluctuate, especially in north where changes are periodic and related to those of small rodents (see Elton (1942) for analysis of fur returns from trapping). Further south, densities are of order of 1.5 per sq mile (Scott, 1941a) but Korschgen (1959) followed population over 7 years and found one peak with densities of 12 to 20 per sq mile. In north, fur returns give index to numbers: in south, counts of earths and traces generally give valuable information. Wood (1959) tested spacing of traps on trap lines as population index and found traps one-fifth of a mile apart caught greatest numbers.

High embryo rate suggests fairly fast turnover of population, though mortality of young during dispersal probably high and proportion not reaching breeding age unknown. Sheldon (1949) determined age of 82 skulls and believed 8.5% were more than 5 years old. Age of ten years not uncommon in captivity. Lord (1961) used ingenious method with Gray Fox of capturing, spaying and releasing females and observing effect on ratio of young : old in population. From this he calculated total population.

FOOD Systematic study in America shows that foxes usually prey on species according to availability. Thus Cook & Hamilton (1944) found mice and rabbits predominate in winter with birds only 5–10% occurrence, fruit taken from late spring to autumn, grasshoppers and beetles in summer. However, Karpuleon (1958) found rabbits taken in excess of availability. In British Isles Southern & Watson (1941) found rabbits were far most frequent prey. This was confirmed by Hurrell (1962). Lever (1959), after myxomatosis, found Short-tailed Vole increased in importance. Sheep's wool, often from carrion, common in stomachs of hill foxes, but voles, hares, Rabbits, Ptarmigan and Red Deer may be found (Lever, 1959; Lockie, 1956; Watson, 1955). Schofield (1960) found staple winter food in Michigan was illegally killed deer. Foxes also take appreciable numbers of small birds as well as game species and poultry, a variety of insects, especially beetles of genera *Carabus* and *Geotrupes*, and fruit and berries, especially whortleberries and blackberries. Lever (loc. cit.) found rodents eaten most in autumn and winter, birds (including poultry) in spring and summer and insects and fruit in summer and autumn.

Most of above information from stomach contents. Feeding tests on captive foxes made by Lockie (1959) and Scott (1941b) show that most food items identifiable in faeces. Scott used per cent occurrence method, but Lockie found best estimate was by relative bulk of undigested material. Both investigators found daily food requirements just under 1 lb per day.

PREDATORS Mainly man with hounds or gun: cubs may be killed by various predators, including feral cats. From Nov 1959 to March 1960 some 1,300 foxes known to have died in eastern England in unusual circumstances, many in convulsions. At first thought due to virus disease, but later shown to have been from eating pigeons and other birds poisoned by toxic seed dressings.

RELATIONS WITH MAN Equivocal. Regarded with affection by many country people besides the Hunts; heartily disliked by those who keep sheep, poultry and game. Lever (1959) found game and poultry represented half to two-thirds of all bird remains and Middleton (1957) showed foxes can be important predators of partridge nests.

FAMILY URSIDAE

Bears mainly distributed in northern hemisphere, though one species found in S. America. Divided into six genera by Simpson.

GENUS *Ursus*

Holarctic. Various species and many races described, but good reasons for putting all in the one species below.

†**Brown Bear** *Ursus arctos* L.

Still occurs in most European countries, though only in small numbers and in very limited areas of mountain forests in W. Europe. Ranges over much of Russia and Siberia, Asia Minor, C. Asia, N. India and N. China. Also in N. America.

Skeletal remains and literary references indicate species found in part of British Isles until at least time of Roman occupation. May have lingered in Scotland until 9th or 10 cent. A.D. Date of extinction in Ireland also unknown.

FAMILY MUSTELIDAE

World-wide except for Australasia. Simpson divides into following sub-families: Mustelinae (marten, stoat, weasel, wolverine, etc.); Mellivorinae (African honey badger); Melinae (Old and New World badgers); Mephitinae (skunks); and Lutrinae (otters).

GENUS *Martes*

Genus widespread throughout Holarctic Region with one sub-genus (*Charronia*) extending into Oriental Region (to India, Malaya and E. Indies). Palaearctic Region has six species, Pine Marten (*M. martes*), the only one occurring in British Isles, distributed in Europe down to Mediterranean except S. Spain and Balkans, Beech Marten (*M. foina*) with more southerly range in Europe than Pine Marten, but wide overlap, and extending to Asiatic mountains over to Mongolia (Hagmeier, 1961), Sable (*M. zibellina*) mainly Asiatic but reaches to N. Finland, Japanese Marten (*M. melampus*) and two species grouped under subgenus *Charronia*, Yellow-throated Marten (*M. flavigula*) extending from E. Siberia to E. Indies, and *M. gwatkinsi* in S. India. The Nearctic Region has four species, American Marten (*M. americana*) east of Rocky Mountains, Pacific Marten (*M. caurina*) west of Rockies, *M. atrata* from Newfoundland, and one species in subgenus *Pekania*, the Fisher (*M. pennanti*). Most of this genus provide valuable pelts for fur trade and some bred on fur-farms.

Pine Marten *Martes martes* (L.)

DISTRIBUTION Europe up to tree line (approx. 70° N.) and down to N. Spain, Italy, Jugo-Slavia, east to Urals in N. and to Caucasus and W. Siberia, up to 5,500 ft (1,800 m). Pattern of variation complicated: seven subspecies named, largest in Caucasus (Schmidt, 1943); some tendency to increase in size northwards (Lampio, 1951), but decline eastwards to Russian race, *M. m. ruthena* (Reinwaldt & Erkinaro, 1959).

In British Isles formerly widely distributed, even to Hebrides. Greatly reduced in 19th cent. and now restricted to N.W. Scottish Highlands, Lakeland, Wales and Ireland. Was much persecuted for pelt. Has slightly increased in last 15 to 20 years, especially in N.W. Highlands, and since 1959 several records south of Caledonian Canal. Odd records far from native haunts.

DESCRIPTION See Field Identification Characters. Colour varies from rich chestnut-brown to almost black on both upper and under sides. Creamy-white throat patch is distinctive feature, often tinged with orange when moult just completed, variable in size, sometimes extending up sides of neck. Prominent ears with pale edges. Moult starts with head and legs in late spring and by June animal appears in short, dark summer coat with thinner tail (Schmidt, 1943, from observations on captive animals). For captive American *M. caurina*, Markley & Bassett (1942) state that winter coat grown in Sept and first half of Oct, starting on tail and legs and finishing on back and face. Tail notably more bushy than in summer. H.G.Hurrell (unpubl.) confirms this from captive specimens of *M. martes* from Germany. Males larger than females (see below under Measurements). Juvenile takes 6 months before tail reaches adult thickness.

MEASUREMENTS Very variable. Schmidt (1943) gives following for 100 German specimens: h.&b. ♂ 480 to 530 mm, ♀ 400 to 450 mm; tail ♂ 250 to 280 mm, ♀ 230 to 260 mm. Weight varies between 900 and 1,500 g according to sex and age. Schmidt noted in captive animals weight varied with season, rising to highest peak in June, and secondary peak in October.

HABITAT Predominantly woodland animal, especially characteristic of northern conifer belt up to tree line. American species noted to keep to forest during winter, but to come out on to rocky slopes, scrub and meadow in summer (Marshall, 1951a). In some parts of British Isles (e.g. Sutherland), now mainly inhabits open rocky ground.

GENERAL HABITS Usually silent. Deep 'huffy' noise, emphatically repeated with long drawn-out moan, when slightly alarmed or annoyed. High-pitched chattering squeal when angry or fighting is noise most often heard from wild Marten. When on heat female clucks as she goes about depositing scent and urine: during copulation both sexes purr and growl (Markley & Bassett, 1942).

FIG. 45. Four medium-sized, terrestrial carnivores found in the British Isles. Above, Pine Marten (*Martes martes*), now rare and confined to hill country; middle, Polecat (*Mustela putorius*), also restricted but not uncommon now in parts of Wales; bottom, Stoat (*M. erminea*), distinguished by larger size and black-tipped tail from the Weasel (*M. nivalis*).

Call of lost cub like tearing of cloth, or call of Snipe. Rarely adult may make this call for company.

Locomotion, as with most mustelids, is bounding. Grinnell, Dixon & Linsdale (1937) give measurements of male *M. caurina* (a smaller species than *M. martes*) tracks in snow: length of bound averaged 18 to 30 in. (46 to 76 cm), long and short often alternating. Footprints *c.* 1 in. wide by 1¼ in. (2.5 by 3.3 cm). Can make short rush at great speed; downhill leap of 14 ft (4.3 m) noted in snow (F.Chard, unpubl.). Climbs with great agility.

Indication of presence found in dens (see below) and tracks but mainly in deposits of droppings, which are 4 cm or more in length, round in section and vary between pale and black (see sketches in Lockie, 1961). Said sometimes to smell of violets (Schmidt, 1943).

Social organization not clearly known. Conflicting evidence from American species on whether winter foraging is by loosely knit group (Grinnell, Dixon & Linsdale, 1937), or by mainly single animals, though pairs fairly frequent and up to six together recorded (Marshall, 1951a). Male probably takes little part in rearing of young, and family probably hunts, led by female, until time of dispersal. Mark and recapture experiments in American species (de Vos & Guenther, 1952; Miller, Ritcey & Edwards, 1955; Hawley & Newby, 1957) suggest that Marten, especially females, do not move far. Over 50% of animals marked were recaptured during same winter near place of marking: average movement between recaptures was, in one experiment, just over half a mile (10 records, range 0 to 3 miles), in another 1.1 miles (26 records, range 0 to 4½ miles). Animals released at distances of 1 to 12 miles from point of capture gave evidence of homing capacities. Average area covered given as 0.9 sq miles for male, and 0.3 sq miles for female (Hawley & Newby, 1957). In winter, trappers report movements over home range roughly circular with temporary residence at points along the circle. Whole area with circumference of 5 to 30 miles and overall density 1 Marten to *c.* 3 sq miles. Tracking records show that at any one place, area of *c.* 1 sq mile is hunted. Marshall (1951a), following tracks of one animal, found it travelled on average 5.3 miles each night (6 observations, range 2 to 9 miles). (All N. American observations.) In Lake District asserted that Martens travel from den to den round mountain massif many miles in circumference (H.G. Hurrell, unpubl.).

J.D.Lockie (unpubl.) has kindly supplied following sight observations in Highlands: of 20 Martens seen, 5 were during daylight, 4 at night, and 11 within 2 hours of dark, morning and evening. These may, of course, underestimate night activity.

In British Isles foraging mainly on ground: in American species variously recorded as mainly on or above ground. Arboreal pathways probably adhered to and marked with scent which is set on the branches.

Dens may be temporary or more permanent. In British Isles usually in cairns or crevices in crags, but may use nests of Magpies, or, occasionally, nest-boxes placed for owls. On Continent and in America recorded as using squirrel dreys, woodpecker holes, and hollow fallen trees. Breeding recorded in British Isles in nest of Buzzard on ledge, in hole in peat hag, in river bank and in peat-cap on top of large boulder.

BREEDING Cycle very like that of Stoat; mainly known from animals in captivity. Oestrus occurs after young weaned, July to August, betrayed by marked vulval swelling, which may show two peaks (Markley & Bassett, 1942). Female in oestrus sets scent and urinates frequently. Copulation, which has been observed in tree (Siefke, 1960) lasts *c.* 1 hour, and male drags female round by scruff, purring and growling. Blastocysts remain unimplanted until mid-Jan, young born late March to April. Total period *c.* 270 days. Litters in captivity average 3 (Schmidt, 1943) (41 observ., range 2 to 5). One litter only per year. Young weaned at 6 to 7 weeks.

Sex ratio thought to be about equal, and found to be so in some trapping records (Lampio, 1951), but others show bias, usual in mustelids, towards males. Yeager (1950) found in trapped samples of American species males were 65% in autumn and 55% in winter.

Young born with thin covering of white or yellowish hair. Weight of *M. caurina* at birth *c.* 28 g. At 8 days distinct grey stripes appear, reaching greatest development at 16 days, disappear at 20 days. General colour up to 3 weeks grey, changing after to brown (Markley & Bassett, 1942). Tails have only short hairs at first but begin to bush out at *c.* 3 months. Young emerge from den at *c.* 2 months.

Both sexes reach adult weight in first summer but show no sign of sexual activity until second. In captivity no fertile mating until third or even fourth summer. (All these are records of *M. caurina*.)

POPULATION Figures for density given above (see under General Habits). Marshall (1951b) and Popov (1943) show that sexually immature males can be distinguished from weight of baculum. Hawley & Newby (1957) for American species show that number of juveniles on area with *c.* 15 adults varied between 5 and 0. Yeager (1950) found in 194 specimens 43% belonged to first- and second-year classes, males being more common than females. This, together with relatively low embryo rate, suggests fairly slow turnover of population. Life span in captivity 10 to 15 years (17 recorded). Yeager (1950) found 20% could be designated old, i.e. with very worn teeth, and in these males predominated by 33 : 6.

FOOD Lockie (1961) showed for Scottish Highlands that food varies greatly in size and composition, but rodents and small birds form the bulk at all times of year. Bird prey contains high proportion of tits, wrens and treecreepers. Of small rodents 90% were Short-tailed Voles, a much larger proportion than in trapped samples at same place. Beetles, caterpillars, carrion, fish and berries (especially whortleberries and rowan berries) eaten seasonally.

Höglund (1960) in Sweden found during winter 51% squirrel, 21% small mammals, 13% game birds, 5% other birds, 2% bilberries, etc. There were big differences between winters according to abundance of squirrels and small rodents. Similarly for *M. americana* Quick (1955) found in N. British Columbia that small mammals and Varying Hares predominated in the diet one winter, voles and birds in another. Cowan & Mackay (1950) found in Canadian Rockies that small mammals composed 66% of food in summer and 83% in winter. Parovshchikov (1961) found much the same in N. Russia. In the open ground of Alaska, Lensink, Skoog & Buckley (1955) also found that species of *Microtus* predominated. Schmidt (1943) reckoned from captive animals that daily food intake is *c.* 10% of body weight.

H.G.Hurrell (unpubl.) has observed his tame Martens, when at liberty, to kill frogs, rabbits, rats and small mammals, also bumble bees and cockchafers. Usually ignore slugs but occasionally eaten after being dragged about with fore-paws to remove slime.

PREDATORS In British Isles man is main predator and Marten not infrequently caught in traps set for Foxes. Occasionally Foxes may kill them and there is a saying in Lakeland: 'Where Foxes is rank, Marts is scarce' (Taylor, 1956).

BB

RELATIONS WITH MAN Marten populations subject to constant pressure because of value of pelts. This and vermin trapping account for catastrophic decline in British Isles. Records from America show overall decline in trapping returns over last 50 years.

GENUS *Mustela*

Genus widespread throughout Holarctic Region, reaching into Oriental Region (to Malaya and E. Indies) and into Neotropical (one species down to L. Titicaca); contains many of smaller and medium-sized carnivores. Most authorities now divide into 3 subgenera: *Mustela, sensu stricto*, with about a dozen species, comprising stoats and weasels; *Lutreola*, with 3 species, comprising European and American Mink; and *Putorius*, with 2 species, the Polecat and the Black-footed Ferret. Mink kept widely in fur farms and American species now living ferally in British Isles.

Stoat (Ermine) *Mustela erminea* (L.)

DISTRIBUTION Most widespread species of genus, extending in Palaearctic Region from Arctic down to Pyrenees, Alps and Himalayas; in Nearctic (now that the many described species all lumped in *M. erminea* (see Hall, 1951)) from Arctic down to California, New Mexico and New York. Many subspecies described, highly variable in size geographically with smaller subspecies to S. of range in America (the smallest being scarcely size of Weasel) (Hall, 1951) and to north of range in Europe (Reichstein, 1957).

Three subspecies in British Isles; *M. erminea stabilis* from mainland (detailed information lacking but apparently absent from Lundy, Scillies, some of Inner Hebrides (e.g. Rhum, Arran, Colonsay), Outer Hebrides, Orkney, introduced on mainland of Shetland); present on Jersey and Guernsey (Baal, 1949); *M. erminea hibernica* from Ireland and I. of Man; and *M. erminea ricinae* from Islay and Jura.

Abundance followed closely that of Rabbit except in certain areas, e.g. where open trapping with gins as in S.W. Wales, but, since myxomatosis, has declined in numbers throughout country.

DESCRIPTION See Field Identification Characters. Irish race darker than mainland one, lacking white edging on ear and upper lip and usually dark colour encroaching on belly and throat; 10

to 12 teats in contrast to 8 in all other subspecies (Miller, 1912). *M. e. ricinae* smaller than mainland form. Young animals said to have coats dorsally greyer and duller and ventrally more creamy than adults.

Two moults a year, spring and autumn. Spring moult is slow, progressing from back to belly; autumn moult swift and progressing in reverse direction (Rothschild, 1942). Autumn moult in north of range is to pelage entirely white except for black tip of tail ('ermine' condition); further south, moult is to coat like summer one but denser. In America narrow zone where both types of moult occur, white females preponderating in northern part of zone (Hall, 1951). Same recorded for Yorkshire (Flintoff, 1935b), where various half-way stages noted. Type of winter coat thought to be genetically determined and timed in relation to temperature and daylength but Rothschild (1942) has shown that Stoats which normally stay brown in winter can be induced to turn white, or partly white, by exposure to low temperatures.

MEASUREMENTS Males consistently larger than females. Size varies but males grow to *c.* 270 g by July and reach adult weight of *c.* 320 g by following spring; females grow faster, reaching *c.* 190 g by July and adult weight (*c.* 220 g) by following spring (Deanesly, 1935). Measurements unsatisfactory because of variability but following are from winter and spring specimens (Flintoff, 1935a; Bureau of Animal Population, Oxford, unpubl. records); h.&b. ♂ 297 mm (4 meas., range 275 to 310 mm), ♀ 264 mm (8 meas., range 242 to 292 mm); tail ♂ 110.5 mm (4 meas., range 95 to 127 mm), ♀ 117 mm (8 meas., range 95 to 140 mm). Weight (Deanesly, 1935, Jan–July animals only), ♂ 321.5 g (204 weighed, range 200 to 445 g), ♀ 213 g (99 weighed, range 140 to 280 g). Heaviest male more than thrice weight of lightest female. British race tends to be larger than Continental.

HABITAT Very wide range of habitats from lowland agricultural country, marsh and woodland to moorland and mountains.

GENERAL HABITS Usually silent but, when alarmed, both sexes give what is variously described as a 'bark' or 'a spitting rattle'. Swims readily and well (eye-witness account for closely related *M. frenata* given in Davis, 1942). Climbs well, if necessary (records not infrequent after myxomatosis). Usual gait bounding, average distance of each bound, measured from tracks in snow, being 56 cm (22 in.) for male and 30 cm (12 in.) for female (Nyholm, 1960). Tracks of hind feet register almost exactly in those of fore feet. Can leap distance of 2.5 m (8 ft) (Soper, 1919) and vertically 1 m (3 ft) (Blackmore, 1948). Footprints of male larger than those of female.

No specially defined trackways but will work along hedgerows and inside stone walls. Apparently very curious and can be drawn near to observer, especially if rabbit squeal imitated. Droppings dark and irregularly elongated (see sketch in Lockie, 1961), often piled up in den (Polderboer, Kuhn & Hendrickson, 1941). Sexes usually live separately and female will rear family by herself, though some records of male associating with family. Family may hunt together into autumn and, since families can be large and more than one may join together, this gives rise to reports of Stoats hunting in packs. Possible, however, especially when small mammal prey crashes, that movements, migrations almost, may be performed by many animals.

Home range of one male approximately 50 acres in young Forestry Comm. plantation in Scotland where voles numerous (J.D.Lockie, unpubl.). Winter home ranges in Finland, measured by Nyholm (1960), were: male, 85 acres (34 ha) (17 meas., range 72 to 106 acres (29 to 40 ha)), female 18 acres (7.4 ha) (46 meas., range 9 to 41 acres (4 to 17 ha)). Areas within each range used successively for few days. Distance travelled in night averages c. 2 miles (3 km) but may be up to 5 miles (8 km) (Nasimovich, 1949). Strong musky scent emitted from anal glands, when alarmed, but not known if used for marking home range. Dens may be in hollow tree, rock crevice or burrow (often commandeered from moles or rats) and used as focal point of home range.

Hunting mainly at night but also often in daytime. Prey largely pursued by scent. Notable that single Rabbit will be relentlessly followed through colony whose other members continue to feed. Pursued Rabbit often observed to act in panic-stricken way and to lie down squealing at approach of Stoat. Kill always made by bite at back of neck, which may have given rise to false idea that Stoats and Weasels suck blood of prey. Large prey gripped at back of neck, enfolded by fore-legs and scratched with hind (Hamilton, 1933).

BREEDING Males have active sperm from March to Nov, though regression starts in July. Females ovulate at about monthly intervals throughout year except for break during pregnancy (March–April). Ovulation resumed during lactation. Though copulations may occur throughout active period of males, these are infertile and corpora lutea remain small. Fertilization is only in late spring and summer and implantation delayed until following spring (i.e. for about 280 days), when embryos proceed to develop to full term in 21–28 days. This account by Deanesly (1935, 1943) supported for *M. frenata* by Wright (1947), though Watzka (1940) for European Stoat maintains only two periods of heat, March and June–July, at both of which fertilization can occur, the latter only involving delayed implantation. However, certainly only one litter a year in British Isles.

Deanesly (1935) finds 9 to 10 ova shed at each ovulation, whatever season and age of animal. Embryo rate 9 (12 observ., range 6 to 13); embryo rate for same species in New York State 6 (5 observ., range 4 to 8) (Hamilton, 1933). Lactation lasts *c.* 5 weeks.

Sex ratio difficult to assess. Trapped samples usually give preponderance of males: Deanesly (1935) found 61% of males in 640 examined and Flintoff (1935b) 63% of 6,221 examined. May be due to selection of heavier males by traps and to greater activity of males. Elder (1945) found 80% males when population was low and 60% when it was increasing.

Young born with coat of fine white hair and between 14 and 21 days of age grow prominent mane behind head (N. American species) (Hamilton, 1933). Black tip to tail appears at 20 days and eyes open at 37 days. Last milk teeth still present at 3 months. In skull, sutures between nasals and premaxillae/maxillae widely open between 3 and 7½ months, still visible 7½ to 10 months, afterwards indistinguishable (Hall, 1951). Males grow to *c.* 270 g by July, remain sexually inactive during winter and reach adult weight in next spring. Weight of baculum stays at 20 to 30 mg until spring of first breeding, when it about doubles. Females grow rapidly to *c.* 190 g by July and have ovulated by May–June. Fertilized by older males, so that whole female population can be pregnant by following spring.

POPULATION May fluctuate widely in numbers, especially where prey species do same. Yearly records of Stoats trapped on 4,000 acres in Hampshire, 1947–60 (Anon., 1960) range from 136 to 302 before myxomatosis and from 13 to 58 afterwards. Figures quoted for density vary from 1 per 40 acres (Polderboer, Kuhn & Hendrickson, 1941, on *M. frenata*) to 1 per 70 acres (Soper, 1919). Nasimovich (1949) found from winter track index in Russia that numbers varied less than those of Weasel. In same country percentage of young in population may vary between 65 and 19 in different years (Popov, 1943).

FOOD Until myxomatosis Rabbit was staple food of Stoat in British Isles. Where no Rabbits present food is mainly small mammals. Thus Polderboer, Kuhn & Hendrickson (1941) in Iowa found over 70% occurrence of voles and mice in faeces, Aldous & Manweiler (1942) in Minnesota found 59% 'mice' and 23% shrews and Hamilton (1933) in New York State found 47% 'mice' and 20% shrews. This varies with abundance of prey and with season and Nasimovich (1949) in Russia found 8% voles, 25% insects and 71% juniper and other berries. In British Isles known to take also birds and their eggs, reptiles and fish. Little known about daily requirements of food but Howard (1957) found that *M. frenata* of 230 g ate average of 77 g (33% of its own weight) of rats per day over 398 days. Hamilton (1933) states that *M. erminea* eats about one-third of its weight per day and drinks frequently.

PREDATORS At moment man probably most important predator in British Isles but occasionally adults and, more frequently, young taken by hawks, owls, and larger predatory mammals. Suffers from nematode parasite, *Skrjabingylus nasicola*, which makes cavities in skull but not so frequently as in Weasel, nor known how often and under what circumstances condition can be fatal.

RELATIONS WITH MAN Since adults, young and eggs of poultry and game birds, as well as other birds are taken, Stoat is treated as 'vermin' and trapped heavily by gamekeepers who used special system of strategically sited tunnels with gin traps inside. However, Stoat's destruction of rabbits, rats, mice and voles may counterbalance this. When kept in captivity rather timid and less aggressive than Weasel (J.D.Lockie, unpubl.).

Weasel *Mustela nivalis* (L.)

DISTRIBUTION Weasels at present divided into two main species, *M. nivalis*, with *c.* 17 subspecies distributed over whole Palaearctic

Region, and *M. rixosa*, with 4 subspecies distributed over Canada down to the northern United States. Hall's revision (1951) of N. American weasels suggests that *M. rixosa* extends westwards over the U.S.S.R. to central Europe, where it meets *M. nivalis*. Critical revision of material from whole range may reveal that they are conspecific, as already suggested by Reichstein (1957).

British Isles have type subspecies only, distributed over whole mainland but missing from Ireland and all islands except Skye.

DESCRIPTION See Field Identification Characters. Colour similar to that of Stoat but lacks straight line between brown upper parts and white underparts of latter: often spots and blotches of dark colour on underparts. Tail relatively short and without black tip. Latham (1953) states fur of *M. rixosa* fluoresces under ultra-violet light with lavender glow. Males larger than females (see below under Measurements). Details of moult not known but probably twice a year, as Stoat, since in north of range they turn white in winter. However, southern limit of white forms further north than in Stoat and only rare records for British Isles. Young have greyer and duller back colour and more creamy underparts than adults.

MEASUREMENTS Highly variable. Maintained by some authorities (e.g. Zimmermann, 1940) that two species are concerned, the Common Weasel and the Dwarf Weasel, latter distributed in Europe in patches among Common. However, variability produced by age distribution (there are two litters a year which grow at different speeds, see below under Breeding) suggests more information needed to settle point. Data below from animals caught Jan to June, kindly supplied by Dr Ruth Deanesly, except where specified otherwise.

H.&b., ad. ♂ 202 mm (46 meas., range 175 to 220 mm), ♀ 177.5 mm (12 meas., range 165 to 190 mm); tail ♂ 60 mm (46 meas., range 40 to 75 mm), ♀ 49.5 mm (12 meas., range 40 to 65 mm). Weight, ad. ♂ (data in Hill, 1939) 115 g (162 weighed, range 70 to 170 g), ♀ 59 g (36 weighed, range 35 to 90 g).

HABITAT Widely spread from lowland farming country and woodland up to moorlands and mountains. Broadly found wherever there are voles and mice. Nasimovich (1949) found in Russia woodlands preferred to open ground in winter.

GENERAL HABITS Voice varied. Guttural hiss when alarmed and has short, screaming bark when provoked. Young have shrill scream. Very aggressive in captivity and will hiss, bark and snap at slightest provocation (I.Linn, unpubl.). Moves much like Stoat but length of bounds only 20 to 30 cm (7½ to 12 in.) (Nasimovich, 1949). Uses no regular runways but, unlike Stoat, can follow along tracks and burrows of voles and mice. Frequently seen standing vertically on hind legs investigating surroundings (*Photograph 42*). Droppings similar to those of Stoat but smaller (see sketch in Lockie (1961)): sometimes accumulate in large numbers in dens. Sexes remain separate and have own home ranges. In Scotland range of males is 3 to 9 acres in young Forestry Commission plantation where voles are numerous (J.D.Lockie, unpubl.). Whole territory hunted regularly. Nyholm (1960) found in Finland that range of male only slightly larger than that of female, viz. 1.7 ha (4 acres) compared with 1.2 ha (3 acres). Polderboer (1942) gives smaller figure of 0.8 ha (2 acres) for 4 Weasels studied in Iowa. By following tracks in snow Nasimovich (1949) in Russia determined the average distance travelled in night's hunting was 1.5 to 2 km (0.9 to 1.2 miles). Shelters were not used permanently. This contrasts with Criddle's observations (1947) in Canada that winter dens lined with fur of prey which accumulates. One had fur lining nearly 1 in. thick weighing 22 g.

Most hunting presumably at night but Weasels very frequently seen during day. Weasels small enough to hunt through burrows of mice and voles and to penetrate through mouse-infested cornricks. Prey killed by bite at back of neck.

BREEDING Male cycle investigated by Hill (1939); season lasts April to August, though early stages of spermatogenesis present throughout winter. Deanesly (1944) showed for females anoestrus lasts Sept to Feb and pregnancies may occur any time between March and August, coinciding closely with male cycle. Hall (1951) records for *M. rixosa* in America pregnancies in most months of year with peaks in spring and mid-winter. Breeding season presumably adaptable to fluctuating food supply. Ovulation may occur only on stimulus of copulation. In British Isles normally two litters a year in April–May and in July–August. No delayed implantation; gestation *c.* 6 weeks, mean number corpora lutea 7.1 (32 observ., range 4 to 11). Lactation *c.* 4 to 5 weeks.

Sex ratio in trapped samples presumably suffers from same bias as that of Stoat. Thus animals investigated by Deanesly and Hill (loc. cit.) comprised 327 males and 126 females.

Young males of spring litter grow quickly and by June (2 months of age) weigh 70 to 90 g; by July have reached adult weight (95 to 135 g); and by August are producing active sperm. Those of second litter grow more slowly and do not become sexually mature until following spring. Females of first litter also grow fast, being 50 to 55 g in June, and some become pregnant in year of birth.

As with Stoat, age is best determined from the skull sutures. Wear of teeth difficult to assess and milk teeth all shed by 2 to $2\frac{1}{2}$ months.

POPULATION Little known. Numbers fluctuate with abundance of mice and voles. Yearly records of Weasels trapped on 4,000 acres in Hampshire (Anon., 1960) show little effect of myxomatosis in contrast to Stoats. Between 1947/8 and 1956/7 numbers varied between 50 and 180, but in 1957/8, a year of mouse and vole abundance throughout the country, 348 were trapped. Nasimovich (1949) in Russia found that the number of tracks seen per 10 km in snow varied from 6 to 0.1 according to year. Dependence on small mammals probably means its numbers fluctuate more than those of Stoat. Average expectation of life unknown but has survived up to 8 years in captivity.

FOOD Specialist in small mammals, though few systematic studies made. Nasimovich (1949) found from analysis of faeces in Russia that 100% contained remains of voles. Kutcheruk & Rubina (1953) examined 2 ricks infested by small mammals and found in them 13 and 10 Weasels. Criddle (1947) examined one den of *M. rixosa* which contained remains of nearly 50 voles and a heap of faeces with fur and bones. I.Linn (unpubl.) kept male (126 g) and female (56 g) in captivity and found mean daily consumption of male was 32 g (25% of body weight) and of female was 17.5 g (31% of body weight). Llewellyn (1942) kept *M. rixosa* (32 g) and found it ate *c.* 20 g per day over 6 days. Also takes young Rabbits, small birds, eggs and occasionally poultry.

PREDATORS Hawks, owls and larger mammals will kill an occasional Weasel but in British Isles man is most important predator. One record (Polderboer, Kuhn & Hendrickson, 1941) of *M. frenata* eating a *M. rixosa*. In addition, Stoats and Weasels sometimes compete for food. Hall (1951) notes that in New York

State, where Stoats exceptionally small, Weasels do not occur but Nasimovich (1949) found Weasel numbers more quickly reduced than those of Stoat when mice and voles scarce, since Stoat here had more varied diet. Incidence of the nematode parasite *Skrjabingylus nasicola* is high; Hall (1939) reports 10% of young and 70% of adults infected.

RELATIONS WITH MAN Regarded widely as vermin, yet Linn (1962) showed that a family of Weasels could account for *c.* 2,000 mice and voles in a year.

American Mink *Mustela vison* Schreber

DISTRIBUTION Nearctic, spreading over most of Canada and U.S.A. except Arctic islands and south-west parts of U.S.A. Kept on fur ranches in many parts of world and escaped animals have built up wild populations, e.g. in Iceland. In British Isles fur farms first established 1929, escaped animals living ferally recorded from then onwards. First breeding in the wild noted in 1956 in upper reaches of R. Teign, Devon. Now known to be established and breeding in Hampshire, Wiltshire, Pembroke, Carmarthen, Cardigan, and probably the common border of Banffshire and Aberdeenshire.

DESCRIPTION Medium-size mustelid, rich dark brown all over, including belly, small white spot on lower lip and chin and, sometimes, few white hairs or scattered white spots on underside. Size variable; male markedly larger than female. Colour varieties raised on ranches range from white through trade-favoured mutants like 'Sapphire' and 'Silverblu' to almost black. Light-coloured animals found occasionally in British feral populations.

MEASUREMENTS H.&b. 302 to 430 mm (12 to 17 in.), tail 127 to 229 mm (5 to 9 in.). Weight 565 to 1,020 g (1¼ to 2¼ lb), ♂ in captivity may exceed 2,260 g (5 lb).

HABITAT Always by rivers, streams and lakes.

GENERAL HABITS Very silent except during mating season when both sexes make purring noises. Shrieks when alarmed. Largely aquatic: swims well and catches much food in water. Sexes mostly live independently. In spring females stay within relatively small home range: males wander long distances.

BREEDING Season of feral Mink in British Isles not clearly defined but young so far recorded in spring. In captivity Stevenson (1959) gives following information. First-year and older males become sexually active in February. Female has about four oestrous cycles which occur between late Feb and early April, each lasting 7–10 days. Ovulation only after copulation (or artificial stimulus like being handled) but much variation in interval before implantation, minimum period of 'gestation' being 39 days, average 45 to 52 days and maximum of 76 days recorded. Normal litter 5–6 but larger numbers (up to 17) recorded. Data for U.S.A. confirm (Enders, 1952). If feral populations become permanently established in British Isles, will be interesting to see if these breeding arrangements persist. Stevenson notes great consistency in ranch-living Mink all over the world, breeding condition being attained c. 100 days after shortest day on both sides of equator.

FOOD In America winter food largely mammals, especially aquatic species, but also birds and fish; summer food includes many crayfish (Jackson, 1961). Few records for British Isles yet. Reports usually concentrate on raiding of chicken coops. Clearly status as possible major pest needs watching.

RELATIONS WITH MAN Relatively easy to rear in captivity and high financial returns ensure popularity on fur farms. May, perhaps, be reckoned as established member of our fauna.

Polecat *Mustela putorius* (L.)

DISTRIBUTION Most of Palaearctic Region except high north. Divided into c. 15 subspecies. Introduced into New Zealand, probably from wild W. European stock (McCann, 1956). In British Isles once widely spread, even to Hebrides (first specimen shown at London Zoo trapped in Regent's Park in 1828). By beginning of 20th century almost exterminated but now recovering. though practically confined to Wales, especially central Wales (Condry, 1954; Taylor, 1952). Possibly some truly wild ones also in Devon and Cornwall and in Lake District. Otherwise specimens reported probably escaped polecat-ferrets, to which wild form closely related or ancestral. Probably always absent from Ireland and the Scottish Polecat (named *M. p. caledoniae*) now almost certainly extinct. This subspecific name and that of other form separated as British (*M. p. anglius*) of very doubtful validity.

DESCRIPTION See Field Identification Characters. Upper coat long, almost black, often with purplish sheen; sparse, showing buff underfur. Varying but usually small amount of creamy-white on muzzle, behind eyes (sometimes extending as band across forehead) and on throat. Ears short, rounded, edged with white. Colour variable, a few approaching paleness of E. European *M. p. eversmanni*; reddish form known for at least 50 years around Tregaron, Cardiganshire, now spread north of Dovey estuary (Matheson, 1963). Moult not described in detail for Europe but McCann (1956) found captive specimens in New Zealand had only one moult which was prolonged. Females began at time of first oestrus in early spring. This continues slowly throughout summer and new coat appears below old in early autumn, then grows faster and complete by beginning of winter. In male each stage some weeks later.

Distinctions between Polecat and Ferret (especially the Polecat-ferret, or fitchet, which is coloured rather like wild Polecat in contrast to usual albino type of Ferret) not always clear-cut. Ashton (1955) and Ashton & Thomas (1955) state only constant skull difference is in post-orbital constriction which has a 'waist' in Ferret but not in Polecat. However, Tetley (1945) observed that the few extant specimens of Scottish Polecat had this 'waist' and it is also known to occur in the E. European *M. p. eversmanni*. Still probably true to say that in British Isles Ferrets have this constriction more marked than wild Polecat; also Ferret skull usually smaller and with smaller teeth than Polecat. Ashton & Thomson (1955) add that colour of Polecat usually darker than that of Polecat-ferret and the ring of pale colour on face normally broken by dark on throat in wild Polecat but unbroken in Polecat-ferret. Coat of cubs lighter in colour than that of adults.

MEASUREMENTS Male larger, h.&b. *c.* 410 mm, tail *c.* 180 mm; weight *c.* 1,250 g (up to 2,150 g): female, h.&b. *c.* 350 mm, tail 140 mm, weight *c.* 800 g.

HABITAT In Wales found in wide variety of habitats from dunes up into mountains, where may occur in plantations up to 1,500 ft and over. Commonly in thickets and woods where it makes den among rocks, in tree roots and in rabbit holes. In Russia found in broken woodlands and glades rather than in continuous forest (Novikov, 1956).

GENERAL HABITS Normally silent but may utter series of short yelps and variety of chattering and clucking noises. Characteristic growling noted during copulation (Eibl-Eibesfeldt, 1955). Much less agile than Marten; poor climber but swims well. Little known about organization of home range or social habits but marks its area with anal gland secretion mixed with urine. This secretion has foetid smell, hence local name of Foumart or Foulmart. Hunts usually by night and daytime spent in den. Prey located mostly by sound and scent in contrast to Marten which uses sight more; prey caught by head or neck and shaken violently. This killing bite not innate but learned so that young animals sometimes grip prey in wrong place and suffer in consequence (Eibl-Eibesfeldt, 1955, 1956). Same author observed nest being made of grasses and moss bitten off and dragged into den backwards, as with Badger. Young remain with den as base until about 3 months old, when they disperse.

BREEDING Both sexes come into breeding condition during March and pair late March to early April. Gestation 41 to 42 days and young born late April and May. Not known whether second litter later in year but stated that, if first litter lost, female, who normally becomes anoestrous 10–20 days after copulation, will come on heat again after 2 to 3 weeks (Rempe, 1957). Copulation may last up to one hour and female is grasped by 'neck-bite' and pulled around like prey. During courtship these roles may be reversed (Eibl-Eibesfeldt, 1955). Few records of embryo rate or litter size; quoted as 4 to 5 but Rempe (1957) records two litters of 8, one of 9 and one of 10 in captivity.

Breeding of Ferret closely studied and very similar to that of Polecat (see, e.g., Hammond & Marshall, 1930; Rowlands, 1957). Breeding condition takes 4 to 5 weeks to develop, being complete by March. Female shows marked vulval swelling, which may persist for whole season, if not mated, since ovulation occurs only after copulation. After fertilization female becomes anoestrous in about a week. Litter weaned at 6 to 8 weeks and oestrus recurs c. 2 weeks after that. Two litters a year normal. Average size (counted at 4 weeks of age to avoid disturbance) between 6 and 7. If mating infertile, pseudo-pregnancy occurs.

Young Ferrets practically naked at birth; weight c. 10 g. Eyes open at 4 weeks but even before this they begin to crawl about

out of nest and eat solid food. At 6 to 8 weeks they are very active and can be weaned.

POPULATION Very little known. Popov (1943) has shown that young males can be distinguished until they come into breeding condition after their first winter by weight of baculum, which averages 146 mg in contrast to 337 mg for adults. Recorded as living up to 13 years in captivity.

FOOD No systematic studies. In British Isles undoubtedly lived largely on rabbits before myxomatosis. Also takes poultry, young game birds and eggs, but probably also accounts for many rodents. Known to eat fish (especially eels), snakes and frogs.

PREDATORS Man the most serious and, until recently, many were caught in rabbit traps. Formerly hunted with hounds in Wales and Lake District. Fees varying from fourpence to one shilling a head appear in churchwardens' and other accounts from 17th cent. onwards.

RELATIONS WITH MAN Classed as vermin. In early 19th cent. used extensively in fur trade and small numbers still used by furriers.

GENUS *Meles*

This genus contains only the European Badger.

Badger *Meles meles* (L.)

Formerly called Brock (from Gaelic 'Broc') which is included in many place names such as Brockenhurst, Brockworth, Brockhampton, etc. Local names: Grey, Pate, Bawson or Badget.

DISTRIBUTION Practically all countries of Europe including some of Mediterranean islands, and across Asia to Japan, limits north, being roughly line just south of Arctic circle and south, the Himalayas.

Type subspecies (*M. m. meles*) occurs over most of Europe. Twenty-four subspecies based on such characters as size and variation in dentition but for many of them not enough data available to say whether rank of subspecies justified.

Widely distributed in British Isles. Found in every county of England, Wales and Ireland and in most of the counties of Scotland. In England rarest in flat lands of E. Anglia and most common in parts of Cornwall, Devon, Somerset, Gloucestershire, the New Forest area, Monmouthshire, Hertfordshire, Yorkshire, Cumberland and Durham. In Wales most numerous in south and west and scarcest in Caernarvon. In Scotland widely distributed but nowhere really common; largest populations being in East Lothian, Perthshire and Spey Valley. Absent from islands round Britain except Anglesey. Common in most parts of Ireland.

DESCRIPTION Appears grey from distance owing to colour of individual hairs which are light at base and tip with a dark patch between, nearer to tip. Hair colour shows a good deal of variation, the light areas ranging from white through cream to sandy yellow and the dark part from black to reddish brown. Albinos occur. Legs and underside of body darker than upper side. Head white with conspicuous black stripes on either side including eye region. Single, very prolonged moult, lasting most of summer (Novikov, 1956). Eyes small, ears short and tipped with white. Body somewhat wedge-shaped, legs short but very powerful for digging. Five toes on each foot with large claws on front feet. Tail short. Skull with prominent interparietal ridge in mid-line. Lower jaw articulated in such a way that dislocation is impossible without fracturing skull.

MEASUREMENTS Average adult 915 mm (36 in.), including 100 mm (4 in.) for tail. Average adult weight, ♂ 12.3 kg (27 lb), ♀ 10.9 kg (24 lb) (50 records). Weights of over 18 kg (40 lb) not unusual and three of over 27 kg (60 lb) recorded. Animals are heaviest in Dec and Jan, lightest in early spring. Sexes difficult to distinguish in field as marking similar, but male (boar) has broader head and a relatively thicker neck. Female (sow) has sleeker appearance.

HABITAT Badgers make their sets in wide variety of places, but most typically in woods or copses especially when they border pastureland. Slopes preferred and old rabbit warrens often taken over. Also found on cliffs by sea, in quarries, on mountain sides and even hedgerows, very occasionally in flat fields. Breeding sets known up to 1,700 ft. Low-lying marsh areas are avoided.

GENERAL HABITS Cubs make high-pitched whickering when tiny and loud squeals if danger threatens. When older they make 'puppy' noises when playing.

Adults utter deep growl of warning followed by staccato bark if other animals approach too near. Sow makes single note of warning like cry of moorhen.

At mating season boar uses deep purring noise and when excited this is prolonged and becomes higher in pitch. Sow also uses a purring noise to encourage cubs.

Screaming occurs, especially between Jan and April. Said to be made by both sexes. Significance still doubtful.

The set is complex labyrinth of tunnels and chambers often with many entrances. Tunnels may go into hillside up to 100 yd but typically 10 to 20. They may be at several levels. Plans of excavated burrow systems are given by Likhachev (1956).

Chambers lined with heaps of bedding brought in on dry nights. May consist of bracken, grass, bluebells, moss, leaves, etc. Twenty to 30 bundles may be brought in on a single night by both boar and sow at any time of year but especially Jan to May and August to October. Periodically, old bedding discarded in winter and may be aired at entrance on sunny mornings. Very occasionally nests made above ground in which young reared. Foxes, rats and rabbits may also use Badger sets.

Movements occur in relation to reproductive cycle and food supply. Adult males wander long distances in early spring to find mates. Complete families often move from one set to another, especially after cubs are weaned, or if danger threatens. Several families can live together especially during late summer.

Mainly crepuscular and nocturnal except in remote parts. Emergence from set usually at dusk but this varies according to sex, age, season and environmental conditions such as nearness to habitation and light intensity. Activity of one sow Nov to June recorded by implanting radio transmitter under skin (Bonnin-Lafargue & Canivenc, 1961).

When feeding, Badgers choose particular locality according to weather and season, e.g. on wet nights they would search pastures for earthworms but would take any food as opportunities occur until satisfied.

Winter activity reduced, especially in Dec, but no true hibernation. Can go without food for long periods and may remain below ground for several days at a time (much fat stored up under skin) but even in coldest spells some Badgers are about.

Faeces deposited in series of shallow pits within 20 yds or so of set; usually not covered in. Occasionally, in large set, certain chambers underground used for same purpose. Also regular places for defaecation as much as mile from set. Faeces vary according to diet, but usually looser than those of dog and often very yellow; Faeces very muddy after feeding on earthworms. Mammal hairs and beetle elytra often conspicuous contents. Faecal analysis gives fair qualitative estimate of diet except in terms of softer animal foods which are completely digested, but is useless for quantitative work.

Musk glands situated in anal region well developed and secrete yellowish oily liquid with strong musky odour. Scent emitted as result of fear or excitement; also deliberately set by squatting on a stone, root or bare ground. By setting a scent trail when in unfamiliar country Badger can find its way back. Scent setting also on objects in vicinity of set and may be concerned with marking out territory; also used at mating season for informing potential mate. Boar may also back on to sow and set scent on her before copulation.

BREEDING Complex and unusual. Copulation can occur in every month from Feb to Oct but not necessarily followed by fertilization. Main period Feb to May when copulation usually prolonged. Fertilization usually occurs at this time. Copulation stimulates ovulation (Notini, 1948). Long period of delay before implantation of blastocysts (up to nine months). Implantation in British Isles usually in December. Young born Jan to May and typically in Feb in S. England.

Possible for sow during period of delay to undergo further periods of oestrus when she will receive male. These copulations are of short duration (up to two minutes) and may result in further ovulation but fertilization does not appear to take place. If, however, earlier matings have not resulted in fertilization, copulation may be prolonged and fertilization follow (Neal & Harrison, 1958).

In England sows usually breed every year. Litter size 1 to 5, the latter being unusual; most reports of high numbers due to two families living together. Data from embryos gives average of 3.1 per litter. Numbers deduced from observations at eight weeks or later gives average 2.3 (50 families)—9 singles; 23 twins; 11 triplets; 7 quads (S.W. England).

CC

Cubs remain underground *c*. 8 weeks. Weaning starts at *c*. 12 weeks. Sow regurgitates semi-digested food at this stage (Notini, 1948). Cubs search for food independently of sow after 12 to 14 weeks; live with sow at least until autumn and sometimes over winter.

Female cubs usually mature in S. England when 12 to 15 months old. Male cubs take one or two years.

POPULATION Largest number of resident Badgers in a colony found between May and September. Could consist of adult males, adult females with cubs, female cubs of the previous year (probably fertilized) and male cubs of the previous year (possible but unlikely). Two sows with their cubs may be present. Total at this time of year may be as many as 12. By winter, number reduced at least by sows which are later to have their first litters if older ones still in residence.

Density of three adults per sq mile is possible in typical Badger country. Disease causing death seldom noted, but large numbers killed when crossing roads and railways. Badgers can live more than 12 years but few data available. Appears to have been marked increase in Badger population in British Isles during past 60 years.

FOOD Truly omnivorous, diet largely dependent upon availability. Animal matter includes rabbits (especially young), mice, rats, voles, moles, hedgehogs, amphibians, slugs, snails, earthworms, wasp grubs, beetles and other large insects. Poultry taken occasionally but not typically; lamb killing extremely rare, but still-born lambs occasionally taken. Carrion eaten occasionally.

Vegetable food includes underground storage organs of woodland plants, fruits of all kinds from windfall apples, pears and plums to acorns, beech mast and blackberries. Green food including grass taken especially during winter; oats occasionally eaten and mushrooms and other fungi sampled.

Most important single item of diet is earthworm; young rabbits (previous to myxomatosis) were also important. In autumn, acorns are major food in districts where common.

Andersen (1955) concluded for Denmark that oats (July and August), earthworms (most of the year, especially spring and autumn), amphibians (summer), insects such as *Geotrupes* (May), bumble bees and wasps (July and August), small mammals especially voles and shrews (May to July) were major items of diet. Figures from Russia (Likhachev, 1956) show similarly wide diet.

RELATIONS WITH MAN Badger is of little economic importance. With medium densities they do little harm and quite a lot of good. This applies to most of Britain. In places of high density when near habitation poultry killing may sometimes be nuisance especially in spring, but this usually confined to few individuals which get into the habit. Where natural foods are plentiful (especially earthworms, young mammals, insects and various food such as acorns) Badgers do more good than harm.

Badger baiting is illegal, but at one time was regularly practised. Badger digging with terriers still occurs in some parts. Badger gassing is illegal.

Badger cubs make charming pets, but should be reared from small cubs. They are easily house-trained. When sexually mature become restless and are likely to go off in search of mate. Extremely strong and, if kept shut up, this should be kept in mind. They need some dark place to use as set, and strips of sacking makes better bedding than hay. One meal a day at dusk is sufficient. They will eat practically anything, but some meat should be given occasionally. The more they are handled the better.

GENUS *Lutra*

World-wide. Many attempts to split this genus, but all otters so variable within groups and yet so alike that no satisfactory divisions made with possible exception of *Aonyx*. About 12 species.

Common Otter *Lutra lutra* (L.)

DISTRIBUTION Whole Palaearctic and into Indo-Malayan Regions, where it interdigitates with *L. sumatrana*. Canadian species close to European. Widely distributed in British Isles, most numerous in E. Anglia and large river systems. S.E. England with short streams less well populated than other areas. All western counties, especially Wales and Lake District, have no lack of Otters which may alternate between sea and freshwater habitats. Scotland well populated, with many marine-living ones around Hebrides, Orkney and Shetland. Density never very high and, in opinion of some hunters, 1 per 6 miles of stream normal. Type subspecies (*L. l. lutra*) extends over most of Palaearctic Region;

several races described from Continental part of range. Irish and
Scottish specimens tend to be darker than English (Tetley, 1945).

DESCRIPTION See Field Identification Characters. Most distinctive features flat head (often all that is seen in water) (*Photograph
44*), long, thick, tapering tail ('rudder'), webbed feet (5th toe sometimes shows in footprints or 'seal') dense brownish fur, on which
guard hairs mat into spiky appearance when Otter emerges from
water. Lower jaw locked to skull, capable only of up-and-down
movement. Tone of pelage variable, occasional specimens cream
or white recorded; also varies with season, being richer and darker

FIG. 46. Otter (*Lutra lutra*). Note the broad muzzle on the flat
head, small ears and thickened base to the tail.

brown in winter after moult; information needed on number and
duration of moults. Novikov (1956) suggests only one moult which
lasts long time and progresses almost imperceptibly. Females
look more compact than males which tend to be 'lankier', but
thicker about the neck.

MEASUREMENTS Vary according to age. Stephens (1957) gives
following from own data and from those of Southwell (for animals
considered adult, i.e. over 4.5 kg (10 lb)): total length, ♂ 118.6 cm
(47.5 in.) (23 measured, range 96 to 136 cm (38 to 54 in.)),
♀ 104 cm (41 in.) (12 measured, range 94 to 112 cm (37 to 44 in.));
tail ♂ 43.2 cm (17 in.) (10 measured, range 35.6 to 47 cm (14 to
18½ in.)), ♀ 39 cm (15.4 in.) (4 measured, range 35 to 42 cm (14 to
16½ in.)). Weights, ♂ 10.3 kg (23 lb) (12 weighed, range 5.5 to

16.8 kg (12½ to 39 lb)), ♀ 7.4 kg (16 lb) (7 weighed, range 6.4 to 12.3 kg (14½ to 28 lb)). Exceptionally large Otters quoted up to 166 cm and 23 kg (65 in. and 50 lb).

HABITAT Lakes, rivers, streams and marshes. Frequently lives in coastal waters and has been caught in crab and lobster pots. Sometimes found far from water, but usually when crossing watershed from one system to another. In more mountainous areas suggested that Otters move up to head waters when fish migrate there to spawn, then come down to lower reaches and coast in spring.

GENERAL HABITS Otters often silent for long periods. Use of whistle noted in both tame and wild Otters, but use of other noises observed in tame Otters (H.G.H.). Characteristic whickering of cubs and also high-pitched piping (which may turn into whistle of adult?). Piping used as means of keeping in contact (J.D.L.). Whistle, about a second in duration, sometimes repeated at intervals, is contact call. Long-drawn-out moan probably denotes apprehension; a chortle in rather low pitch commonly used when pleased; a hiss or high-pitched chatter when annoyed (H.G.H.).

Faeces ('spraints') easy to recognize with distinctive smell. Typically black or blackish, turning paler slowly as they weather. Spraints often deposited on rocks or grassy mounds by water. Sometimes Otters scrape up sand, mud or wisps of grass into heaps and spraint on top (H.G.H.).

Usually nocturnal. During day lie up in burrows, drains, hollow trees; sometimes these lined with reeds and bitten wood. In summer occasionally lie up in woods and reed-beds. Little definite known about movements, nightly or seasonal. Usually assumed Otters will travel long distances, e.g. have been tracked for miles in snow, but experienced otter hunters report that scent ('drag') from one night's activity not usually followed for more than 2-3 miles (H.G.H.). Certainly seem to occupy stretch of water, then abandon it. More precise information wanted.

BREEDING Very little known. Records of bitches with cubs of reliably estimated age, gathered together in Stephens (1957), fairly evenly spread over year (134 reports). But some authors report peak breeding in spring, others in autumn and winter. With *L. canadensis*, Liers (1951) found heat lasted Dec to early

April. Not known when Otters begin to breed, but not in first summer; after this probably one litter per year. Gestation generally stated to be *c*. 62 days, but several records (Liers, 1951) between 9 and 12 months for *L. canadensis* (with delayed implantation). Breeding holt often away from main stream, lined with reeds, grass and moss. Number of young 2 to 3, reared entirely by bitch. Blind up to 35 days (Cocks, 1881, 1882). Juvenile pelage dark and fine. Stay in nest probably 8 weeks; remain with bitch long time wandering about country, perhaps until she mates again. Captive pair of cubs (Stephens, 1957) grew in gentle curve from 1.2 kg to 6.4 kg in 15 months. At the start the male was 340 g heavier than female, at the end 2,275 g heavier.

POPULATION No proper census figures, only estimates like that given under Distribution, which may be wildly out. Hunting figures show no more than that population probably constant; number killed in *c*. 600 hunting days per year, 248 (1939), 198 (1949), 161 (1950), 207 (1951), 202 (1952) and 249 (1953). Animals examined during Stephens's survey showed only 2 out of 19 bitches visibly pregnant; presumably most of catch young.

In Canadian Otter size and weight of baculum used to separate age groups of males (Friley, 1949). Closure of skull sutures used by Hooper & Ostenson (1949), who found in spring-trapped sample of 139 specimens (90 males, 49 females) that 9 were a few months old, 49 were 10–15 months, 54 were in 3rd and 4th year and 27 were still older. Lack of young animals probably due to selection by traps. Life span in captivity *c*. 20 years.

FOOD Great controversy about damage to fishing interests; probably normal density too low to cause serious loss in most habitats, but in fish hatcheries at spawning time may do serious damage to trout and salmon stocks. Stephens (1957) showed that a half- to three-quarters-grown Otter in captivity ate 12 to 20 lb (5.5 to 9 kg) food per week. Food analysis from spraints collected all over country showed that of 294 food item occurrences Salmonidae were 21%, Anguillidae (eels) 18% and Cyprinidae (carp, roach, dace, bream, etc.) 11%. However, samples examined from specialized habitats gave following figures: fish hatcheries (23 food item occurrences), Salmonidae 3%, Anguillidae 13%, and Cyprinidae 9%: R. Camlad, Shropshire (100 food item occurrences), Salmonidae 7%, Anguillidae 11%, Cyprinidae 9%,

Gasterosteidae (sticklebacks) 12%, *Astacus* (crayfish) 18%; R.
Clettwr, Cardiganshire (53 food item occurrences), Salmonidae
40%, Anguillidae 11%. Many minor food groups constitute fair
proportion of total, e.g. frogs, birds, rodents, beetles. H.G.H. has
observed also newts, slugs, earthworms, frog tadpoles and freshwater shrimps (*Gammarus*) sought.

PREDATORS Presumably man only.

RELATIONS WITH MAN Hunting still carried on over much of
British Isles. Otherwise Otters only trapped when doing notable
damage (e.g. in fish hatcheries) or when value of pelt increases.
May well be useful in trout and salmon streams by killing eels
which devour eggs of trout and salmon. More data needed.
Trapping for pelts never so highly organized in British Isles as in
Scandinavia and Canada, where fur much denser. Otters frequently reared in captivity, making delightful pets; many published accounts of how to keep them (e.g. Kelway, 1944).

Informants cited by initials are H.G.Hurrell (H.G.H.), and
J.D.Lockie (J.D.L.).

FAMILY FELIDAE

World-wide, except Australasia, containing all the varied
assemblage of cats, great and small, from Lion downwards.
Systematists differ as to whether most of leopards, tigers, ocelots,
pumas and so on should be included in genus *Felis* or whether
they should be split up.

GENUS *Felis*

If genus restricted narrowly (subgenus *Felis* of most authors),
includes only Old World wild cats, distributed over Eurasia into
India and Burma and Africa. E.&M.-S. give 6 genera in Eurasia,
3 of which extend into Africa.

Wild Cat *Felis silvestris* Scheber

DISTRIBUTION From British Isles eastwards through C. and S.
Europe to Asia Minor and Caucasus. Seven subspecies given in
E.&M.-S., but Haltenorth (1953) has revised classification and
includes as subspecies many forms previously regarded as species

(e.g. *F. lybica, F. cafra, F. ocreata, F. ornata*, etc.). Species in this sense found throughout Europe and Africa and much of Asia to W. China.

Subspecies found in British Isles (*F. s. grampia*) distinguished from central European *F. s. silvestris* by darker general colour and more pronounced black markings. Coat said to be lighter in colour in summer owing to fading before moult.

Formerly distributed throughout British Isles, except possibly Ireland, where evidence doubtful: disappeared finally from England, Wales and S. Scotland by mid-19th century. Considerable recovery in Scottish Highlands since World War I, now known in Forestry Commission areas in Ross and Cromarty, Inverness-shire (excluding islands), Moray, Banff, W. Aberdeenshire, Argyllshire (excluding islands) and Perth (Taylor, 1946). Also known Caithness (uncommon), Nairn (increased during 1959–60), Sutherland (uncommon) and Angus (locally common and spreading) (Jenkins, 1962).

DESCRIPTION See Field Identification Characters. Sometimes difficult to separate from feral domestic cats and hybrid domestic ×wild. Most distinctive characters are strong black striping (contrasting with blotching of most domestic tabbies), black bands on thick short tail, blunt black end to tail, generally larger and more robust build (footprints are larger), and horn-coloured claws. Skull larger and more robust than in domestic cat with high arch to nasals and low sagittal crest for attachment of muscles. Teeth larger, especially carnassials. In domestic cat gut is *c.* one-third as long again as in Wild Cat (de Leuw, 1957; Haltenorth, 1957). Development of young and moults apparently undescribed.

MEASUREMENTS Kirk & Wagstaffe (1943) give measurements and weights of 107 specimens killed during winter, only 5 of which were females: h.&b. ♂ 589 mm (102 meas., range 365 to 653 mm), ♀ 571 mm (5 meas., range 545 to 584 mm); tail ♂ 315 mm (103 meas., range 210 to 342 mm), ♀ 311 mm (5 meas., range 293 to 331 mm); weight ♂ 5.1 kg (11 lb) (102 weighed, range 3 to 6.9 kg (6½ to 15¼ lb)), ♀ (6 specimens added from Matthews, 1941) 4 kg (8½ lb) (11 weighed, range 3.2 to 4.5 kg (7 to 10 lb)). Haltenorth (1940) gives larger figures for German specimens, viz. ♂ 7 kg (107 weighed), ♀ 6.3 kg (33 weighed) and Lindemann (1953) cites one of 14.8 kg from E. Carpathians.

Fig. 47. Wild Cat (*Felis silvestris*) (above) and domestic tabby (the ancestral species is not certain) (below). Note the bushy, truncated tail of the Wild Cat. Furthermore, most domestic tabby cats have blotchy black markings contrasting with the finer stripes of the Wild Cat. 'Striped' tabbies are known but are not nearly as common as blotched ones in the British Isles.

HABITAT Woodland and treeless mountain terrain. In winter wanders widely and recorded as raiding poultry houses. De Leuw (1957) gives for Germany as main habitat in winter, and as refuge in summer, dense woodland. Hunts frequently, however, in open fields.

GENERAL HABITS Most of this section taken from de Leuw (1957). Usual call short 'mau'; deep growl when angry. When at ease or bringing food to kittens a penetrating purr which stops abruptly. Screams noisily. Usually moves about on ground but can climb and swim well. Has favourite resting and sunning places, such as fallen trees and ledges, which are used over long periods. Droppings large and black, not covered over like those of domestic cat: usually found near where prey captured. These and urine used to mark range (Lindemann, 1955).

Wild Cats hunt either solitarily or as pair, except that female rears family away from male, who is known to kill kittens. Home range 60 to 70 ha (150 to 175 acres) defended by male, organized into system of tracks, resting places and claw-sharpening trees. Latter may be method of marking home range by secretion from foot glands (de Leuw, 1957). In hard winter may wander outside range in search of food; male also may wander during rut.

Activity basically nocturnal with peaks at dusk and dawn, but also controlled by weather, since Wild Cats tend to lie up during rain. In sunshine frequently lie out in favourite places basking and in summer will hunt during day. Most frequently seen during autumn when they hunt hard to lay up fat for winter.

Hunting often organized in circuit, moving round areas where mice abundant; in summer this takes them into open fields. Method is by stalking or lying in wait and leaping on prey. Vision and hearing keen; scent subordinate. Large prey usually have head torn off and may be left with only brains eaten. Smaller prey often taken off to store, though during night prey more often eaten where killed. Domestic cats' habit of bringing back live prey and playing with it unknown in Wild Cat. Prey killed by Wild Cat have only claw marks in contrast to those killed by Fox which leaves saliva on body. Cockchafers and grasshoppers caught with great adroitness, also fish, but snakes apparently avoided. Dens made among rocks, under tree-stumps, and occasionally in large birds' nests.

BREEDING Exact season of male not known but female comes into oestrus in British Isles in first half of March (Matthews, 1941). In Germany de Leuw (1957) places beginning of rut mid-Feb to end March, according to weather. Marked by much noise and wandering by male. Copulation once observed in open by de Leuw, presumed usually under cover. Gestation 63 days, compared with average of 58 days for domestic cat (Haltenorth, 1957). Number of kittens usually 2 to 4 born early to mid-May. Said to be second oestrus end May and second litter August (Matthews, 1941) and even third one in autumn but not certain whether this due to admixture of feral domestic strains. Haltenorth (1957) gives 1 litter only a year for Wild Cat.

True sex ratio not known. Trapped samples show bias towards males.

At 4 to 5 weeks kittens emerge and play with female; at 10 to 12 weeks they go out hunting with her and den is frequently moved near to hunting grounds. Weaned at c. 4 months and family breaks up at 5 months. At 10 months they are fully grown though further slight growth made up to 2 years. Sexual maturity attained in year after birth.

POPULATION Practically nothing known. Matthews (1941) examined sample of 25 of which 5 were juveniles with unfused epiphyses, 9 'subadults' with partly fused epiphyses (probably in second year) and 11 adults. Suggests fairly heavy juvenile mortality. In younger classes males preponderated (11 : 3). De Leuw (1957) notes corpses found in hard weather, presumably from starvation.

FOOD In Scotland notably Mountain Hares, Rabbits, grouse (Millais, 1904). Can kill animals as large as Roe Deer fawn or well-grown lamb, but probably takes many small mammals and birds. Stomach analyses from E. Carpathians (28 examined: Lindemann, 1953) show 65% small mammals, mainly Wood Mice and Short-tailed Voles, 12% squirrels, 5% hares and marmots, 8% game birds and 6% small birds. Haltenorth (1940) notes stomach contents mainly mice and shrews.

PREDATORS Only serious predator man.

RELATIONS WITH MAN Widely regarded as vermin to beginning of 20th century. Many still trapped, but since World War I some estates and Forestry Commission ground have become refuges from which it has spread over Highlands. Has been maintained and bred in captivity but usually remains untameable.

FAMILY PHOCIDAE

Streamlined elongated body without pronounced neck, covered in short, coarse hair; all digits bearing claws but more pronounced in fore-limb; hind-limbs trailing on land and not used then for propulsion but principal means of swimming in sea; external ear very small and inconspicuous; head rather dog-like; multicuspidate molar teeth (Fig. 43).

Comprises four sub-families: Phocinae, northern seals (except Hooded) in Arctic, Atlantic and Pacific Oceans (circumboreal) with some adjacent seas and lakes; Monarchinae, monk seals of Mediterranean Sea, West Indies and Hawaiian Islands; Lobodontinae, Weddell, Ross, Leopard and Crab-eater Seals of Antarctic Ocean and Cystophorinae, Hooded and Elephant Seals of Arctic, Antarctic and Californian waters.

GENUS *Phoca*

Circumboreal southward to north temperate waters in Pacific and Atlantic Oceans and adjacent seas and lakes including Caspian and Baikal. Now generally split into monotypic genera (*Phoca*, *Histriophoca*, *Pagophilus*) and *Pusa* with 3 species.

Common Seal (Harbor Seal) *Phoca vitulina* L.

DISTRIBUTION Circumboreal, N. Pacific to N. China and California, N. Atlantic to New England and France, but mainly along coastlines. Five subspecies recognized by Scheffer (1958), two in each of the Oceans (eastern and western) and one isolated in lakes in N. Labrador. British form is type subspecies.

Breeding centres in British Isles: shallow areas of Wash and E. Anglian Coast, Shetland, Orkney, E. and W. Coasts of Scotland, Inner and Outer Hebrides; N. Ireland. Little known of relative status. In non-breeding season animals more generally distributed all round British coasts (including Irish). Large breeding colonies on Dutch, Frisian and Danish coasts. Interchange of individuals with British possible but unknown.

DESCRIPTION Colour, darkish-grey on back, lighter below, mottled with many small black spots, fairly uniformly. Sexual difference is not great; bull has broader and blunter muzzle. Retroussé nose, rounded cranium, and nostril angle (Fig. 43) are sole field identification characters. Molar teeth tricuspid, the front and back cusps being well marked (Fig. 43). Pups born in first adult pelage (grey), very few with white puppy coat, lost within day or two.

MEASUREMENTS Adults: head to tip of flipper (h. to f., see under Grey Seal) ♂ 153 to 198 cm (5 to 6½ ft), ♀ 137 to 168 cm (4½ to 5½ ft); weight ♂ 202 to 253 kg (4 to 5 cwt), ♀ 100 to 150 kg (2 to 3 cwt) (R.J.H.). Length at birth 75 to 90 cm (2½ to 3 ft), weight 9 to 11 kg (20 to 25 lb).

HABITAT In the south, usually associated with sandbanks, mud-banks and estuaries, as one name (Harbor Seal) suggests. Haul out on highest points of sandbanks (with ease of escape) as tide recedes (*Photograph 46*); large bull commonly at highest point on watch. In Shetland and N. Ireland, where coast is rock-bound with only sandy or pebble bays, haul out on rocks in preference to bays (L.&U.V.). In Outer Hebrides use shell-sand beaches on western side. Numbers hauled out depend upon sea swell, state of tide and adequate air temperature; they like rain. Remain in shallow coastal waters, sea lochs and around island archipelagos.

GENERAL HABITS Voice, mewing in pups, adults growl when cornered, but otherwise generally silent (R.J.H.); dog-like yelps and howls when excited (Venables & Venables, 1957).

Locomotion as for Grey Seal but Common Seals frequently do a porpoise jumping swim, repeatedly coming clear of surface. Much more aquatic than Grey Seal although more prone to limit activities to shallow waters. Feeds during daylight high tides and hauls out during night in Wash (R.J.H.). Havinga (1933) reports the same for Dutch waters. In Shetland low-water haul-out and high-water feeding irrespective of daylight (Venables & Venables, 1955). Times of submergence usually 7–10 minutes; pups 5–6 minutes. Adults have been observed to remain down for 45 minutes (R.J.H.).

No social organization on breeding 'grounds'. Considerable erotic play, water slapping and rolling, apparently resulting in

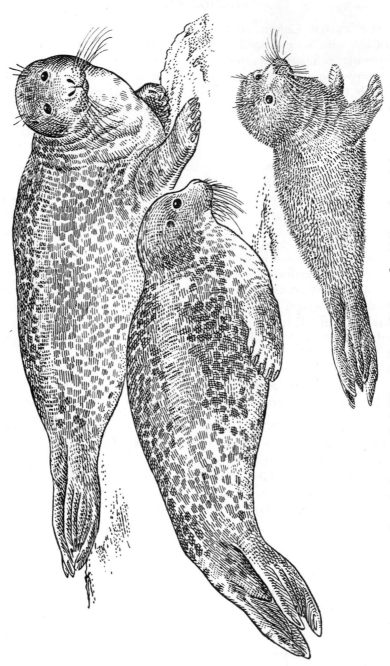

Fig. 48. Common Seal (*Phoca vitulina*), ♂ above, ♀ middle and pup below.

copulation sometimes observed in May in Wash area (R.J.H.) and also in Shetland (Venables & Venables, 1959) up to onset of parturition.

Moult during July to early Sept when large haul-outs occur in Shetland (Venables & Venables, 1955, 1957).

BREEDING Parturition: in Wash 6 June to 24 June; peak at 19 to 23 June (R.J.H.). Shetland dates later, about 14 June to 5 July (Venables & Venables, 1955). 14 June given for Dutch waters (Havinga, 1933), extending into July for Scheldt area (van Bemmel, 1956). Birth takes place in the sea or on temporarily exposed sand banks or rocks, from which pup must swim within few hours. Can swim and dive efficiently from birth, assisted by mother, but hind flippers too weak to haul-out easily until several days old. Suckling under water the rule at least at first. Period of lactation not definitely known but 3 weeks in captivity and the Venables estimate one month in Shetland. Considerable maternal care and protection shown.

Mating takes place after moult in Shetland but no information for Wash where copulation seen from end of July to early Sept at water's edge and in water. In Shetland mating seen from 7 Sept to 9 Oct (Venables & Venables, 1957) always on or close to sea-bottom at 2 to 4 fathoms. No sexual behaviour seen ashore. In Shetland mating preceded by rolling and blowing of bubble streams. Slapping water with fore-flippers also part of erotic play. Probably monogamous but possibly promiscuous. (Ratio of sexes present at mating period not known.) No territorial behaviour by bulls.

Mating followed by period of delayed implantation. Implantation after 1 Nov and before Jan (R.J.H.). For *P. v. concolor* implantation in late Sept (Fisher, 1954).

Picture complicated by vernal erotic behaviour (Venables & Venables, 1959) and by presence of blastocysts in May (R.J.H.). Much work needs still to be done.

POPULATION Estimated in Wash area at 2,000 (Sergeant, 1951). S.W. Shetland *c.* 400 and many more in other parts of archipelago (Venables & Venables, 1957), numerous in Orkneys (H.R.H.), *c.* 350 counted in June on coast of Ulster (Venables & Venables, 1960). Relation of these numbers to real population unknown and numbers elsewhere quite unknown.

FOOD Feeds on available fish and shell-fish; dab, plaice, flounder, goby, whiting, various mollusca, shrimps, prawns and crabs all reported from East Anglia (Sergeant, 1951). Dutch records lay emphasis on flat-fish (van Bemmel, 1956).

ENEMIES Man principal enemy in all areas; Killer Whales may account for some.

Note.—So little has been published on this seal that we are indebted to personal communications for the Wash area to Professor R.J.Harrison (R.J.H.), and for Shetland, Orkney and N. Ireland to L.S.V. and U.M.Venables (L.&U.V.).

GENUS *Halichoerus*

This genus contains only the Grey Seal.

Grey Seal (Atlantic Seal) *Halichoerus grypus* (Fab.)

DISTRIBUTION Broadly speaking, in temperate N. Atlantic; but not in mid-ocean, i.e. off Canadian Atlantic coast, Greenland, Iceland, European coasts north of Brittany, Baltic Sea. Breeding colonies on coasts of Nova Scotia, Labrador and (probably) Greenland, Iceland (possibly), Faeroes, Norwegian coast, Gulfs of Finland and Bothnia, coasts of British Isles. Information on colonies other than British very scanty. Possibly three geographical races but not described or named.

Breeding colonies around British Isles: Ireland—Clare I., Great Saltee, Lambay I., and probably on west and south-west coasts but no information available; Wales—Pembrokeshire coast and islands, smaller numbers on Cardiganshire coast; England— isolated groups in Scilly Isles and on Cornish coasts, Lundy and I. of Man (very few), Farne Islands off Northumberland coast (numerous), Scroby Sands off Norfolk coast (very few); Scotland —large and small colonies on Inner and Outer Hebrides, N. Rona and Orkney (very numerous); Shetland (numbers unknown); small numbers on N. and E. Scottish coasts.

Very large colonies have about 2,500 pups each year, small colonies as few as a dozen. Numbers around breeding colonies high also during period of moult. At other times of year dispersed along coasts and out to sea. Range only definitely known for first year of life. Despite overlap of dispersal areas of colonies some evidence that colonies are discrete and individuals return to same colony group to breed and even to same spot (J.M.B.).

DESCRIPTION Pelage variable with age, sex, nearness to moult and individually. Bulls darker than cows from black or dark-brown to mid-grey or mid-brown, with small lighter spots or patches. Cows mid-light-grey to fawn, usually with conspicuously lighter chest and belly, both back, sides and belly with dark spots. Colour *as such* unreliable for identification of species or separation of bulls and cows. Both sexes appear darker when wet (Hewer & Backhouse, 1959). Straight (cows) or slightly rounded (bulls) profile, flattish cranium and nostril angle (see Fig. 43) are only field identification characters.

Molar teeth with large cusp and two much smaller ones, one in front and one behind (cf. Common Seal with three quite distinct cusps (Fig. 43).

Adult bulls with much blubber on neck and shoulders, the skin thrown into folds. Male muzzle much heavier and broader, but old cows can look rather like young bulls. Both sexes become browner and tawnier after breeding as moult approaches. Cows moult approximately Jan to March, bulls in March to May (H.R.H., K.M.B., E.A.S.). Pups with creamy-white, long, curly fur, lost after about 3–4 weeks, to become moulters with blue-black to light grey pelage showing same sexual differences of pattern as adults. Next moult after approximately 15 months' interval. A 12-month-old moulter is often pale tawny or cream and may be mistaken for a pup.

MEASUREMENTS Three made on length: (1) head and body, to base of tail measured along dorsal curve of body, base of tail approximately above anus (h.&b.); (2) head and body and tail measured as before (h.&b.&t.); (3) tip of snout to tip of hind flippers (h. to f.) i.e. overall length as seen in field.

Adults: h. to f. ♂ 232 cm (93 in.) (14 meas., range 216 to 254 cm (85 to 100 in.)), ♀ 204 cm (80.5 in.) (31 meas., range 185 to 220 cm (73 to 87 in.)); h.&b.&t. ♂ 208 cm (82 in.) (3 meas.), ♀ 178 cm (70 in.) (13 meas.); tail ♂ and ♀ 10 cm (4 in.) (H.R.H.). At birth: h. to f. 96.5 to 107 cm (38 to 42 in.). During suckling length increases by 21%, girth by 56% (J.C.C.). During first year, at three months, 117 cm (46 in.) (23 meas.), at six months, 125 cm

DD

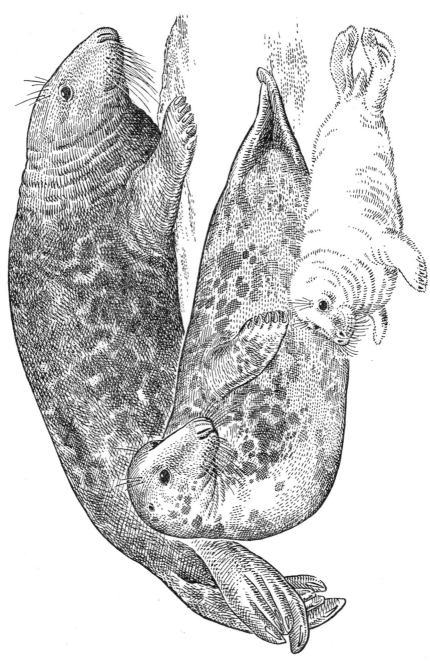

Fɪɢ. 49. Grey Seal (*Halichoerus grypus*), ♂ above, ♀ middle and pup below.

(49 in.) (17 meas.), at nine months 145 cm (57 in.) (5 meas.). In fourth year 162 to 175 cm (64 to 69 in.) (6 meas.). In sixth year av. 195 cm (77 in.) (6 meas., range 188 to 200 cm (74 to 79 in.)). Thereafter little increase in cows, but bulls may increase by further 20% (H.R.H.). Weight at birth 14.7 kg (32½ lb) (74 weighed, range 9 to 19 kg (20 to 42 lb)). Growth rate during suckling 1.8 kg (4 lb) per day (> 50 weighed), male pups reaching 44.5 kg (98 lb), females reaching 42 kg (93 lb). Loss after weaning until taking to sea at rate of 0.5 kg (1.2 lb) per day (16 meas.) (Coulson, 1959). Cows may lose 45 kg (100 lb) during lactation (Matthews, 1950). Growth of teeth and jaws follows similar pattern to overall length.

HABITAT When ashore usually remains close to water's edge, always with easy access to open sea by water. In Outer Hebrides, N. Rona and, to lesser extent, Orkney and Farnes breeding colony inland may cover a small island or reach 250 ft above sea-level. Moulting haul-outs always close to sea and at maximum at low-water.

Usually associated with rocky shores, stormy water and islands inaccessible to man. Within this range, may haul out on small sandy, pebble or rocky beaches or coves. Rarely seen in estuaries except mouth of Tweed, Humber, Dee (Wirral) and other salmon rivers.

GENERAL HABITS Characteristically vocal, particularly females (hence Norse and Gaelic legends linking it with man). Pups, hissing snarl when approached, high-pitched 'bawling' note (like human child) when hungry. Cows, hooting or singing note against bulls and each other (*Photograph 47*); when in numbers and jostling occurs produces moaning sound audible for some distance. Bulls, hisses and throaty snarl most common but can also hoot. At sea practically silent but alarm given by hind-flippers hitting surface as animal dives.

Locomotion at sea by side to side sweeps of large hind-flippers. Fore-flippers used as hydroplanes and for slow inshore motion. Ashore body hitches and, for climbing only, the fore-flippers are flexed and hook into ground or rocks. Characteristic track on sand, broad groove with lateral fore-foot holes. Pungent oil-odour left on rocks.

Social organization only during breeding season (*Photograph 48*).

At other times haul-out at traditional places which are *usually not* those used for breeding. Moulting haul-outs with females or males predominating (*Photograph 49*).

During breeding season, breeding bulls acquire territory. Cows only maintain area around pup. Bulls mate with cows in territory but do not possess or maintain true harem. Bull to cow ratio, 1 : 10–12 on average (range 1 : 1 to 1 : 20). Erotic behaviour in spring in Pembrokeshire colony (Backhouse & Hewer, 1958).

No evidence of directional migration, but some individuals travel up to 600 miles from breeding ground during dispersal phase of first year. No day–night rhythms. Activity during breeding season same day and night, except in Pembrokeshire where cows leave beaches at night. Main activities keyed to tides and weather, e.g. haul out at low water, stay at sea in storms and freezing weather.

Adult bulls and cows do not feed during breeding; i.e. bulls starve for *c.* 2 months, cows for 2–3 weeks. Feeding intermittent during moult, but intensive (apparently) between end of moult (March for cows, May for bulls) and onset of breeding (late August). Tend to feed on rising tide when in inshore waters. Feeding movements appear related to movements of fish.

Breeding behaviour differs in two sexes and, in detail, in different colonies. Bulls arrive first and establish territories on land (N. Hebrides, Orkney, Farnes) or off-shore (S. Hebrides, Pembrokeshire). Some evidence of pre-breeding contests between bulls (*Photograph 47*). (Details of behaviour of bulls and cows in Hewer (1960b) and Hewer & Backhouse (1960)). Differences between colonies appear largely dictated by geography. Bulls mate with cows in their territory 2 to 3 weeks after parturition. Bulls remain on station about 2 months; cows about 3 weeks.

Dispersal for feeding after breeding but return to haul-out for moult a few months later before final dispersal.

BREEDING Bulls potent only from August to December. Parturition in autumn and early winter. Some variation between colonies: Pembrokeshire—mainly in Sept and Oct but also infrequent births from May to August, small batch born also late March (Backhouse & Hewer, 1957). No precise date determined for peak. Hebrides, Sept, Oct and early Nov, peaks for Shillay, 6–7 Oct (Hewer, 1957), N. Rona 9–10 Oct (Boyd, Lockie & Hewer, 1962).

Orkneys, as for Hebrides but peak about 15–16 Oct (E.A.S.). Farnes, end Oct, Nov and Dec, peak on 19 Nov (J.C.C.).

Oestrus 2 to 3 weeks after parturition, fertilization followed by delayed implantation. Implantation, following moult, from mid-Feb to mid-April. Gestation 11½ months including delay, active growth for 7½ months only. Not known if other oestrus periods occur in non-pregnant cows. One embryo only (twins unknown), normally in alternate uterine horns in successive years. Lactation 2 to 3 weeks (variable). Sex-ratio at birth 1 : 1. Earlier births predominantly male, later ones female (Coulson & Hickling, 1961).

Females usually sexually mature (first ovulation) at 5 years (first pup possible when 6 years old), male usually mature at 6 years of age, but not holding territory until later.

Milk contains over 50% fat, 64% total solids (Matthews, 1950).

Pups' milk dentition absorbed *in utero*. Permanent dentition erupts just before birth and/or during puppyhood.

POPULATION Relatively little known. All figures up to 1960 guesses, but apparent increase in last 30–40 years. Direct census impossible. Population bears relation to number of pups, about 3.5:1. Number of pups per annum for British Isles is of the order of 10,000. Total British population therefore is about 35,000. Baltic, Norwegian, Iceland, Greenland and Canadian numbers still very incomplete (E.A.S., J.M.B.). Mortality figures not known although certainly heavy in first year, up to 20% possible before becoming moulters. Death of pups due to starvation, injury or drowning. Drowning and predators principal causes later. Population turnover slow. Longevity of females up to 34 years, of males up to 23 years (H.R.H.). Some evidence of high differential mortality of bulls upon entering breeding colony class (II.R.II.).

FOOD Catholic but little positive information. Crabs, lobsters, conger eel, lump-sucker, saithe, pollock, mackerel, wrasse, pilchard, herring, salmon and cephalopods recorded. External surface of nose and long stiff whiskers probably important for locating prey. Light not essential (although flattened cornea is adaptation for underwater vision) as feeds in muddy water and totally blind animals appear well nourished. Fifteen lb per day estimated by Steven (1936) but this is more than required in zoos. Several weeks in year without feeding during breeding; even at other times probably spasmodic as in other carnivores.

PREDATORS Man still principal enemy. Killer Whales probably take toll as of other seals. Numerous parasites both internal and external.

RELATIONS WITH MAN Has been persecuted from time immemorial as competitor for fish and as source of fat and hides. Less now than heretofore. Protected from 1 Sept to 31 December.

Note. Much information not published but supplied by personal communications acknowledged as follows: H.R.H., H.R.Hewer; K.M.B., K.M.Backhouse; J.C.C., J.C.Coulson; E.A.S., E.A. Smith; J.D.L., J.D.Lockie; J.M.B., J.Morton Boyd.

Order Perissodactyla

The 'odd-toed' ungulates, including Horse, Tapir and Rhinoceros. Only representative in British Isles is the Horse.

FAMILY EQUIDAE

Contains Horse, Donkey and Zebra.

GENUS *Equus*

Palaearctic and Ethiopian Regions.

Wild Pony *Equus caballus* (L.)

Breeds of semi-wild ponies occur in New Forest, on Dartmoor and Exmoor, in Lake District and on Northumberland and Cumberland fells, in Welsh mountains, Shetland, Western Islands and Connemara.

Order Artiodactyla

'Even-toed' ungulates form important order among world's mammals, with 86 living, and many fossil genera. Of modern forms, pigs and hippopotamuses grouped together, and seem very different from rest, but examination of intermediate forms, chevrotains and some fossil groups, indicates clearly common origin of all artiodactyls. By far greatest number of genera Old

World, especially concentrated in Africa. They are, on the whole, large animals which have specialized as browsers or grazers of vegetation. Have relied on speed and often social habits to counterbalance their relative unaggressiveness, and live mainly on open steppe or savannah, or in thorn scrub and forest margin. Artiodactyls are source of many domesticated forms cultivated by man during evolution of pastoral habits. In British Isles, deer are our only wild, large land mammals. Have been much persecuted and survival largely due to highly developed senses, cud-chewing and nocturnal habits, and speed in flight from danger.

Most characteristic morphological feature of artiodactyls is equal development of digits 3 and 4 with axis of limb passing between them; this contrasts with perissodactyls, with axis passing down centre of digit 3. Other morphological specializations, especially in all speedy forms, include (a) reduction and elongation of digits, (b) a complex four-chambered stomach, and (c) characteristic, high-crowned teeth (hypsodont) or long-crowned teeth with crescent-shaped ridges (selenodont). Development of horns or antlers also characteristic of this group. Antlers, which are shed yearly, characterize the deer; rest have horns with bony core and horny sheath, neither of which is shed. Another common feature is reduction or omission of upper incisors, food being either plucked with tongue, as in cattle, or pulled with lower incisors pressed against maxillary pad, as in deer.

Order comprises 3 suborders: (1) Suiformes (Pig and Hippopotamus), (2) Tylopoda (Camel) and (3) Ruminantia (cattle, deer, antelopes, Giraffe).

Suiformes suborder contains 3 families: Suidae which are Palaearctic and African with 4 genera (Pig, Wart-hog, Forest Hog, Babirussa); Tayasuidae, New World, 1 genus (Peccary); and Hippopotamidae, Africa, 2 genera.

The Tylopoda contains only one family, the Camelidae of S. America and Asia with 2 genera (Camel and Llama).

Largest suborder, Ruminantia, contains five families: Tragulidae, Asia and Africa, 2 genera (Chevrotain); Cervidae, world-wide except Africa and Australia, 17 genera (true deer); Giraffidae, Africa, 2 genera (Giraffe and Okapi); Antilocapridae, America, 1 genus (Pronghorn); and finally large assemblage of Bovidae, world-wide except for Australia and S. America, though only few have reached N. America, 53 genera (Antelope, Bison,

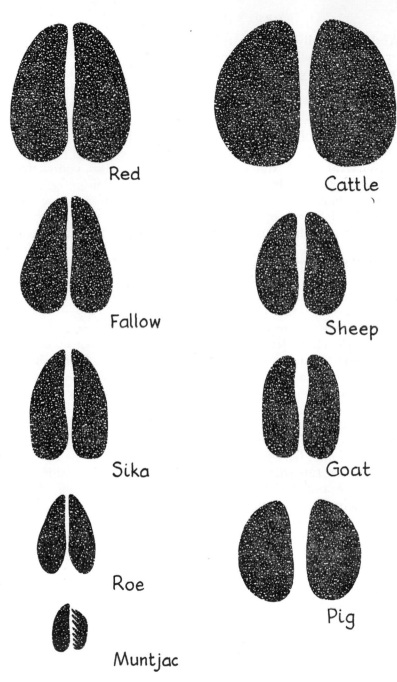

Red

Cattle

Fallow

Sheep

Sika

Goat

Roe

Pig

Muntjac

FIG. 50. Footprints of species of deer found in the British Isles (left). Footprints of domestic animals with which these may be confused are shown on the right.

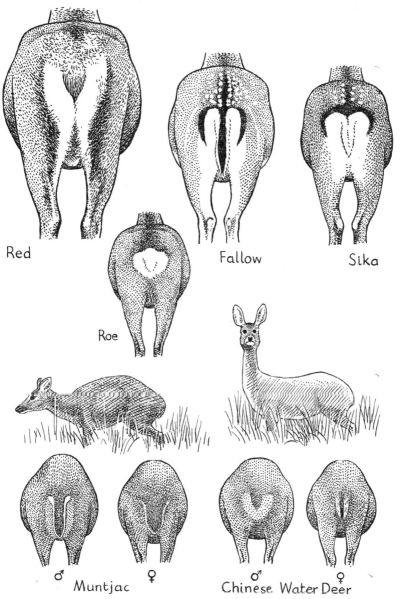

Red   Fallow   Sika

Roe

♂ Muntjac ♀   ♂ Chinese Water Deer ♀

FIG. 51. Rump patterns of species of deer found in the British Isles, with characteristic silhouettes of Muntjac (*Muntiacus muntjak*) and Chinese Water Deer (*Hydropotes inermis*).

Buffalo, Goat, Musk-ox and Sheep). Only two families of ruminants, the Cervidae and Bovidae represented in the British Isles. Suiformes were represented by Wild Boar up to about three hundred years ago.

FIELD IDENTIFICATION CHARACTERS

(1) Deer. Native and introduced British species can be identified by size, colour and antlers, rump patterns and footprints. (See *A Field Guide to British Deer*, ed. F.J.Taylor Page, for detailed keys, and Figs. 50 & 51.) Red Deer (*Cervus elaphus*) is largest of these, with reddish-brown, grey or buff summer coat, brownish-grey winter coat, pale yellow rump and relatively short tail. Antlers in older males complex, usually with brow, bay and tray tines and additional top points. Common in Scotland, Lake District and Exmoor, few and local elsewhere.

Other native species, Roe (*Capreolus capreolus*) is small animal which shows preference for young plantations with dense undergrowth. Summer coat reddish-brown, becoming greyer in winter; rump horizontally oval, white in winter, fawn in summer; tail very short; and antlers small, with rough cylindrical beam producing usually one forward tine and above it one backward tine. Introduced Siberian Roe (*C. c. pygargus*) larger, but only likely to be seen around Woburn, Bedfordshire, and probably extinct.

Fallow Deer (*Dama dama*) is medium size. Adult buck with antlers can be at once identified by way in which beam spreads into palmate form. Colour variations range from fawn with white spots to drab grey-brown without spots. Rump white, outlined with darker hair, and tail relatively long, dark, edged with white. This species commonly kept in parks. Escapes have established themselves in woodlands all over British Isles.

Remaining species introduced relatively recently, and their distributions fairly limited. Japanese Sika (*Cervus n. nippon*) most widely dispersed. Similar to Red Deer, but smaller in size. Summer coat buff-brown with faint white spots, winter coat dark grey-brown; rump white, heart-shaped and bordered with black; tail white, medium length. Antlers similar to Red Deer but simpler and smaller.

Two species of Muntjac (*Muntiacus muntjak* and *M. reevesi*) have been introduced. Former probably no longer feral. Latter fairly widespread in Home Counties and Midlands. Smaller than Roe and have short limbs and more crouching carriage. Coat reddish-yellow, turning to deeper brown in winter. Rump white, vertically elongated, and tail moderately long and thin. Antlers small, with only short brow tines; pedicles are long and extend as ridges on to face. Upper canines form short tusks in male.

Another species escaped from Woburn is Chinese Water Deer (*Hydropotes inermis*). Has spread only slightly. Same applies to escapes from parks in Shropshire and Hampshire. Almost as small as Muntjac, has fawn coat, very light underneath, lacks antlers and has large tusk-like upper canines in male.

Finally there is the Reindeer (*Rangifer tarandus*) which has also been introduced. Small herd semi-feral in Cairngorms in Scotland. Reindeer are grey or brown in colour with white underparts. Both male and female carry large, somewhat palmated antlers. Large brow tine also palmated and branched.

(2) Goat (*Capra hircus*). Odd feral herds occur in C. and N. Wales, Cheviots and Scottish Highlands and Islands. Introduced on Lundy.

(3) Sheep (*Ovis aries*). Nearest to truly wild sheep found on Soay (St Kilda). Introduced on Hirta (St Kilda) and on Lundy.

(4) White cattle (*Bos taurus*). Several imparked herds of small size preserve features of ancient wild cattle, e.g. Chillingham herd in Northumberland.

SUBORDER SUIFORMES

FAMILY SUIDAE

Contains 4 genera (pigs, Wart-hog, Forest Hog and Babirussa) in Palaearctic and Africa.

GENUS *Sus*

Two species, the Wild Boar and *S. salvanius*, the Pygmy Hog of N. India.

†**Wild Boar** *Sus scrofa*. L.

Palaearctic and Indian regions. Became extinct in British Isles in early 17th century. Apparently never recorded for Ireland.

SUBORDER RUMINANTIA
FAMILY CERVIDAE

Widespread family occurring all over world except Australia and Africa. Contains sub-families Moschinae, with 1 Asiatic genus, Musk Deer (*Moschus*); Muntiacinae, with 2 Asiatic genera, *Muntiacus* and *Elaphodus*; Cervinae, with 4 genera, all Eurasian except *Cervus*, large genus with species in N. America; and Odocoileinae with 5 genera in S. America, 1 (Mule Deer, *Odocoileus*) from N. and S. America, 2 Holarctic (Elk, *Alces* and Reindeer, *Rangifer*), 1 Palaearctic (Roe, *Capreolus*) and 1 Asiatic (Water Deer, *Hydropotes*).

GENUS *Muntiacus*

Genus has 5 species, all small animals with simple antlers and tusk-like canines, and all confined to S. and S.E. Asia apart from introductions. Recorded up to 6,500 ft in Himalayas.

*Indian Muntjac (Barking Deer) *Muntiacus muntjak* (Zimm.)
*Chinese Muntjac *M. reevesi* (Ogilby)

DISTRIBUTION First species has eight subspecies distributed from China through India down to Malaya and E. Indies. Introduced at Woburn in 1890. Chinese species has one main form from China and dubious one from Formosa. Introduced at Woburn *c.* 1900. This species, or its hybrid with Indian species, now found in Buckinghamshire, Hertfordshire, Northamptonshire and Warwickshire, as well as Bedfordshire; occasionally also in E. Anglia, Cambridgeshire, Derbyshire, Dorset, Huntingdonshire, Leicestershire, Middlesex, Oxfordshire, Gloucestershire, Staffordshire and Worcestershire (Pickvance & Chard, 1960).

DESCRIPTION Indian Muntjac has reddish or yellowish-brown coat above, and lighter brown underparts. Chinese Muntjac has deeper red, with back of ears dusky, changing in winter to olive-brown. Female slightly lighter and black tufts of hair replace antlers. Chin, throat and rump white; tail moderately long, bushy and prominently white beneath. Fawns dark brown, white spotted on flanks. Antlers short, simple, with single brow tine. Pedicles long and hairy, arising from frontal bones and continued as convergent ridges, marked by dark lines of hair, on to face. In male, upper canines are tusk-like and curved.

MEASUREMENTS Height at shoulder 37.5 to 42.5 cm (15 to 17 in.); antlers 10 cm (4 in.); weight ♂ 18 to 22 kg (40 to 50 lb) ♀ c. 13 kg (30 lb).

HABITAT Generally in woodland with dense herb and shrub layers, through which well-defined runs made to feeding places and 'lavatories'. Presence often difficult to detect, and may go unsuspected. May wander far during summer through standing crops without being observed.

GENERAL HABITS Diurnal, grazing in clearings, often singly, sometimes in pairs. Have been observed lying up in larger numbers in thick undergrowth or in open sunny places in snow. Move rapidly through close-growing vegetation with head held low. Makes rhythmical, barely audible growling noise as it travels, produced by rapid expulsion of breath. Barks loudly and at regular intervals when alarmed or disturbed. Trees frayed along regularly used runs, and marked with scent from frontal and sub-orbital glands by males, for attraction of females between late Oct and early March.

Droppings small rounded pellets under ½ in. in length, drawn out to slight point at one end. Tracks small, about ¾ in. wide at heel. The step is under 1 ft at normal walk and, unlike other deer, two halves of foot uneven in size.

BREEDING Bucks and does associate Oct to March. One, occasionally two, fawns born late in summer. Also recorded, Nov and December.

POPULATION Nowhere dense. Known that many die of starvation in severe British winter.

FOOD Shrubs, grass, roots and fruits. Little damage to trees, but visits farm crops and orchards and is known to damage brassicas and roots. Some bark-stripping occurs. Damage to crops more noticeable in recent years, and in some places control necessary.

Much general information is contained in Whitehead (1950, 1954a) and Taylor Page (1957).

GENUS *Dama*

Genus confined to European Mediterranean and Asia Minor. Two species only, one of which, *D. mesopotamica*, from Persia and Iraq, verging on extinction; the other, *D. dama* now widespread, through introductions, all over Europe, and to Australia and New Zealand.

Fallow Deer *Dama dama* (L.)

DISTRIBUTION Western Europe up to about 60° N. lat. and Asia Minor (Haltenorth, 1959). Evidence for Fallow Deer being indigenous to British Isles disputable. Recorded in Domesday Book as well-established. Descendants of original herds still living wild in Epping Forest, New Forest, Rockingham Forest and Cannock Chase. Feral herds, developed from park escapes, now common in most woodland areas of England. Less common in Wales, Scotland and Ireland.

DESCRIPTION Many colour varieties, but most usual summer coat deep fawn with prominent white spots on flanks and black hair along back and tail. Black tail with white underside distinguishes Fallow from Sika, which has tail predominantly white. Winter coat greyish-fawn. Black variety with spots almost obscured fairly common. Fawns at first heavily spotted. Antlers appear in second year, and by sixth year fully developed with broad palmate area. Antlers cast in May, regrown by August and clear of velvet by end of August. No upper canines. First upper incisor expanded.

MEASUREMENTS Height at withers ♂ 90 to 95 cm (35 to 37 in.), ♀ slightly smaller; nose to tail 170 cm (67 in.); antlers, length 65 to 78 cm (25 to 31 in.), circumference of beam 11.2 to 12.2 cm (4 to 5 in.); weight (clean) *c.* 63.6 kg (140 lb), but large animal might be up to 110 kg (240 lb).

HABITAT Extensive deciduous or mixed woodland, preferably but not essentially with thick herb and shrub layers, and often close to deer parks from which escape has been made.

GENERAL HABITS Feral herds rarely large except locally in late winter and spring. Safety sought in cover rather than in flight. Gait often stilted and jerky. Herds tend to move in single file at steady shuffling gallop. In summer, does with fawns may adopt bouncing gait.

Usually silent, except for resonant bark of alarm, rutting call which is rhythmic mixture of bark and grunt, and bleat used by fawns. Bedding areas and assembly points traceable by trampled ground. Droppings sometimes have component pellets adherent like those of sheep. Pellets of male slightly elongated (just over $\frac{1}{2}$ in.), pointed at one end, concave at other; those of female have more marked point and no concavity. Tracks medium size, up to *c.* $2\frac{1}{4}$ in. wide at heel. Feeding is at dusk and on to dawn, along woodland margins and on adjacent fields. Where undisturbed, may become more diurnal, especially in winter. Older males mainly nocturnal and rarely seen.

BREEDING Assembly within traditional rutting area starts in second week of October. Males spend summer apart from does and fawns while new antlers grow (*Photograph 51*). Oldest buck marks mating area to be defended, by fraying young trees and urinating in scrapes beneath them. Scent from urine and post-orbital gland transferred during fraying to antler palms, from which it disperses efficiently (J.S.R.Chard, unpubl.). Younger males establish territories down-wind and uphill of older buck. Noisy challenging, and some rounding up of does (*Photograph 52*). Rut lasts *c.* four weeks, but does coming into delayed oestrus may be covered as late as January. First pregnancies occur at age of two years, and single fawn (occasionally twins and rarely triplets) born in May or June. Records as late as November. Gestation eight months. After rut, small parties of separate sexes remain together until about May. Herds begin to re-form after mid-summer (Carne, 1960).

POPULATION Little known. Forestry Commission regards as acceptable density of one deer per 70 acres. The sex ratio about equal, and mortality among young animals high.

FOOD Mainly grasses and herbs, nuts and berries; bark-stripping by females found mainly in smooth-barked hardwood plantations. In warm weather, Fallow Deer usually drink before feeding, but can exist without surface water.

PREDATORS Good evidence that Foxes are main predators on young fawns.

RELATIONS WITH MAN Since 11th century Fallow Deer have frequently been enclosed in deer parks. Escapes have constantly occurred. During this century increasing numbers of feral deer have established themselves. Damage to forest and farm crops sometimes severe. Culling often indiscriminate, but attempts now being made by the Forestry Commission and some estates to control systematically.

General information can be found in Millais (1897), Whitehead (1950, 1954b) and Taylor Page (1957).

GENUS *Cervus*

Most important genus in sub-family Cervinae, distributed principally in E. Palaearctic and Oriental Regions (6 species). A seventh, Red Deer (*Cervus elaphus*), extends right over Palaearctic Region, and an eighth (*C. canadensis*), closely related to Red Deer, has reached Nearctic Region.

*Sika Deer *Cervus nippon* (Temminck)

DISTRIBUTION About seven subspecies described, all from E. Palaearctic Region. Japanese subspecies (*Cervus n. nippon*) was one of earliest of 'recent' introductions to British Isles, being brought into parks about mid-19th century. Escapes, especially during two World Wars, have founded feral populations, and herds are known in Essex, Devon, Dorset, Hampshire, Kent, Lancashire, Somerset, Surrey, W. Yorkshire, Westmorland and (in small numbers) Buckinghamshire. In Scotland, established in Argyll, Caithness, Fife, Inverness-shire, Peebles-shire, Ross and Sutherland; in Ireland in Co. Dublin, Fermanagh, Kerry, Tyrone and Wicklow.

DESCRIPTION In summer, flanks warm buff-brown, with very faint spots, deep brown in winter. Head always paler and greyer than flanks. Rump white, bordered with black, extending to heart-shaped flash when animal flees. Calves resemble those of Fallow Deer, but with smaller spots. Tail short (10 cm (4 in.)), usually pure white and a means of distinguishing species from Fallow. Slight mane. Antlers basically like Red Deer, but simpler, cast early April, in velvet (rich red, black tips) in May to July, cleaned by September.

MEASUREMENTS Height at shoulder, ♂ 82 to 90 cm (32 to 35 in.), ♀ 68 to 75 cm (27 to 29 in.); nose to tail *c*. 150 cm (60 in.); weight *c*. 63 kg (140 lb); antlers, length 40 to 63 cm (16 to 25 in.), circumference of beam 8 to 10 cm (3 to 4 in.), extreme spread 40 to 50 cm (16 to 20 in.).

HABITAT Prefers deciduous or mixed woodland, harbouring in hazel, brambles, bracken; in coniferous woodland, found in unthinned plantations. Also on wet ground, such as alder carr and estuarine reed-beds (Carne, 1958).

GENERAL HABITS During rut, male has characteristic whistle, rising, falling and ending in grunt, usually given three to four times, then silence of up to one hour's duration. Sharp scream of alarm typically given by hind with calf, and also by stag; often repeated several times and audible up to half a mile. Movements like Red Deer, with heavy, bounding gallop. Droppings not adherent, pellets rounded and intermediate in size between those of Fallow and Roe. Tracks about 2 in. wide at heel. Lies up in thick cover during day, forages from late evening to just before dawn in open woodland, heaths and fields, sometimes in field crops in warm weather. Only moderately gregarious, and lone animals seen about as often as small herds. Stags usually alone or in small groups, but band together at end of winter when antlers being cast. Hinds mainly solitary in summer but in parties of two or three for rest of year (Carne, 1959).

BREEDING Rut starts end of Sept, peak in first half Oct, over by end of November. Polygamous, each male herding five to six hinds. Calves, usually singles, born in late May.

FOOD Mainly herbs and grass, but stripping of bark from tree branches and browsing of young shoots occurs.

Little known about population or predators. Feral herds can damage trees and crops. General information can be found in Whitehead (1950), Tait (1953) and Taylor Page (1957).

Red Deer *Cervus elaphus* (L.)

DISTRIBUTION Seventeen subspecies described, covering Palaearctic Region as far as Manchuria and reaching into Oriental Region along southern slopes of Himalayas. Validity of many of

EE

these doubtful because species varies widely according to environment. Thus forest-living forms generally bigger and heavier than mountain forms, but also gradient from east to west in Europe with smaller animals to west. In addition average size of British Red Deer has decreased since Ice Age (Lowe, 1961). Introduced and widely spread in Australia and New Zealand, especially the South Island.

In British Isles indigenous stock probably now confined to Exmoor, Quantocks and Brendon Hills, Lake District, Scottish Highlands and Islands and part of Co. Kerry. Established in many other localities from introductions and escapes, viz. S.W. counties east to Hampshire, Surrey and Sussex (Ashdown Forest), Thetford Chase in E. Anglia, N. Staffordshire (The Roches), Sherwood Forest, Lancashire, Cheshire, W. Yorkshire, Durham, Scottish Lowlands, Co. Donegal and Co. Wicklow.

DESCRIPTION Coat dark red to brown in summer, but considerable variation. Inner sides of thighs white to creamy yellow, rump same. Tail tufted, c. 15 cm (6 in.), often with black central streak. Stag develops mane during rut. Winter coat dark brown, greybrown or grey, rough and thick. Moult starts about May. Calves variable, usually brown flecked with white.

Antlers develop as simple spikes or knobs at eight to ten months; in second year brow point is added; thereafter additional points appear on main body of antler until there may be more than twelve in all. In Scottish Red Deer development slower, brow point not added until third year (V.P.W.Lowe, unpubl.). Size and weight of antlers vary greatly. Woodland deer develop larger heads than those on hills. Males sometimes found which grow no more points above the brow tine (switch), others remain without antlers (hummel). Antlers cast about March, old stags casting first, young ones may delay until August or Sept (V.P.W.Lowe unpubl.), and new ones begin to grow at once, reaching full size by about July and being cleaned by end of August (*Photographs 53 & 54*).

MEASUREMENTS Largest British species. Height at withers, ♂ 105 to 140 cm (41 to 54 in.), ♀ c. 105 cm (41 in.). Weight very variable; average old stag from Scottish forest c. 95 kg (15 stone), from English woodland up to 189 kg (30 stone), from E. European woodland 255 kg (40 stone). Antlers also variable but average about 100 cm (39½ in.) in length, 75 cm (30 in.) span, 12.5 cm (5 in.) beam, and 7 kg (151 lb) in weight per pair. Scottish antlers average less than this.

HABITAT Normally beasts of forest, especially of forest margin. In Highlands move seasonally between open moors above tree line (summer) and forest on lower ground (winter) where damage to forests and farm crops may occur (Whitehead, 1960; Lowe, 1961).

GENERAL HABITS Most characteristic sound made by Red Deer is well-known 'roaring', mostly confined to stags during rut. Stags otherwise silent, though will bark, like hinds, especially when frightened. Hinds have gruff bark and nasal bleating call when alarmed; occasionally roar in summer (V.P.W.Lowe, unpubl.). Calves give high-pitched bleat or scream, if in danger.

Gait most frequently adopted is lazy stride or steady trot which breaks into gallop when rapid flight needed. Droppings sometimes adherent, pellets *c.* ¾ in. long. Those of male shaped like acorn cut across and concave at wide end; those of female more rounded. Tracks about 2½ in. wide at heel.

Greatest activity occurs at dusk and early morning, but if little disturbed, not markedly nocturnal. Day spent resting on hill or in shade of woodland; in evening move to feeding and drinking places, following paths which may be of great antiquity. Highly developed social life (Darling, 1937; Perry, 1953), with matriarchal system, guides distribution and movements. Hinds with their families occupy territories on lower ground in winter (*Photograph 57*), moving up to summer grazing, calving and rutting grounds during rest of year. Stags often have own grounds and may live singly or in small groups. Sometimes large mixed herds in summer and winter but, in spring, hinds nearly always away from mature stags, and often on higher ground.

BREEDING Incidence of rut variable: early Sept to mid-October. Stags round up as many hinds as can be searched out, and defend them from other stags (*Photographs 55 & 56*). During this time they roar constantly. By Oct–Nov, main part of rut is over, but some hinds come into oestrus late, and these often fertilized by young stags. Habit of wallowing in peat hags and muddy pools increases before and during rut (*Photograph 58*).

Hinds fertile in their third year bearing first calf in fourth year

Fig. 52. Fallow Deer (*Dama dama*).

Fig. 53. Japanese Sika (*Cervus nippon*).

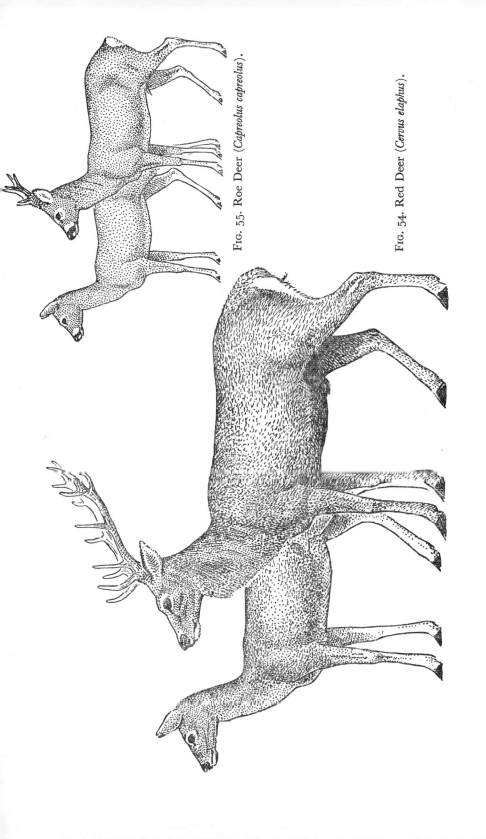

FIG. 55. Roe Deer (*Capreolus capreolus*).

FIG. 54. Red Deer (*Cervus elaphus*).

(Lowe, 1961); gestation eight months, so peak of calving usually end May to early June. Births have been recorded as late as October. Normally single calf born. Calves suckled for eight to ten months and remain with hind until second autumn. Growth slows after third year. Mean expectation of life is 5 years and life span 20 years.

POPULATION Little really known of Red Deer populations in woodland; Forestry Commission suggest that one per 120 acres is limit above which serious damage can occur. For Highland deer forests, there are accounts by Darling (1937), which state that one per 40 acres is limit beyond which vegetation will become impoverished, and by Evans (1890) (privately printed, but some information available in Cameron (1923)), which give vital statistics of Jura deer over ten-year period. This herd was maintained for stalking at high density of one per 15.5 acres. Clear that density affects condition, incidence of mortality, birth rate and the life table generally; also that overgrazing, especially combined with burning, may deplete soil fertility (Darling, 1937). Too great densities in relation to food are almost certainly cause of winter damage to trees and farm crops. Environment, management and population densities vary so much at the moment, that no details quoted about life table could be regarded as average. Population research now being undertaken should provide valuable information (Lowe, 1961).

FOOD Grasses and young shoots of trees and heather form main bulk of food. Fruits added in autumn. Where coastline available, seaweed eaten. On farmland, damage done to root crops and vegetables; in forests, young trees may be barked or thrashed. During rut, stags eat little.

PREDATION Young calves taken by Foxes, Golden Eagles and Wild Cats. Adult deer have no enemies except man, unless various parasitic organisms are included whose effects may only be fatal for animals already weakened by starvation.

RELATIONS WITH MAN Deer stalking of great economic, importance in 19th century, now becoming less important as sport. Owing to overpopulation and escapes, now broadly regarded as pest, and attempts made to control them. Sale and processing of venison are slowly regaining some importance.

General information may be found in Cameron (1923), Millais (1897), Ritchie (1920) and Lowe (1961).

GENUS *Hydropotes*

Monospecific genus, placed by Simpson in sub-family Odocoileinae, and by E.&M.-S. in separate sub-family Hydropotinae. Notable as being only deer without antlers. Distribution China and Korea. Sub-family Odocoileinae exhibits somewhat more primitive arrangement of metacarpals and metatarsals than Cervinae.

*Chinese Water-deer *Hydropotes inermis* (Swinhoe)

DISTRIBUTION Introduced in British Isles at Woburn *c*. 1900. Dates of escapes unknown, but now fairly widespread in Bedfordshire, Hertfordshire and Buckinghamshire. Some of Woburn stock, introduced in N. Hampshire and at Walcot Park, Shropshire, now feral in woods in those areas.

DESCRIPTION Small deer about size of Muntjac. Coat uniform pale chestnut stippled with black, head and ears buff, white round nose, eyes, chin and inside ears. Small, dark tail over inconspicuous rump patch. Long curved and movable upper canine teeth in male; smaller in female. Ears narrow and pointed. Winter coat similar but darker. Sexes hardly distinguishable. Fawns sparsely and indistinctly spotted in lines.

MEASUREMENTS Height at shoulder 50 cm (20 in.); length 90 cm (35 in.); tail 6 cm (2 in.); weight up to 16 kg (35 lb).

HABITAT In China, inhabits swampy country; in British Isles has adapted itself to woodland and open grassland.

GENERAL HABITS Like Muntjac, active day and night. Usually solitary, but very little information available about habits in wild state in this country. Males utter whistling call during rut; alarm call a scream resembling that of wounded hare.

BREEDING Rut takes place December; fawns born late May to early June. Litters number five to six in China (Hamilton, 1871), but fewer in park conditions in this country.

FOOD Mainly grasses, vegetables and root crops.

RELATIONS WITH MAN Easily reared by hand in this country.

General information also in Aitchison (1946) and Whitehead (1949).

GENUS *Capreolus*

Genus placed in sub-family Odocoileinae, which contains many New World deer and, in Old World, Reindeer, Elk and Chinese Water-deer.

Genus monospecific, and distributed widely throughout Palaearctic Region, but absent from extreme north, from N. Africa and from N.W. India.

Roe Deer *Capreolus capreolus* (L.)

DISTRIBUTION Small species with antlers having only three tines; mainly inhabitant of open woodland and forest margin. Many subspecies described, but reduced to three by E.&M.-S. Fairly constant differences, however, between British and, e.g. Scandinavian Roe Deer, former being darker generally and greyer in winter. Largest subspecies, *C. c. pygargus* (Pallas) from W. Siberia, released in vicinity of Woburn in 1900, but doubtful if any now feral in this area.

Roe is an indigenous British species, widespread until restriction of forests narrowed its range during 18th century to Scotland, Border counties, Lake District, and possibly W. Sussex and Surrey. More recently, has spread out again, and now known in sixteen English counties. Absent from Wales and Ireland.

DESCRIPTION Summer coat bright red-brown, slightly paling underneath; rump buff, horizontally oval and inconspicuous; tail not distinguishable. Lips and sides of muzzle black; front of muzzle and chin white. Winter coat assumed Oct to Nov, thicker with long, brittle grey hairs tipped with brown. Rump prominently white. This coat shed April onwards. Varieties rare, though melanism and albinism recorded. Young red-brown flanked with white spots and paler underneath. Antlers lack brow tines, beam is upright, forked at top and with one tine about halfway up. Beam often ridged. Shed Nov to December. New antlers grown and cleaned by early May.

MEASUREMENTS Height at shoulder 65 to 73 cm (26 to 29 in.); nose to tail 120 cm (47 in.); weight 23 to 32 kg (50 to 70 lb); cleaned weight, ♂ 16 to 27 kg (35 to 60 lb), ♀ 11 to 21 kg (24 to 46 lb). Antlers, length 22.5 cm (9 in.), circumference at base 11 cm (4 in.). Weights and antler size vary much with condition.

HABITAT Shows preference for broken up, or open, woodland (*Photograph 50*). Will lie up in deep shade and thickets, but also on open, high ground (especially in Scotland), where young frequently dropped. In winter, found in denser parts of woodlands and plantations.

GENERAL HABITS Voice a gruff bark often uttered as animal bounds away in alarm. Does call to young with high-pitched 'pee-you' or 'peep-peep'; faint piping will attract buck during rut from considerable distance. Young have shrill bleat and scream when alarmed.

Normal gait an easy canter with head high, frequently stopping and looking back. Hearing good, but sight and smell not so acute as in Red Deer. Droppings small, tapering, usually non-adherent. Tracks of medium size 2.5 to 3.2 cm (1 to 1¼ in.) at heel; step *c.* 38 cm (1¼ ft) at normal walk.

Can be very elusive and nocturnal, but where undisturbed will feed during day, though main activity is at dusk and dawn. Day activity may increase during rut and in hard winter conditions. Once antlers clean, territory marking by buck commences. Trees frayed, and intruders driven off. Much ground scraping. Scrapes may be marked by scent passed in urine. Much chasing of doe by buck, often in regularly used ring or figure-of-eight patterns which produce worn pathways round focal objects (*Photograph 59*).

BREEDING Oestrus last few days in late July and early August. After copulation (Roe are unusual in being, as a rule, monogamous), buck leaves doe until autumn. Delayed implantation normal (Tegner, 1951; Stieve, 1950). Occurs late December. Development takes about five months, young being born late May. Two young frequent; three occasionally recorded. Later in summer, doe may rejoin buck, and family parties may be observed, but these have no permanent social importance because young are driven away in early spring of following year.

POPULATION Little precise information about densities of

population or how they are estimated. Andersen (1953) found, by complete shooting out in Denmark, density of 60 to 65 per 100 ha (*c.* one per 4 acres), three times as high as had been estimated before shooting. This was peak population, and various figures guessed as an 'economic density' vary from one to 15 acres to one to 40 acres. Probable expectation of life five to seven years.

FOOD Said to eat 3 to 4% of its own weight daily ('Snaffle', 1904). Browses on leaves and berries. Foods may include blackberry, privet, rose and juniper. Sometimes pine shoots, yew, heather, clover and fungi. Bark rarely eaten. Will travel some distance to drink.

PREDATORS No systematic information. Foxes and Eagles probably take some young, especially in Scotland. Various parasites may, as with Red Deer, kill off animals already weakened.

RELATIONS WITH MAN Main damage results from fraying and browsing in young forests (Fooks, 1958) (*Photograph 60*).

GENUS *Rangifer*

Genus comprises Reindeer and New World Caribou. Specialized for living in Arctic and sub-arctic, and distinguished by both sexes bearing antlers.

†*Reindeer *Rangifer tarandus* (L.)

Probably became extinct in British Isles towards close of 12th cent. (Ritchie, 1920). Long domesticated in Lapland and Siberia. Introduced into Cairngorms in Scotland in 1952 and small herd is well-established there.

FAMILY BOVIDAE

Vast family containing antelope, buffalo, cattle, goat, musk-ox and sheep. An obviously important source of domestic animals.

GENUS *Bos*

Four species (including Yak) according to E.&M.-S., all from Oriental and S.E. Palaearctic Regions, but systematics obscure.

White Cattle *Bos taurus* (L.)

Herds kept at Chillingham (Northumberland), Cadzow (Lanark-shire), Dynevor and Vaynol (Carmarthenshire), and Woburn (Bedfordshire), which are thought to be related to the ancestral type (Whitehead, 1953).

GENUS *Capra*

Four species (including Ibex) of Palaearctic and Indian distribution. Domestic goat derived from species below (Harris, 1962).

Wild Goat *Capra hircus* (L.)

DISTRIBUTION Present range of truly wild goats is from Greece, through Asia Minor to Baluchistan. Feral herds found in remote parts of western Scottish Highlands, some Hebridean islands, Holy Island, Lundy, Cheviot Hills, the fells above Kielder Forest, Northumberland, and C. and N. Wales (Rhinogs, the Douallt-Rhobell, Fawr-Foel Dhu area S.W. of Bala Lake, the Moelwyns, and the Glyder range in Snowdonia). Mostly among high and inaccessible crags. In Eire, Achill Island still said to support a few, and in N. Ireland some still exist on Rathlin Island, and Fair Head, Co. Antrim.

From time immemorial, goats have escaped into mountainous regions and become feral. Sometimes intentionally released to graze at high level and keep sheep to lower and more suitable territory. Some, especially those in Wales and Wester Ross in Scotland, may be of very ancient stock either indigenous, or introduced in very early times (Fitter, 1959).

DESCRIPTION Colour usually creamy white, black and brown, brown and white, or black and white. Horns like those of ancestral Persian wild goat (*Capra hircus aegagrus*).

MEASUREMENTS Average length 75 cm (30 in.); span of horns 75 cm (30 in.), record 111.5 cm (43¾ in.).

GENERAL HABITS Small herds led by master billy. Fighting may precede mating which occurs in Oct and November. Kids born in Feb and March. Reversion to wild type from domestic is rapid, taking place within few generations (Watt, 1937).

GENUS *Ovis*

Five species, of which one Nearctic (Bighorn), rest (including Mouflon, Argali and Urial) Palaearctic.

Wild Sheep *Ovis aries* (L.)

Various domesticated races of British sheep are like wild ones in appearance, especially those on Soay in St Kilda (Boyd, 1953; Fitter, 1959).

Bibliography

CHECK-LISTS AND OTHER WORKS OF GENERAL REFERENCE

ALLEN G.M. (1939) A check-list of African mammals. *Bull. Mus. Comp. Zool. Harvard Coll.* **83**

CABRERA A. (1957) Catalogo de los mamiferos de America del Sur. 1. Metatheria.—Unguiculata-Carnivora. *Rev. Mus. Argent. Cienc. Nat. 'Bernadino Rivadavia.' Zool.* **4**, 1–307

CHASEN F.N. (1940) A handlist of Malaysian mammals. A systematic list of the Malay peninsula, Sumatra, Borneo and Java, including the adjacent small islands. *Bull. Raffles Mus.* **15**

ELLERMAN J.R. & SCOTT T.C.S. MORRISON- (1951) *Checklist of Palaearctic and Indian Mammals, 1758 to 1946.* London, Brit. Mus. (Nat. Hist.). **Referred to throughout text as E.&M.-S.**

ELLERMAN J.R. & SCOTT T.C.S. MORRISON- (1955) *Supplement to Chasen, 1940. A Handlist of Malaysian Mammals, Containing a Generic Synonymy and a Complete Index.* London, Brit. Mus. (Nat. Hist.)

HALL E.R. & KELSON K.R. (1959) *The Mammals of North America.* New York, Ronald Press Co.

HAMILTON G.E.H. BARRETT- & HINTON M.A.C. (1910–21) *A History of British Mammals.* London, Gurney & Jackson. Unfinished. **Referred to throughout text as B.-H.&H.**

IREDALE T. & TROUGHTON E. le G. (1934) A check-list of the mammals recorded from Australia. *Mem. Austr. Mus.* **6**

LAURIE E.M.O. & HILL J.E. (1954) *List of Land Mammals of New Guinea, Celebes and Adjacent Islands, 1758–1952.* London, Brit. Mus. (Nat. Hist.)

MILLER G.S. (1912) *Catalogue of the Mammals of Western Europe.* London, Brit. Mus. (Nat. Hist.)

MILLER G.S. & KELLOGG R. (1955) List of North American recent mammals. *U.S. Nat. Mus. Bull.* **205**, 1–954

SIMPSON G.G. (1945) The principles of classification and a classification of mammals. *Bull. Amer. Mus. Nat. Hist.* **85**, 1–350

DETAILED REFERENCES

ADAMS L.E. (1909) Some notes on the breeding habits of the common mole. *Mem. Manchr. lit. phil. Soc.* **54**, 1–9

ADAMS L.E. (1913) The harvest mouse. *Wild Life*, **2**, 7–18

AITCHISON J. (1946) Hinged teeth in mammals. *Proc. zool. Soc. Lond.* **116**, 329–38

ALDOUS S.E. & MANWEILER J. (1942) The winter food-habits of the short-tailed weasel in northern Minnesota. *J. Mammal.* **23**, 250–5

ALLANSON M. (1933) The reproductive processes of certain mammals. Part V. Changes in the reproductive organs of the male grey squirrel. *Phil. Trans.* B, **222**, 79–96

ALLANSON M. (1934) Seasonal variation in the reproductive organs of the male hedgehog. *Phil. Trans.* B, **223**, 277–303

ALLEE W.C. *et al.* (1949) *Principles of Animal Ecology.* Philadelphia, W.B. Saunders Co.

ALLEN D.L. (1954) *Our Wildlife Legacy.* New York, Funk & Wagnalls Co.

ALLEN G.M. (1916) Whalebone whales of New England. *Mem. Bost. Soc. nat. Hist.* **7**, 1–105

AMOROSO E.C. & MATTHEWS J.H. (1951) The growth of the grey seal (*Halichoerus grypus*) from birth to weaning. *J. Anat., Lond.* **85**, 426–8

ANDERSEN J. (1953) Analysis of Danish roe deer population based upon extermination of the total stock. *Dan. Rev. Game Biol.* **2**, 127–55

ANDERSEN J. (1955) The food of the Danish badger (*Meles meles danicus* Degerbøl) with special reference to the summer months. *Dan. Rev. Game Biol.* **3**, 1–75

ANDERSEN J. (1957) Studies in Danish hare-populations. 1. Population fluctuations. *Dan. Rev. Game Biol.* **3**, 85–131

ANDERSEN J. (1962) Roe-deer census and population analysis by means of modified marking release technique. In *The Exploitation of Natural Animal Populations,* ed. LE CREN E.D. & HOLDGATE M.W. Oxford, Blackwell

ANDREWES C.H., THOMPSON H.V. & MANSI W. (1959) Myxomatosis: present position and future prospects in Great Britain. *Nature, Lond.* **184**, 1179–80

ANON. (1954) *Instructions for Collectors. No. 9a. Invertebrate Animals other than Insects,* 2nd ed. London, Brit. Mus. (Nat. Hist.)

ANON. (1957) Nutrias in the United States. *U.S. Fish & Wildlife Serv. Lflt. 389*

ANON. (1959) *Traps for Grey Squirrels.* London, Forestry Commiss.

ANON. (1960) Vermin bag records. *Ann. Rep. (1959) Imp. Chem. Ind. Game Services*

ASHTON E.H. & THOMSON A.P.D. (1955) Some characters of the skulls and skins of the European polecat, the Asiatic polecat and the domestic ferret. *Proc. zool. Soc. Lond.* **125**, 317–33

ASHTON E.H. (1955) Some characters of the skulls of the European polecat, the Asiatic polecat and the domestic ferret. *Proc. zool. Soc. Lond.* **125**, 807–9

BAAL H.J. (1949) The indigenous mammals, reptiles and amphibians of the Channel Islands. *Bull. Soc. jersiaise*, **15**, 101–110.

BACKHOUSE K.M. & HEWER H.R. (1956) Delayed implantation in the grey seal, *Halichoerus grypus* (Fab.). *Nature, Lond.* **178**, 550

BACKHOUSE K.M. & HEWER H.R. (1957) A note on spring pupping in the grey seal (*Halichoerus grypus* Fab.). *Proc. zool. Soc. Lond.* **128**, 593–4

BACKHOUSE K.M. & HEWER H.R. (1957) Behaviour of the grey seal (*Halichoerus grypus* Fab.) in the spring. *Proc. zool. Soc. Lond.* **129**, 450

BAKER J.R. (1930) The breeding-season in British wild mice. *Proc. zool. Soc. Lond.* (1930), 113–26

BAKER J.R. (1950) *Cytological Technique*, 3rd ed. London, Methuen

BAKER J.R. & RANSON R.M. (1932a) Factors affecting the breeding of the field mouse (*Microtus agrestis*). Part I. Light. *Proc. roy. Soc.* B, **110**, 313–22

BAKER J.R. & RANSON R.M. (1932b) Factors affecting the breeding of the field mouse (*Microtus agrestis*). Part II. Temperature and food. *Proc. roy. Soc.* B, **112**, 39–46

BAKER J.R. & RANSON R.M. (1933) Factors affecting the breeding of the field mouse (*Microtus agrestis*). Part III. Locality. *Proc. roy. Soc.* B, **113**, 486–95

BALSAC H. HEIM DE & GUISLAIN R. (1935) Evolution et spéciation des campagnols du genre *Arvicola* en territoire français. *Mammalia*, **19**, 367–90

BARBER H.N. (1954) Genetic polymorphism in the rabbit in Tasmania. *Nature, Lond.* **173**, 1227

BARNETT S.A. (1958) An analysis of social behaviour in wild rats. *Proc. zool. Soc. Lond.* **130**, 107–52

BARRINGTON R.M. (1880) On the introduction of the squirrel into Ireland. *Sci. Proc. roy. Dublin Soc.* N.S., **2**, 615–31

BAUMGARTNER L.L. & MARTIN A.C. (1939) Plant histology as an aid in squirrel food-habit studies. *J. Wildlife Manag.* **3**, 266–8

BECKER K. (1952) Über das Vorkommen schwarzer Wanderratten (*Rattus norvegicus* [Erxl.]). *Zool. Gart. Lpz.* **19**, 223–33

BECKER K. (1955) Über Art- und Geschlechtsunterschiede am Becken einheimischer Spitzmäuse (*Soricidae*). *Z. Säugetierk.* **20**, 78–88

BEMMEL A.C.V. VAN (1956) Zeehonden in Nederland. *De Levende Nat.* **59**, 1–12

BENTLEY E.W. (1959) The distribution and status of *Rattus rattus* L. in the United Kingdom in 1951 and 1956. *J. Anim. Ecol.* **28**, 299–308

BERNARD J. (1959) Note sur le période de reproduction du renard (*Vulpes vulpes* Linné, 1758) dans le Luxembourg belge. *Säugetierk. Mitt.* **7**, 110 13

BEZEM J.J., SLUITER J.W. & HEERDT P.F. VAN (1960) Population statistics of five species of the bat genus *Myotis* and one of the genus *Rhinolophus*, hibernating in the caves of S. Limburg. *Arch. Néerl. Zool.* **13**, 511–39

BISCOE C.H. TYNDALE (1953) A method of marking rabbits for field studies. *J. Wildlife Manag.* **17**, 42 5

BISHOP I.R. (1962) Studies on the Life Histories, Ecology and Systematics of Small Mammals inhabiting the Channel Islands. M.Sc. unpubl. thesis, Univ. of Southampton

BISHOP I.R. & DELANY M.J. (1963a) The ecological distribution of small mammals in the Channel Islands. *Mammalia*, **27**, 99–110

BISHOP I.R. & DELANY M.J. (1963b) Life histories of small mammals in the Channel Islands in 1960–61. *Proc. zool. Soc. Lond.* (in press)

BLACKMORE M. (1948) *Mammals in Britain.* London, Collins

BLACKMORE M. (1956) An occurrence of the mouse-eared bat *Myotis myotis* Borkhausen in England. *Proc. zool. Soc. Lond.* **127**, 201–3

BLAIR W.F. (1943) Criteria for species and their subdivisions from the point of view of genetics. *Ann. N.Y. Acad. Sci.* **44**, 179–88

BLAIR W.F. (1950) Ecological factors in speciation of *Peromyscus. Evolution*, **4**, 253–75

BOBACK A. (1954) Zur Frage des Harnspritzens beim Feldhasen, *Lepus europaeus.* Pallas, 1778. *Säugetierk. Mitt.* **2**, 78–9

BOOTH Y. SPENCER- (1956) Shrews (*Crocidura cassiteridum*) on the Scilly Isles. *Proc. zool. Soc. Lond.* **126**, 167–70

BOYD J.M. (1953) The sheep population of Hirta, St Kilda. *Scot. Nat.* **65**, 25–8

BOYD J.M. (1957) Aerial studies of a breeding colony of grey seals, *Halichoerus grypus* (Fab.) at Gasker, Outer Hebrides, in 1955 and 1956. *Proc. zool. Soc. Lond.* **129,** 333–42

BOYD J.M. (1959) Observations on the St Kilda field-mouse *Apodemus sylvaticus hirtensis* Barrett-Hamilton. *Proc. zool. Soc. Lond.* **133,** 47–65

BOYD J.M., LOCKIE J.D. & HEWER H.R. (1962) The breeding colony of grey seals on North Rona, 1959. *Proc. zool. Soc. Lond.* **138,** 257–77

BRAMBELL F.W. ROGERS (1935) Reproduction in the common shrew (*Sorex araneus* L.). *Phil. Trans.* B, **225,** 1–62

BRAMBELL F.W. ROGERS (1942) Intra-uterine mortality of the wild rabbit, *Oryctologus cuniculus* (L.). *Proc. roy. Soc.* B, **130,** 462–79

BRAMBELL F.W. ROGERS (1948) The reproduction of the wild rabbit. *Proc. zool. Soc. Lond.* **114,** 1–45

BRAMBELL F.W. ROGERS & HALL, K. (1937) Reproduction of the lesser shrew (*Sorex minutus* Linnaeus). *Proc. zool. Soc. Lond.* 1936 (1937), 957–69

BRAMBELL F.W. ROGERS & MILLS I.H. (1948) Studies on sterility and pre-natal mortality in wild rabbits. IV. The loss of embryos after implantation. *J. exp. Biol.* **25,** 241–69

BRAMBELL F.W. ROGERS & ROWLANDS I.W. (1936) Reproduction of the bank vole (*Evotomys glareolus* Schr.). 1. The oestrous cycle of the female. *Phil. Trans.* B, **226,** 71–97

BRIGGS A.R. MEAD- & RUDGE A.J.B. (1960) Breeding of the rabbit flea, *Spilopsyllus cuniculi* (Dale): requirement of a 'factor' from a pregnant rabbit for ovarian maturation. *Nature, Lond.* **187,** 1136–7

BRINK F.H. VAN DEN (1955) *Zoogdierengids van Europa ten Westen van 30° Oosterlengte.* Amsterdam, Elsevier

BROCKIE R.E. (1959) Observations on the food of the hedgehog (*Erinaceus europaeus* L.) in New Zealand. *N.Z. J. Sci.* **2,** 121–36

BROCKIE R. (1960) Road mortality of the hedgehog (*Erinaceus europaeus* L.) in New Zealand. *Proc. zool. Soc. Lond.* **134,** 505–8

BROWN J.A. HARVIE- (1880–81) The squirrel in Great Britain. *Proc. phys. Soc. Edinb.* **5,** 343–8; **6,** 31–63, 115–83

BROWN L.E. (1956a) Field experiments on the activity of the small mammals (*Apodemus, Clethrionomys* and *Microtus*). *Proc. zool. Soc. Lond.* **126,** 549–64

BROWN L.E. (1956b) Movements of some small British mammals. *J. Anim. Ecol.* **25,** 54–71

BUECHNER H.K., HARTHOORN A.M. & LOCK J.A. (1960a) Recent advances in field immobilization of large mammals with drugs. *Trans. 25th N.A. Wildlife Conf.* 415–22

BUECHNER H.K., HARTHOORN A.M. & LOCK, J.A. (1960b) The immobilization of African animals in the field with special reference to their transfer to other locations (U.S. Translocation). *Proc. zool. Soc. Lond.* **135,** 261–4

BULLOUGH W.S. (1951) *Vertebrate Sexual Cycles.* London, Methuen

CAIN A.J. (1954) *Animal Species and their Evolution.* London, Hutchinson

CAMERON A.G. (1923) *The Wild Red Deer of Scotland.* Edinburgh, Blackwood

CAMPBELL J.L. (1955) The hedgehog in the Inner Hebrides. *Scot. Nat.* **67,** 122–3

CARNE P.H. (1958) Wild deer in southern England. *Field,* **211,** 695–6

CARNE P.H. (1959) Japanese deer in Britain. *Field*, **213**, 185

CARNE P.H. (1960) Fallow deer. *Countryman*, **5**, 311–14

CARRICK R. (1957) What is the best free-feeding system for furrow-poisoning the rabbit? *C.S.I.R.O. Wildlife Res.* **2**, 74–84

CHARD J.S.R. (1936) *British Animal Tracks*. London, C. Arthur Pearson

CHITTY D. (1937) A ringing technique for small mammals. *J. Anim. Ecol.* **6**, 36–53

CHITTY D. (1938) A laboratory study of pellet formation in the short-eared owl (*Asio flammeus*). *Proc. zool. Soc. Lond.* A, **108**, 267–87

CHITTY D. (1952) Mortality among voles (*Microtus agrestis*) at Lake Vyrnwy, Montgomeryshire in 1936–9. *Phil. Trans.* B, **236**, 505–52

CHITTY D. (1954) The study of the brown rat and its control by poison. In *Control of Rats and Mice*, vol. I, ed. CHITTY D.H. & SOUTHERN H.N. Oxford, Clarendon Press

CHITTY D. (1957) The field vole (*Microtus agrestis* L.) and the Orkney vole (*Microtus orcadensis*, Millais 1904). In *The UFAW Handbook on the Care and Management of Laboratory Animals*, ed. WORDEN A.N. & LANE-PETTER W. London, Univ. Feder. Anim. Welfare

CHITTY D. (1958) Self-regulation of numbers through changes in viability. *Cold Spr. Harb. Symp. Quant. Biol.* (*1957*), **22**, 277–80

CHITTY D. & KEMPSON D.A. (1949) Prebaiting small mammals and a new design of live trap. *Ecology*, **30**, 536–42

CHITTY D. & SHORTEN M. (1946) Techniques for the study of the Norway rat (*Rattus norvegicus*). *J. Mammal.* **27**, 63–78

CHITTY D. & SOUTHERN H.N. ed. (1954) *Control of Rats and Mice*. 3 vols. Oxford, Clarendon Press

CHITTY H. (1957) The oestrous cycle and gestation period in the lactating field vole, *Microtus agrestis*. *J. Endocr.* **15**, 279–83

CHURCH B.M., JACOB F.H. & THOMPSON H.V. (1953) Surveys of rabbit damage to wheat in England and Wales, 1950–52. *Plant Pathology*, **2**, 107–12

CHURCH B.M., WESTMACOTT M.H. & JACOB F.H. (1956) Survey of rabbit damage to winter cereals, 1953–54. *Plant Pathology*, **5**, 66–9

CHURCH H.F. (1957) The times of emergence of the pipistrelle. *Proc. zool. Soc. Lond.* **128**, 600–2

CHURCHER C.S. (1959) The specific status of the New World red fox. *J. Mammal.* **40**, 513–20

CLARK W.E. LE GROS (1955) *The Fossil Evidence for Human Evolution*. Chicago, Univ. Chicago Press

CLARK W.E. LE GROS (1959) *The Antecedents of Man*. Edinburgh, Univ. Press

COCKS A.H. (1881) Note on the breeding of the otter. *Proc. zool. Soc. Lond.* 249–50

COCKS A.H. (1882) On the breeding of the otter. *Zoologist*, Ser. 3, **6**, 201–4

COLLETT R. (1881) On *Halichoerus grypus* and its breeding on the Fro Islands off Trondhjems-fjord in Norway. *Proc. zool. Soc. Lond.* (1881) 380–7

COLLETT R. (1911–12) *Norges Pattedyr*. Kristiania, H. Aschehoug & Co.

CONDRY W. (1954) The polecat in Wales. *Oryx*, **2**, 238–40

CONSTANTINE D.G. (1958) An automatic bat-collecting device. *J. Wildlife Manag.* **22**, 17–22

Cook D.B. & Hamilton W.J. (1944) The ecological relationships of red fox food in Eastern New York. *Ecology*, **25**, 91–104

Corbet G.B. (1960) Wood mice at high altitude in Scotland. *Proc. zool. Soc. Lond.* **133**, 486–7

Corbet G.B. (1960) The Distribution, Variation and Ecology of Voles in the Scottish Highlands. Ph.D. unpubl. thesis, Univ. of St. Andrews

Corbet G.B. (1961) Origin of the British insular races of small mammals and of the 'Lusitanian' fauna. *Nature, Lond.* **191**, 1037–40

Corbet G.B. (1963) An isolated population of the bank-vole *Clethrionomys glareolus* with aberrant dental pattern. *Proc. zool. Soc. Lond.* **140**, 316–19

Corbet G.B. (1964) Regional variation in the bank-vole *Clethrionomys glareolus* (Schreber). *Proc. zool. Soc. Lond.* (in press).

Coulson J.C. (1959) The growth of grey seal calves on the Farne Islands, Northumberland. *Trans. nat. Hist. Soc. Northumb.* N.S. **13**, 86–100

Coulson J.C. & Hickling G. (1960a) Grey seals of the Farne Islands, 1958 to 1959. *Trans. nat. Hist. Soc. Northumb.* N.S. **13**, 151–78

Coulson J.C. & Hickling G. (1960b) The grey seals of the Farne Islands. An interim report dealing mainly with the 1959 breeding season. *Trans. nat. Hist. Soc. Northumb.* N.S. **13**, 196–214

Coulson J.C. & Hickling G. (1961) Variation in the secondary sex-ratio of the grey seal, *Halichoerus grypus* (Fab.) during the breeding season. *Nature, Lond.* **190**, 281

Cowan I. McT. & Mackay R.H. (1950) Food habits of the marten (*Martes americana*) in the Rocky Mountain region of Canada. *Canad. Field.-Nat.* **64**, 100–4

Craggs J.D. & Ellison N.F. (1960) Observations on the seals of the (Welsh) Dee estuary. *Proc. zool. Soc. Lond* **135**, 375–85

Craighead J.J. & Stockstad D.S. (1960) Color marker for big game. *J. Wildlife Manag.* **24**, 435–8

Cranbrook Earl of (1957) Long-tailed field mice (*Apodemus* sp.) from the Channel Isles. *Proc. zool. Soc. Lond.* **128**, 597–600

Cranbrook Earl of (1959) The feeding habits of the water shrew, *Neomys fodiens bicolor* Shaw, in captivity and the effect of its attack upon its prey. *Proc. zool. Soc. Lond.* **133**, 245–9

Cranbrook Earl of & Crowcroft P. (1958) The white-toothed shrews of the Channel Islands. *Ann. Mag. nat. Hist.* Ser. 13, **1**, 359–64

Cranbrook Earl of & Crowcroft P. (1961) Small mammals from Herm Island. *J. Linn. Soc.* (*Zool.*), **44**, 365–8

Creed R.F.S. (1960) Observations on the reproduction of the wild red fox (*Vulpes vulpes*). *Brit. Vet. J.* **116**, 419–26

Criddle S. (1947) A nest of the least weasel. *Canad. Field-Nat.* **61**, 69

Croft P.G. (1957) Anaesthesia and euthanasia. In *The UFAW Handbook on the Care and Management of Laboratory Animals*, 2nd ed., ed. Worden A.N. & Petter W. Lane-. London, Univ. Feder. Anim. Welfare

Crowcroft P. (1954a) The daily cycle of activity in British shrews. *Proc. zool. Soc. Lond.* **123**, 715–29

Crowcroft W.P. (1954b) An Ecological Study of British Shrews. D.Phil. unpubl. thesis, Univ. of Oxford

CROWCROFT P. (1955) Territoriality in wild house mice, *Mus musculus* L. *J. Mammal.* **36**, 299–301

CROWCROFT P. (1956) On the life span of the common shrew (*Sorex araneus* L.). *Proc. zool. Soc. Lond.* **127**, 285–92

CROWCROFT P. (1957) *The Life of the Shrew*. London, Reinhardt

CROWCROFT P. (1959) A simple technique for studying activity rhythms by direct observation. *Acta theriol.* **3**, 107–111

CROWCROFT P. & GODFREY G.K. (1960) On the taxonomy of the Jersey vole (*Clethrionomys glareolus caesarius* Miller). *Ann. Mag. nat. Hist.* Ser. 13, **2**, 737–43

CROWCROFT P. & INGLES J.M. (1959) Seasonal changes in the brain-case of the common shrew (*Sorex araneus* L.). *Nature, Lond.* **183**, 907–8

CROWCROFT P. & JEFFERS J.N.R. (1961) Variability in the behaviour of wild house mice (*Mus musculus* L.) towards live traps. *Proc. zool. Soc. Lond.* **137**, 573–82

CROWCROFT P. & ROWE F.P. (1957) The growth of confined colonies of the wild house-mouse (*Mus musculus* L.). *Proc. zool. Soc. Lond.* **129**, 359–70

CROWCROFT P. & ROWE F.P. (1958) The growth of confined colonies of the wild house-mouse (*Mus musculus* L.): the effect of dispersal on female fecundity. *Proc. zool. Soc. Lond.* **131**, 357–65

CROWCROFT P. & ROWE F.P. (1961) The weights of wild house mice (*Mus musculus* L.) living in confined colonies. *Proc. zool. Soc. Lond.* **136**, 177–85

DALIMIER P. (1952) Remarque au sujet de polymorphisme du Mulot en Belgique. *Bull. Inst. Sci. Nat. Belg.* **28**, 1–11

DARE P.J. (1961) Ecological Observations on a Breeding Population of the Common Buzzard (*Buteo buteo* L.), with particular reference to the Diet and Feeding Habits. Ph.D. unpubl. thesis, Univ. of Exeter

DARLING F.F. (1937) *A Herd of Red Deer: a Study in Animal Behaviour*. Oxford, University Press

DARLING F.F. (1939) *A Naturalist on Rona*. Oxford, Clarendon Press

DARLING F.F. (1947) *Natural History in the Highlands and Islands*. London, Collins

DARLINGTON C.D. (1953) *The Facts of Life*. London, Allen & Unwin

DARLINGTON P.J. (1957) *Zoogeography*. New York, John Wiley & Sons Inc.

DARWIN C.R. (1881) *The Formation of Vegetable Mould through the Action of Worms, with Observations on their Habits*. London, John Murray

DAVIES J.L. (1949) Observations on the grey seal (*Halichoerus grypus*) at Ramsey Island, Pembrokeshire. *Proc. zool. Soc. Lond.* **119**, 673–92

DAVIES J.L. (1953) Colony size and reproduction in the grey seal. *Proc. zool. Soc. Lond.* **123**, 327–32

DAVIES J.L. (1956) The grey seal at the Isles of Scilly. *Proc. zool. Soc. Lond.* **127**, 161–6

DAVIES J.L. (1957a) The geography of the grey seal. *J. Mammal.* **38**, 297–310

DAVIES J.L. (1957b) A hedgehog road mortality index. *Proc. zool. Soc. Lond.* **128**, 606–8

DAVIS D.E. (1953) The characteristics of rat populations. *Quart. Rev. Biol.* **28**, 373–401

DAVIS D.E. ed. (1956) *Manual for Analysis of Rodent Populations*. Issued privately from Pennsylvania State Univ., Univ. Park, Penn.

DAVIS D.E., EMLEN J.T. & STOKES A.W. (1948) Studies on home range in the brown rat. *J. Mammal.* **29,** 207–25

DAVIS D.H.S. (1933) Rhythmic activity in the short-tailed vole, *Microtus*. *J. Anim. Ecol.* **2,** 232–8

DAVIS R.A. (1960) A note on the distribution of the coypu (*Myocastor coypus*) in Great Britain. *J. Anim. Ecol.* **29,** 397

DAVIS R.A. (1961) A simple live-trap for small mammals. *Proc. zool. Soc. Lond.* **137,** 631–3

DAVIS R.A. (1963) Feral coypus in Britain *Ann. appl. Biol.* **51,** 345–8

DAVIS W.B. (1942) Swimming ability of two small mammals. *J. Mammal.* **23,** 99

DEAN F. (1947) Some observations on a colony of water voles. *Naturalist, Lond.* (1947), 105–7

DEANESLY R. (1934) The reproductive processes of certain mammals. Part VI. The reproductive cycle of the female hedgehog. *Phil. Trans.* B, **223,** 239–76

DEANESLY R. (1935) The reproductive processes of certain mammals. Part IX. Growth and reproduction in the stoat (*Mustela erminea*). *Phil. Trans.* B, **225,** 1–62

DEANESLY R. (1943) Delayed implantation in the stoat (*Mustela mustela*). *Nature, Lond.* **151,** 365

DEANESLY R. (1944) The reproductive cycle of the female weasel (*Mustela nivalis*). *Proc. zool. Soc. Lond.* **114,** 339–49

DEANESLY R. & WARWICK T. (1939) Observations on pregnancy in the common bat (*Pipistrellus pipistrellus*). *Proc. zool. Soc. Lond.* **109,** A, 57–60

DEHNEL A. (1949) [Studies on the genus *Sorex* L.]. *Ann. Univ. M. Curie-Skłodowska*, C, **4,** 17–102

DEHNEL A. (1950) [Studies on the genus *Neomys* Kaup.]. *Ann. Univ. M. Curie-Skłodowska*, C, **5,** 1–63

DELANY M.J. (1961) The ecological distribution of small mammals in north-west Scotland. *Proc. zool. Soc. Lond.* **137,** 107–26

DELANY M.J. & BISHOP I.R. (1960) The systematics, life-history and evolution of the bank vole (*Clethrionomys* Tilesius) in north-west Scotland. *Proc. zool. Soc. Lond.* **135,** 409–22

DICE L.R. (1947) Effectiveness of selection by owls of deer-mice (*Peromyscus maniculatus*) which contrast in colour with their background. *Contrib. Lab. vert. Biol.* **34,** 1–20

DODGE W.E. & SNYDER D.P. (1960) An automatic camera device for recording wildlife activity. *J. Wildlife Manag.* **24,** 340–2

DOWNING R.L. & MARSHALL C.M. (1949) A new plastic tape marker for birds and mammals. *J. Wildlife Manag.* **23,** 223–4

DRUMMOND D.C. (1960) The food of *Rattus norvegicus* Berk. in an area of sea-wall, saltmarsh and mudflat. *J. Anim. Ecol.* **29,** 341–7

DUBLIN L.I. & LOTKA A.J. (1936) *Length of Life*. New York, Ronald Press Co.

DUNCAN A. (1952) A small colony of grey seals (*Halichoerus grypus* Fabricius) in the south of the Isle of Man. *Rep. Mar. biol. Sta. Pt. Erin*, No. 64, 22–31

DUNCAN A. (1956) Notes on the food and parasites of grey seals (*Halichoerus grypus* Fabricius) from the Isle of Man. *Proc. zool. Soc. Lond.* **126,** 635–44

DUNNET G.M. (1957) Notes on emergence behaviour of the rabbit, *Oryctolagus cuniculus* (L.), and its bearing on the validity of sight counts for population estimates. *C.S.I.R.O. Wildlife Res.* **2**, 85–9

EALEY E.H.M. & DUNNET G.M. (1956) Plastic collars with patterns of reflective tape for marking nocturnal mammals. *C.S.I.R.O. Wildlife Res.* **1**, 59–62

ECKE D.H. (1954) An invasion of Norway rats in southwest Georgia. *J. Mammal.* **35**, 521–5

EDWARDS J.T.G. (1957) The European hedgehog (*Erinaceus europaeus* L.). In *The UFAW Handbook on the Care and Management of Laboratory Animals*, 2nd ed., ed. WORDEN A.N. & PETTER W. LANE-. London, Univ. Feder. Anim. Welfare

EDWARDS V.C. WYNNE- (1954) Field identification of the common and grey seals. *Scot. Nat.* **66**, 192

EIBESFELDT I. EIBL- (1955) Zur Biologie des Iltes (*Putorius putorius* L.). *Verh. dtsch. zool. Ges. Erlangen 1955. Zool. Anz. Suppl.* **19**, 304–14

EIBESFELDT I. EIBL- (1956) Angeborenes und erworbenes in der Technik des Beutetötens (Versuche am Iltis, *Putorius putorius* L.). *Z. Säugetierk.* **21**, 135–7

EISENTRAUT M. (1930) Beobachtungen über den Winterschlaf der Haselmaus (*Muscardinus avellanarius* L.). *Z. Säugetierk.* **4**, 213–39

EISENTRAUT M. (1937) Die deutschen Fledermäuse, eine biologische Studie. *Zbl. Kleintierk.* **13**, 1–184

EISENTRAUT M. (1949) Beobachtung über Begattung bei Fledermäuse in Winterquartur. *Zool. Jahrb. (Syst: Oekol.)* **78**, 297–300

ELDER W.H. (1945) Determination of weasel sex ratios by pelt examination. *J. Wildlife Manag.* **15**, 114–16

ELTON C. (1942) *Voles, Mice and Lemmings: Problems in Population Dynamics.* Oxford, Clarendon Press

ELTON C.S. (1953) The use of cats in farm rat control. *Brit. J. Anim. Behav.* **1**, 151–5

ELTON C. & LAURIE E.M.O. (1954) A sample census of rats and house mice in English corn-ricks in January to July 1943–7. In *Control of Rats and Mice*, vol. II, ed. CHITTY D.H. & SOUTHERN H.N. Oxford, Clarendon Press

ELTON C. & MILLER R.S. (1954) The ecological survey of animal communities: with a practical system of classifying habitats by structural characters. *J. Ecol.* **42**, 460–96

ELTON C. & NICHOLSON M. (1942) The ten-year cycle in numbers of the lynx in Canada. *J. Anim. Ecol.* **11**, 215–44

EMLEN J.T. *et al.* (1957) Dropping boards for population studies of small mammals. *J. Wildlife Manag.* **21**, 300–14

ENDERS R.K. (1952) Reproduction in the mink (*Mustela vison*). *Proc. Amer. Phil. Soc.* **96**, 691–741

ERRINGTON P.L. & BERRY R.M. (1937) Tagging studies of red foxes. *J. Mammal.* **18**, 203–5

EVANS A.C. (1948) The identity of earthworms stored by moles. *Proc. zool. Soc. Lond.* **118**, 356–9

EVANS, F.C. (1942) Studies of a small mammal population in Bagley Wood, Berkshire. *J. Anim. Ecol.* **11**, 182–97

EVANS F.C. & VEVERS H.G. (1938) Notes on the biology of the Faeroe mouse (*Mus musculus faeroensis*). *J. Anim. Ecol.* **7,** 290–7

EVANS H. (1890) *Some Account of Jura Red Deer*. Derby. Privately printed

FARROW E.P. (1925) *Plant Life on East Anglian Heaths*. Cambridge, Univ. Press

FELDMAN H.W. (1926) Unit character inheritance of colour in the black rat, *Mus rattus* L. *Genetics*, **11,** 456–65

FELTEN H. (1952) Untersuchungen zur Oekologie und Morphologie der Waldmaus (*Apodemus sylvaticus* L.) und der Gelbhalsmaus (*Apodemus flavicollis* Melchior) im Rhein-Main-Gebiet. *Bonn. Zool. Beitr.* **3,** 187–206

FISHER H.D. (1954) Delayed implantation in the harbour seal *Phoca vitulina* L. *Nature, Lond.* **173,** 879–80

FISHER H.D. & MACKENZIE, B.A. (1955) Food habits of seals in the Maritimes. *Fish. Res. Bd. Canada Progress Repts. Atl. Coast Sta.* No. 61, 5–9

FITTER R.S.R. (1959) *The Ark in our Midst*. London, Collins

FITZGERALD, B. VESEY- (1949) *British Bats*. London, Methuen

FLINTOFF R.J. (1935a) The weights and measurements of stoats and weasels. *North Western Nat.* **10,** 29–34

FLINTOFF R.J. (1935b) Stoats and weasels, brown and white. *North Western Nat.* **10,** 214–29

FLUX J.E.C. (1962) The Ecology of the Scottish Mountain Hare *Lepus timidus scoticus* Hilzheimer. Ph.D. unpubl. thesis, Univ. of Aberdeen

FLYGER V.F. (1955) The Social Behaviour and Populations of the Gray Squirrel in Maryland. D.Sc. unpubl. thesis, Johns Hopkins Univ.

FLYGER V.F. (1955) Implications of social behaviour in gray squirrel management. *Trans. 20th N. Amer. Wildl. Conf.* 381–9

FOOKS H.A. (1958) *The Roe Deer*. London, Forest. Comm. Tech. Notes No. 6

FORD E.B. (1945) Polymorphism. *Biol. Rev.* **20,** 73–88

FRANK F. (1956) Das Duftmarkieren der Grossen Wühlmaus, *Arvicola terrestris* (L.). *Z. Säugetierk.* **21,** 172–5

FRANK H.R. (1940) Die Biologie des Dachses. *Z. Jagdk.* **2,** 1–25

FRASER F.C. (1952) *Handbook of R.H. Burne's Cetacean Dissections*. London, Brit. Mus. (Nat. Hist.)

FRASER F.C. & PARKER H.W. (1953) *Guide for the Identification and Reporting of Stranded Whales, Dolphins, Porpoises and Turtles of the British Coasts*, 2nd ed. London, Brit. Mus. (Nat. Hist.)

FRAZER J.F.D. (1959) *The Sexual Cycles of Vertebrates*. London, Hutchinson

FRILEY C.E. (1949) Age determination, by use of the baculum, in the river otter, *Lutra c. canadensis* Schreber. *J. Mammal.* **30,** 102–10

GERSDORF E. (1958) Fressen Feldhasen (*Lepus europaeus*) Feldmäuse (*Microtus arvalis*). *Säugetierk. Mitt.* **6,** 103–5

GIBB J. (1954) Feeding ecology of tits, with notes on treecreeper and goldcrest. *Ibis*, **96,** 513–43

GIBB J. (1956a) Food, feeding habits and territory of the rock pipit *Anthus spinoletta*. *Ibis*, **98,** 506–30

GIBB J. (1956b) Automatic recorders at nests. In *The Ornithologists' Guide*, ed. H.P.W. HUTSON. London, Brit. Ornith. Union.

GILBERT O. (1948) On bats in west Suffolk. *Trans. Suffolk Nat. Soc.* **6,** 163–5

GIRONS M.-C. SAINT- (1957) Les mammifères des Pyrénées orientales. I. Observations sur quelques mammifères recueillis dans la région de Banyuls et plus particulièrement le mulot *Apodemus flavicollis*. *Vie et Milieu*, **8**, 287–96

GIRONS M.-C. SAINT- (1959) Les charactéristiques du rhythme nycthéméral d'activité chez quelques petits mammifères. *Mammalia*, **23**, 245–76

GODFREY G.K. (1953) The food of *Microtus agrestis hirtus* (Bellamy, 1839) in Wytham, Berkshire. *Säugetierk. Mitt.* **1**, 148–51

GODFREY G.K. (1954) Tracing field voles (*Microtus agrestis*) with a Geiger-Müller counter. *Ecology*, **35**, 5–10

GODFREY G.K. (1955) A field study of the activity of the mole (*Talpa europaea* L.). *Ecology*, **36**, 678–85

GODFREY G.K. (1957) Observations on the movements of moles (*Talpa europaea* L.) after weaning. *Proc. zool. Soc. Lond.* **128**, 287–95

GODFREY G.K. & CROWCROFT P. (1960) *The Life of the Mole*. London, Museum Press

GODFREY J. (1958) The origin of sexual isolation between bank voles. *Proc. R. phys. Soc. Edinb.* **27**, 47–55

GORDON A. (1951) Water shrew in Isle of Skye. *Scot. Nat.* **63**, 199

GRIFFIN D.R. (1958) *Listening in the Dark*. New Haven, Yale Univ. Press

GRINNELL J., DIXON J.S. & LINSDALE J.M. (1937) *Fur-bearing Mammals of California*, vol. 1. Berkeley, Univ. Calif. Press

GRODZIŃSKI W. (1959) The succession of small mammal communities on an overgrown clearing and landslip mountain in the Beskid Średni (western Carpathians). *Ekologia Polska*, **7**, 83–143

GROSSER O. (1903) Die physiologische bindegewebige Atresie des Genital-kanales von *Vesperugo noctula* nach erfolgter kohabitation. *Verh. anat. Ges. Jena*, **23**, 109–30

GRULICH I. (1959) [Wühltätigkeit des Maulwurfes (*Talpa europaea*) in der ČSR]. *Práce Brn. Základ. Čsl. Akad. Věd.* **31**, 157–212

GRÜNEBERG H. (1943) *The Genetics of the Mouse*. Cambridge, Univ. Press

HACKER H.P. & PEARSON H.S. (1951) Distribution of the long-tailed field mouse, *Apodemus sylvaticus*, on South Haven Peninsula, Dorset, in 1937, with some observations on its wandering and homing powers. *J. Linn. Soc. (Zool.)*, **42**, 1–17

HAGMEIER E.M. (1961) Variation and relationships in North American marten. *Canad. Field-Nat.* **75**, 122–38

HALL E.R. (1951) American weasels. *Publ. Mus. nat. Hist. Univ. Kans.* **4**, 1–466

HALTENORTH T. (1940) Beiträge zur Kenntnis der Wildkatze (*Felis silvestris* Schreber): Systematik, Verbreitung, Körpermasse, und -gewicht, Darm-länge, Mageninhalt, Wurfgrösse, Wachstum. *Sitz. Ber. Ges. Naturf. Fr. Berl.* (1940) 1–36

HALTENORTH T. (1953) *Die Wildkatzen der Altenwelt*. Leipzig

HALTENORTH T. (1957) Appendix in DE LEUW, 1957 (q.v.)

HALTENORTH T. (1959) Beitrag zur Kenntnis des Mesopotamischen Dam-hirsches—*Cervus (Dama) mesopotamicus* Brooke, 1875—und zur Stammes- und Verbreitungsgeschichte der Damhirsche allgemein. *Säugetierk. Mitt.* **7**, 1–89

HAMILTON E. (1871) Remarks on the prolific nature of *Hydropotes inermis*. *Proc. zool. Soc. Lond.* 258

HAMILTON W.J. (1933) The weasels of New York. *Amer. Midl. Nat.* **14**, 284–344

HAMMOND J. & MARSHALL F.H.A. (1930) Oestrus and pseudo-pregnancy in the ferret. *Proc. roy. Soc.* B, **105**, 607–30

HARRIS D.R. (1962) The distribution and ancestry of the domestic goat. *Proc. Linn. Soc.* (*Zool.*), **173**, 79–91

HARRISON G.A. (1959) Environmental determination of the phenotype. In *Function and Taxonomic Importance*, ed. CAIN A.J. Systematics Assn. Publ. No. 3. London, Systematics Assn.

HARRISON J.L. (1960) A simple trap for squirrels. *J. Mammal.* **41**, 142–3

HARTING J.E. (1895) The harvest mouse. *Zoologist*, Ser. 3, **19**, 418–25

HATTINGH I. (1956) Measurements of foxes from Scotland and England. *Proc. zool. Soc. Lond.* **127**, 191–9

HAVINGA B. (1933) Der Seehund (*Phoca vitulina* L.) in den Holländischen Gewässern. *Tijdschr. ned. dierk. Ver.* Ser. 3, **3**, 79–111

HAWKINS A.E. & JEWELL P.A. (1962) Food consumption and energy requirements of captive British shrews and the mole. *Proc. zool. Soc. Lond.* **138**, 137–55

HAWKINS A.E., JEWELL P.A. & TOMLINSON G. (1960) The metabolism of some British shrews. *Proc. zool. Soc. Lond.* **135**, 99–103

HAWLEY V.D. & NEWBY F.E. (1957) Marten home ranges and population fluctuations. *J. Mammal.* **38**, 174–84

HAYDN J. & KIRKBY P. (1954) Bats in the Bishop's Stortford area. *Oryx*, **2**, 325–8

HAYNE D.W. (1949) Two methods for estimating populations from trapping records. *J. Mammal.* **30**, 399–411

HEDIGER H. (1948) Die Zucht des Feldhasen (*Lepus europaeus* Pallas) in Gefangenschaft. *Physiol comp.* **1**, 46–62

HEINRICH G. (1951) Die deutschen Waldmäuse. *Zool. Jb.* (*Syst.*), **80**, 99–122

HERTER K. (1938) Die Biologie der europäischen Igel. *Zbl. Kleintierk.* **14**, 1–222

HEWER H.R. (1955) Notes on the marking of Atlantic seals in Pembrokeshire. *Proc. zool. Soc. Lond.* **125**, 87–93

HEWER H.R. (1957) A Hebridean breeding colony of grey seals, *Halichoerus grypus* (Fab.) with comparative notes on the grey seals of Ramsey Island, Pembrokeshire. *Proc. zool. Soc. Lond.* **129**, 23–66

HEWER H.R. (1960a) Age determination of seals. *Nature, Lond.* **187**, 959–60

HEWER H.R. (1960b) Behaviour of the grey seal (*Halichoerus grypus* Fab.) *Mammalia*, **24**, 400–21

HEWER H.R. & BACKHOUSE K.M. (1959) Field identification of bulls and cows of the grey seal, *Halichoerus grypus* Fab. *Proc. zool. Soc. Lond.* **132**, 641–5

HEWER H.R. & BACKHOUSE K.M. (1960) A preliminary account of a colony of grey seals *Halichoerus grypus* (Fab.) in the southern Inner Hebrides. *Proc. zool. Soc. Lond.* **134**, 157–95

HEWER H.R. & NEAL E.G. (1954) Filming badgers at night. *Discovery*, **15**, 121–4

BIBLIOGRAPHY 435

HEWSON R. (1948) Some observations on the Orkney vole, *Microtus o. orcadensis* (Millais). *Northw. Nat.* **23,** 7–10

HEWSON R. (1953) An apparently isolated colony of the Scottish field vole *Microtus agrestis neglectus* Jenyns. *Northw. Nat.* **24,** 174–6

HEWSON R. (1954) The mountain hare in Scotland in 1951. *Scot. Nat.* **66,** 70–88

HEWSON R. (1958) Moults and winter whitening in the mountain hare *Lepus timidus scoticus* Hilzheimer. *Proc. zool. Soc. Lond.* **131,** 99–108

HEWSON R. (1961) Collars for marking mountain hares. *J. Wildlife Manag.* **25,** 329–31

HEWSON R. (1962) Food and feeding habits of the mountain hare *Lepus timidus scoticus* Hilzheimer. *Proc. zool. Soc. Lond.* **139,** 415–26

HEWSON R. (1963) Moults and pelages in the brown hare *Lepus europaeus occidentalis* De Winton. *Proc. zool. Soc. Lond.* (in press).

HEYDEMANN B. (1960) Zur Ökologie von *Sorex araneus* L. und *Sorex minutus* L. *Z. Säugetierk.* **25,** 24–9

HICKLING G. (1957) The grey seals of the Farne Islands. *Trans. nat. Hist. Soc. Northumb.* N.S., **12,** 93–133

HICKLING G. (1959) The grey seals of the Farne Islands. *Trans. nat. Hist. Soc. Northumb.* N.S., **13,** 33–64

HICKLING G. (1962) *Grey Seals and the Farne Islands.* London, Routledge & Kegan Paul

HICKLING G., JONES A.W. & TELFER I.M. (1955) The grey seals of the Farne Islands. *Trans. nat. Hist. Soc. Northumb.* N.S., **11,** 153 63

HICKLING G., JONES A.W. & TELFER I.M. (1956) The grey seals of the Farne Islands. *Trans. nat. Hist. Soc. Northumb.* N.S., **11,** 230–44

HILL M. (1939) The reproductive cycle of the male weasel (*Mustela nivalis*). *Proc. zool. Soc. Lond.* **109B,** 481–512

HILL W.C. OSMAN (1953–62) *Primates. Comparative Anatomy and Taxonomy,* vols. 1–5 (continuing). Edinb., Univ. Press

HÖGLUND N.H. (1957) Fortplantningen hos skogsharen (*Lepus t. timidus* L.). *Vildrevy* **1,** 267–82

HÖGLUND N.H. (1960) Studier över näringen vintertid hos mården *Martes m. martes* Linn. i Jamtlands län. *Vildrevy,* **1,** 319–37

HOLISÓVÁ V. (1960) [Die Nahrung der Waldmaus *Apodemus sylvaticus* L. im böhmisch-mährischen Höhenzug.] *Zoolog. Listy,* **9,** 135–58

HOOPER E.T. & OSTENSON B.T. (1949) Age groups in Michigan otter. *Occ. Pap. Mus. Zool. Univ. Mich.* **518,** 1–22

HOOPER J.H.D. & HOOPER W.M. (1956) Habits and movements of cave-dwelling bats in Devonshire. *Proc. zool. Soc. Lond.* **127,** 1–26

HOSKING E. & NEWBERRY C. (1961) *Bird Photography as a Hobby.* London, Stanley Paul

HOWARD W.E. (1949) Dispersal, amount of inbreeding, and longevity in a local population of prairie deer-mice on the George Reserve, Southern Michigan. *Contr. Lab. Vert. Zool. Univ. Mich.* No. 43.

HOWARD W.E. (1957) Amount of food eaten by small carnivores. *J. Mammal.* **38,** 516–17

Hume C.W. (1958) The gin-trap: UFAW'S long battle. *UFAW Courier*, No. 15, 1–10

Hurrell E. (1962) *Dormice*. London, *Sunday Times* Publ. Animals of Britain, No. 10

Hurrell H.G. (1962) *Foxes*. London, *Sunday Times* Publ. Animals of Britain, No. 9

Jackson H.H.T. (1961) *Mammals of Wisconsin*. Madison, Univ. Wis. Press

Jánský L. & Hanák V. (1960) Studien über Kleinsäugerpopulationen in Südböhmen. 11. Aktivität der Spitzmäuse unter natürlichen Bedingungen. *Säugetierk. Mitt.* **8**, 55–63

Jenkins D. (1962) The present status of the wild cat (*Felis silvestris*) in Scotland. *Scot. Nat.* **70**, 126–38

Kalabukhov N.J. (1928) [Über die Nahrung des Igels im Nord-Kaukasus und in der Ukraine. *Mitt. Nordkaukas. Pflanzenschutzstation, Rostow a. Don*], **4**, 62–8

Karpuleon F. (1958) Food habits of Wisconsin foxes. *J. Mammal.* **39**, 591–3

Kästle W. (1953) Die Jugendentwicklung des Zwergmaus, *Micromys minutus soricinus* (Hermann, 1780). *Säugetierk. Mitt.* **1**, 49–59

Kaye S.V. (1961) Movements of harvest mice tagged with gold-198. *J. Mammal.* **42**, 323–37

Keeler B. (1961) Damage to young plantations by the bank vole at Bernwood Forest, 1958–1960. *J. For. Comm.* No. 30, 55–9

Keeler C.E. & King H.D. (1941) Multiple effects of coat color genes in the Norway rat, with special reference to the 'marks of domestication'. *Anat. Rec.* **81**, Suppl. 48–9

Kellogg R. (1928) The history of whales—their adaptation to life in the water. *Quart. Rev. Biol.* **3**, 29–76, 174–208

Kelway P. (1944) *The Otter Book*. London, Collins

Kenneth J.H. & Ritchie G.R. (1953) *Gestation Periods*, 3rd ed. Tech. Comm. Bur. Anim. Breeding, Edinb. No. 5

Kikkawa J. (1959) Habitats of the field mouse on Fair Isle in spring, 1956. *Glasg. Nat.* **18**, 65–77

Kindler V. (1946) [Dormouse damage in the Sneznik Forests (*Muscardinus avellanarius*)]. *Gozd. Vijesn.* **5**, 104–5

Kirk J.C. & Wagstaffe R. (1943) A contribution to the study of the Scottish wild cat (*Felis silvestris grampia* Miller). Part I. Size and weight. *Northw. Nat.* **18**, 271–5

Kirkpatrick C.M. & Hoffman R.A. (1960) Ages and reproductive cycles in a male grey squirrel population. *J. Wildlife Manag.* **24**, 218–21

Knight M. (1962) *Hedgehogs*. London, *Sunday Times* Publ. Animals of Britain, No. 3

Kolosov A.M. (1941) [Reproductive biology of the common hare (*Lepus europaeus* Pall.)]. *Zool. Zh.* **20**, 154–72

Korschgen L.J. (1959) Food habits of the red fox in Missouri. *J. Wildlife Manag.* **23**, 168–76

Koskimies J. (1957) Studies on the winter habitat preferences of the snow hare, *Lepus timidus* L. *Arch. Soc. zool.-bot. fenn. Vanamo*, **12**, 29–37

KRASSOVSKII S. (1935) [Experiment in marking the Arctic fox (*Alopex lagopus*) on Novaya Zemlya]. *Bull. Arct. Inst. Leningr.* No. 9, 281

KUBIK J. (1953) *Micromys minutus* Pall. w Białowieskim parku narodowym. *Ann. Univ. M. Curie-Sklodowska* (1952) C, **7,** 449–95

KUMERLOEVE H. (1956) Kaninchen, *Oryctolagus cuniculus* (Linné, 1758) und Hasen, *Lepus europaeus* Pallas, 1778, als Pilzfresser. *Säugetierk. Mitt.* **4,** 125

KUMMERLÖWE H. (1929) *Plecotus auritus* L. in der Gefangschaft. *Zool. Gart. Lpzg.* **2,** 106–12

KUTCHERUK V.V. & RUBINA M.A. (1953) [The factors determining the species make-up of rodents in stacked crops, straw-haystacks in the southern part of the Moscow province.] *Zool. Zh.* **30,** 495–505

LACK D. (1944) Ecological aspects of species-formation in passerine birds. *Ibis*, **86,** 260–86

LACK D. (1954) *The Natural Regulation of Animal Numbers*. Oxford, Clarendon Press

LAFARGUE M. BONNIN- & CANIVENC R. (1961) Etude de l'activité du blaireau européen. *Mammalia*, **25,** 476–84

LAMPIO T. (1951) On the sex ratio, sex differentiation and regional variation in the marten in Finland. *Pap. Game Res. Helsinki.* No. 7

LANDE O. (1958) Chromosome number in the silver fox (*Vulpes fulvus* Desm.). *Nature, Lond.* **181,** 1353–4

LARINA N.I. (1958) [On the diagnostics problem of closely related species *Apodemus sylvaticus* Linnaeus and *Apodemus tauricus* Pallas.] *Zool. Zh.* **37,** 1719–32

LARKIN P.A. (1948) Ecology of Mole (*Talpa europaea* L.) Populations. D.Phil. unpubl. thesis, Univ. of Oxford

LATHAM R.M. (1953) Simple method for identification of least weasel. *J. Mammal.* **34,** 385

LAURIE E.M.O. (1946a) The reproduction of the house-mouse (*Mus musculus*) living in different environments. *Proc. roy. Soc.* B, **133,** 248–81

LAURIE E.M.O. (1946b) The coypu (*Myocastor coypus*) in Great Britain. *J. Anim. Ecol.* **15,** 22–34

LAURIE E.M.O. & HILL J.E. (1951) Use of *Dermestes* beetles for cleaning mammalian skeletons. *Mus. J.* **51,** 206–7

LE MUNYAN C.D. *et al.* (1959) Design of a miniature radio transmitter for use in animal studies. *J. Wildlife Manag.* **23,** 107–10

LENSINK C.J., SKOOG R.O. & BUCKLEY J.L. (1955) Food habits of marten in interior Alaska and their significance. *J. Wildlife Manag.* **19,** 364–8

LESLIE P.H. (1952) The estimation of population parameters from data obtained by means of the capture-recapture method. II. The estimation of total numbers. *Biometrika*, **39,** 363–88

LESLIE P.H. & CHITTY D. (1951) The estimation of population parameters from data obtained by means of the capture-recapture method. I. The maximum likelihood equations for estimating the death-rate. *Biometrika*, **38,** 269–92

LESLIE P.H., CHITTY D. & CHITTY H. (1953) The estimation of population parameters from data obtained by means of the capture-recapture method. III. An example of the practical application of the method. *Biometrika*, **40,** 137–69

LESLIE P.H., PERRY J.S. & WATSON J.S. (1945) The determination of the median body weight at which female rats reach maturity. *Proc. zool. Soc. Lond.* **115**, 473–88

LESLIE P.H. & RANSON R.M. (1940) The mortality, fertility and rate of natural increase of the vole (*Microtus agrestis*) as observed in the laboratory. *J. Anim. Ecol.* **9**, 27–52

LESLIE P.H. & RANSON R.M. (1954) The amount of wheat consumed by the brown rat. In *Control of Rats and Mice*, vol. II. ed. CHITTY D. Oxford, Clarendon Press

LESLIE P.H. *et al.* (1955) The longevity and fertility of the Orkney vole, *Microtus orcadensis*, as observed in the laboratory. *Proc. zool. Soc. Lond.* **125**, 115–25

LESLIE P.H., VENABLES U.M. & VENABLES L.S.V. (1952) The fertility and population structure of the brown rat (*Rattus norvegicus*) in cornricks and some other habitats. *Proc. zool. Soc. Lond.* **122**, 187–238

LEUTSCHER A. (1960) *Tracks and Signs of British Animals*. London, Cleaver-Hume Press

LEUW A. DE (1957) Die Wildkatze. *Merkbl. Niederwildausschuss des dtsch. Jagdschutzverb.* No. 16. Munich

LEVER R.J.A.W. (1959) The diet of the fox since myxomatosis. *J. Anim. Ecol.* **28**, 359–75

LEVER R.A., ARMOUR C.J. & THOMPSON H.V. (1957) Myxomatosis and the fox. *Agriculture*, **64**, 105–11

LIERS E.E. (1951) Notes on the river otter (*Lutra canadensis*). *J. Mammal.* **32**, 1–9

LIKHACHEV G.N. (1956) [Some ecological traits of the badger of the Tula abatis broadleaf forests.]. In [*Studies of Mammals in Government Preserves*], ed. YURGENSON P.B. Moscow. Trans. 1961 by Israel Program for Sci. Transl.

LINCOLN F.C. (1930) *Calculating waterfowl abundance on the basis of banding returns.* U.S. Dep. Agric. Circ. No. 118.

LINDAHL K. CURRY- (1959) Notes on the ecology and periodicity of some rodents and shrews in Sweden. *Mammalia*, **23**, 389–422

LINDEMANN W. (1953) Einiges über die Wildkatzes der Ostkarpathen (*Felis s. silvestris* Schreber, 1777). *Säugetierk. Mitt.* **1**, 73–4

LINDEMANN W. (1955) Uber die Jugendentwicklung beim Luchs (*Lynx l. lynx* Kerr) und bei der Wildkatze (*Felis s. silvestris* Schreber). *Behaviour*, **8**, 1–45

LINN I. (1954) Some Norwegian small mammal faunas; a study based on trappings in West and North Norway. *Oikos*, **5**, 1–24

LINN I. (1962) *Weasels*. London, *Sunday Times* Publ. Animals of Britain, No. 14

LINN I. & SHILLITO J. (1960) Rings for marking very small mammals. *Proc. zool. Soc. Lond.* **134**, 489–95

LLEWELLYN L.M. (1942) Notes on the Alleghenian least weasel in Virginia. *J. Mammal.* **23**, 439–41

LLOYD H.G. (1959) The distribution of squirrels in England and Wales, 1959. *J. Anim. Ecol.* **31**, 157–65

LOCKIE J.D. (1955) The breeding habits and food of short-eared owls after a vole plague. *Bird Study*, **2**, 53–69

LOCKIE J.D. (1956) After myxomatosis. *Scot. Agric.* **36**, 65–9

LOCKIE J.D. (1959) The estimation of the food of foxes. *J. Wildlife Manag.* **23**, 224–7

LOCKIE J.D. (1961) The food of the pine marten *Martes martes* in west Ross-shire, Scotland. *Proc. zool. Soc. Lond.* **136**, 187–95

LOCKLEY R.M. (1961) Social structure and stress in the rabbit warren. *J. Anim. Ecol.* **30**, 385–423

LORD R.D. (1961) A population study of the gray fox. *Amer. Midl. Nat.* **66**, 87–109

LORENZ K. (1957) The European water shrew (*Neomys fodiens* Pallisant, 1871). In *The UFAW Handbook on the Care and Management of Laboratory Animals*, 2nd ed., ed. WORDEN A.N. & PETTER W. LANE-. London, Univ. Fed. Anim. Welfare

LØVENSKIOLD H.L. (1954) Studies on the avifauna of Spitsbergen. *Skr. Norsk Polarinst.* No. 103, 13

LOVETT W.V. (1961) A feeding population of pipistrelle bats (*P. pipistrellus* Linn.). *Trans. Suffolk Nat. Soc.* **12**, 39–43

LOWE V.P.W. (1957) The wood mouse (common field mouse) (*Apodemus sylvaticus* L.). In *The UFAW Handbook on the Care and Management of Laboratory Animals*, ed. WORDEN A.N. & PETTER, W. LANE-. London, Univ. Fed. Anim. Welfare

LOWE V.P.W. (1961) A discussion on the history, present status and future conservation of red deer (*Cervus elaphus* L.) in Scotland. *Terre et la Vie*, **108**, 9–40

LOZAN M.N. (1961) [Age determination of *Dryomys nitedula* Pall. and of *Muscardinus avellanarius* L.]. *Zool. Zh.* **40**, 1740–3

LUND M.-K. (1959) The red fox in Norway. *Pap. Norweg. Game-Res.* **5**, No. 2

McCANN C. (1958) Observations on the polecat in New Zealand. *Rec. Dom. Mus. Wellington* (1955), **2**, 151–65

McLAUGHLAN J.D. & HENDERSON W.M. (1947) The occurrence of foot-and-mouth disease in the hedgehog under natural conditions. *J. Hyg. Camb.* **45**, 474–9

MADSEN H. (1939) Does the rabbit chew the cud? *Nature, Lond.* **143**, 981

MARKLEY M.H. & BASSETT C.F. (1942) Habits of captive marten. *Amer. Midl. Nat.* **28**, 604–16

MARKUS C.U. (1957) Vergleichende Untersuchungen über den Sexualcyclus weiblicher Rötelmäuse (*Clethrionomys glareolus* Schreber 1780) und Feldmäuse (*Microtus arvalis* Pallas, 1778). *Wiss. Z. Univ. Halle, Math-Nat.* **VI/6**, 1021–32

MARSHALL W.H. (1951a) Pine marten as a forest product. *J. For.* **49**, 899–905

MARSHALL W.H. (1951b) An age determination method for the pine marten. *J. Wildlife Manag.* **15**, 276–83

MATHESON C. (1939) A survey of the status of *Rattus rattus* and its sub-species in the sea-ports of Great Britain and Ireland. *J. Anim. Ecol.* **8**, 76–93

MATHESON C. (1963a) The distribution of the red polecat in Wales. *Proc. zool. Soc. Lond.* **140**, 115–20

MATHESON C. (1963b) The distribution of *Apodemus flavicollis* in Wales and its border counties. *Proc. zool. Soc. Lond.* (in press)

MATHIAK H.A. (1938) A key to the hairs of the mammals of Southern Michigan. *J. Wildlife Manag.* **2,** 251–68

MATTHEWS L.H. (1935) The oestrous cycle and intersexuality in the female mole (*Talpa europaea* Linn.). *Proc. zool. Soc. Lond.* 347–83

MATTHEWS L.H. (1937) The female sexual cycle in the British horseshoe bats *Rhinolophus ferrumequinum insulanus* Barrett-Hamilton and *R. hipposideros minutus* Montagu. *Trans. zool. Soc. Lond.* **23,** 229–66

MATTHEWS L.H. (1941) Reproduction in the Scottish wild cat, *Felis silvestris grampia* Miller. *Proc. zool. Soc. Lond.* **111B,** 59–77

MATTHEWS L.H. (1947) A note on *Crocidura russula* and other mammals in Alderney, Channel Islands. *J. Anim. Ecol.* **16,** 225

MATTHEWS L.H. (1950) [The natural history of the grey seal, including lactation]. *Proc. zool. Soc. Lond.* **120,** 763

MATTHEWS L.H. (1952) *British Mammals*. London, Collins

MATTHEY R. (1956) Cytologie chromosomique comparée et systématique des Muridae. *Mammalia,* **20,** 93–123

MAURICE A. (1931) Le ragondin. *Arch. Hist. Nat. Soc. Nat. d'Acclimatation de France,* No. 7, 1–234

MAYER W.V. (1952) The hair of California mammals with keys to the dorsal guard hairs of California mammals. *Amer. Midl. Nat.* **48,** 480–512

MEHL S. (1939) Die Wühlmaus. *Prakt. Bl. PflBau.* **17,** 1–27

MEHLHARDT D. (1949) *Der Dachs*. Berlin, Naturk. Korr.

MEYLAN A. (1960) Contribution à l'étude du polymorphisme chromosomique chez *Sorex araneus* L. (Mamm. Insectivora). Note préliminaire. *Rev. Suisse Zool.* **67,** 258–61

MEZHZHERIN V.A. (1958) [On feeding habits of *Sorex araneus* L. and *Sorex minutus* L.]. *Zool. Zh.* **37,** 948–53

MIDDLETON A.D. (1931) *The Grey Squirrel*. London, Sidgwick & Jackson

MIDDLETON A.D. (1934) Periodic fluctuations in British game populations. *J. Anim. Ecol.* **3,** 231–49

MIDDLETON A.D. (1957) Game birds on the farm. 2. *Agriculture,* **64,** 345–7

MILLAIS J.G. (1897) *British Deer and their Horns*. London, Sotheran

MILLAIS J.G. (1904–6) *Mammals of Great Britain and Ireland*. London, Longmans Green. 3 vols

MILLER G.S. (1907) The families and genera of bats. *Bull. U.S. Nat. Mus. Washington,* **57,** 1–282

MILLER R.G., RITCEY R.W. & EDWARDS R.Y. (1955) Live-trapping marten in British Columbia. *Murrelet,* **36,** 1–8

MILLER R.S. (1954) Food habits of the wood mouse, *Apodemus sylvaticus* (Linné 1758), and the bank vole, *Clethrionomys glareolus* (Schreber 1780), in Wytham Woods, Berkshire. *Säugetierk. Mitt.* **2,** 109–14

MILLER R.S. (1955) Activity rhythms in the wood mouse, *Apodemus sylvaticus,* and the bank vole, *Clethrionomys glareolus. Proc. zool. Soc. Lond.* **125,** 505–19

MITCHELL P. CHALMERS- (1911) On longevity and relative viability in mammals and birds; with a note on the theory of longevity. *Proc. zool. Soc. Lond.* (1911), 425–548

MOFFAT C.B. (1900) The habits of the hairy-armed bat, *Vesperugo leisleri* Kuhl. *Irish Nat.* **9**, 235–40

MOFFAT C.B. (1922) The habits of the long-eared bat. *Irish Nat.* **31**, 105–11

MOFFAT C.B. (1938) The mammals of Ireland. *Proc. roy. Irish Acad.* **44B**, 61–128

MOHR E. (1952) Die Robben der europäischen Gewässer. *Monog. Wildsäugetiere*, No. 12, 1–283. Frankfurt-am-Main

MOHR E. (1955) *Der Seehund.* Wittenberg Lutherstadt, A. Ziemsen

MÖHRES F.P. (1954) Uber die Ultraschallorientierung der Hufeisennasen (Chiroptera-Rhinolophinae). *Z. vergl. Physiol.* **34**, 547–88

MOORE A.W. (1942) Shrews as a check on Douglas fir regeneration. *J. Mammal.* **23**, 37–41

MOORE J.C. (1959) Relationships among living squirrels of the Sciurinae. *Bull. Amer. Mus. nat. Hist.* **118**, 153–206

MOROT C.H. (1882) Mémoire relatif aux pelotes stomacales des léporides. *Rec. Méd. vet. Paris*, **59**, 635–46

MORRIS B. (1961) Some observations on the breeding season of the hedgehog and the rearing and handling of the young. *Proc. zool. Soc. Lond.* **136**, 201–6

MOSBY H.S., ed. (1960) *Manual of Game Investigational Techniques.* The Wildlife Society, c/o Virginia Co-operative Wildlife Research Unit, Dept. of Forestry and Wildlife, Blacksburg, Virginia

MURIE O.J. (1954) *A Field Guide to Animal Tracks.* Boston, Houghton Mifflin Co.

MYERS K. (1957) Some observations on the use of sight counts in estimating populations of the rabbit, *Oryctolagus cuniculus* (L.). *C.S.I.R.O. Wildlife Res.* **2**, 170–2

MYERS K. & MYKTOWYCZ R. (1958) Social behaviour in the wild rabbit. *Nature, Lond.* **181**, 1515–16

MYKTOWYCZ R. (1958) Social behaviour of an experimental colony of wild rabbits, *Oryctolagus cuniculus* (L.). I. Establishment of the colony. *C.S.I.R.O. Wildlife Res.* **3**, 7–25

NASIMOVICH A.A. (1949) [The biology of the weasel in Kola peninsula in connection with its competitive relations with the ermine]. *Zool. Zh.* **28**, 177–82

NEAL E.G. (1948) *The Badger.* London, Pelican Books

NEAL E.G. & HARRISON R.J. (1958) Reproduction in the European badger (*Meles meles* L.). *Trans. zool. Soc. Lond.* **29**, 67–131

NEWSON R.M. (1960) The Ecology of Vole and Mouse Populations in Different Habitats. D.Phil. unpubl. thesis, Univ. of Oxford

NEWSON R. (1963) Differences in numbers, reproduction and survival between two neighbouring populations of bank voles (*Clethrionomys glareolus*). *Ecology*, **44**, 110–20

NICHOLSON A.J. & WARNER D.W. (1953) The rodents of New Caledonia. *J. Mammal.* **34**, 168–79

NIEUWENHOVEN P.J. VAN (1956) Ecological observations in a hibernation-quarter of cave-dwelling bats in South-Limburg. *Publ. natuurh. Genoots. Limburg*, **9**, 1–55

NORMAN J.R. & FRASER F.C. (1948) *Giant Fishes, Whales and Dolphins*. London, Putnam

NORTH M.E.W. (1956) Tape-recording for the field ornithologist. In *The Ornithologists' Guide*, ed. HUTSON H.P.W. London, Brit. Orn. Union

NOTINI G. (1948) Biologiska undersökinger över grävlingen (*Meles meles*). *Svenska Jägareförbundets Medd*. No. 13

NOVIKOV G.A. (1956) [Carnivorous Mammals of the Fauna of the U.S.S.R.]. Moscow & Leningrad. Keys to the Fauna of the U.S.S.R. No. 62 Translation 1962 by Israel Program for Sci. Trans.

NYHOLM E.S. (1960) [On stoat and weasel and their winter habitat]. *Suom. Riista*, **13**, 106–16 [English abstr. suppl. in mimeo]

ODUM E.P. (1953) *Fundamentals of Ecology*. Philadelphia, W.B. Saunders Co.

OGILVIE A.G. (1957) The initiation of a study of mortality and morbidity in the Farne Island grey seal nurseries. *Trans. nat. Hist. Soc. Northumb*. N.S., **12**, 134–6

OGILVIE A.G. (1959) Morbidity in the Farne Island grey seal nurseries in 1957. *Trans. nat. Hist. Soc. Northumb*. N.S., **13**, 83–5

OKSALA T. (1954) Genetics of the dark phases of the red fox in experiment and in nature. *Pap. Game Res. Helsinki*, No. 11, 3–16

OKSALA T. (1954) On the Samson character of the red fox. *Pap. Game Res. Helsinki*, No. 11, 17–23

OLSTAD O. (1930) Rats and reindeer in the Antarctic. *Sci. Res. Norw. Antarct. Exped*. No. 4

OSGOOD W.H. (1909) Revision of the mice of the American genus *Peromyscus*. *N. Amer. Fauna*, **29**, 1–285

OSTERMAN K. (1956) Zur Aktivität heimischer Muriden und Gliriden. *Zool. Jrb. (Physiol.)*, **66**, 355–88

PAGE F.J. TAYLOR, ed. (1957) *A Field Guide to British Deer*. London, Mammal Society of the British Isles.

PANTIN C.F.A. (1946) *Notes on Microscopical Technique for Zoologists*. Cambridge, Univ. Press

PARKES A.S., ed. (1956–60) *Marshall's Physiology of Reproduction*. London, Longmans Green

PAROVSHCHIKOV V. YA (1961) [On feeding habits of *Martes martes borealis* B. Kuznetz. near Archangelsk]. *Zool. Zh*. **40**, 1112–15

PAVLININ V.N. (1948) [Some studies on the ringing of moles (*Talpa europaea* L.) in the Urals]. *Zool. Zh*. **27**, 555–62

PEARSON J. (1938) The Tasmanian brush opossum: its distribution and colour variations. *Pap. roy. Soc. Tasmania* (1937), 21–9

PEARSON O.P. (1959) A traffic survey of *Microtus-Rheithrodontomys* runways. *J. Mammal*. **40**, 169–80

PERRING F.H. & WALTERS S.M. ed. (1962) *Atlas of the British Flora*. London and Edinburgh, Nelson

PERRY J.S. (1943) Reproduction in the water vole, *Arvicola amphibius* Linn. *Proc. zool. Soc. Lond*. A, **112**, 118–30

PERRY R. (1953) *The Watcher and the Red Deer*. London, Hodge & Co.

PETTER W. LANE- (1951) Mouse ear tattooing forceps. *J. Anim. Tech. Assn*. **2**,
15

PHILIP U. (1957) The wild house-mouse (*Mus musculus* L.). In *The UFAW Handbook on the Care and Management of Laboratory Animals*, ed. WORDEN A.N. & PETTER W. LANE-. London, Univ. Fed. Anim. Welfare

PHILLIPS G.C. & EAST K. (1961) The relative efficiency of some small mammal traps. *Proc. zool. Soc. Lond.* **137**, 637–40

PHILLIPS W.M. (1953) The effect of rabbit grazing on a re-seeded pasture. *J. Brit. Grassland Soc.* **8**, 169–81

PHILLIPS W.M. (1955) The effect of commercial trapping on rabbit populations. *Ann. appl. Biol.* **43**, 247–57

PICKVANCE T.J. & CHARD J.S.R. (1960) Feral muntjac in the West Midlands. *Proc. Bgham. nat. Hist. Soc.* **19**, 1–8

PISANO R.G. & STORER T.I. (1948) Burrows and feeding of the Norway rat. *J. Mammal.* **29**, 374–83

PITT F. (1945) Breeding of the harvest mouse in captivity. *Nature, Lond.* **155**, 700

POLDERBOER E.B. (1942) Habits of the least weasel (*Mustela rixosa*) in northeastern Iowa. *J. Mammal.* **23**, 145–7

POLDERBOER E.B., KUHN L.W. & HENDRICKSON G.O. (1941) Winter and spring habits of weasels in central Iowa. *J. Wildlife Manag.* **5**, 115–19

POPOV V.A. (1943) A new age index in Mustelidae. *C.R. Acad. Sci. U.R.S.S.* **38**, 258–68

PORTER G. (1957) Norway rat (*Rattus norvegicus* Berkenhout, 1769). In *The UFAW Handbook on the Care and Management of Laboratory Animals*, ed. WORDEN A.N. & PETTER W. LANE-. London, Univ. Fed. Anim. Welfare

PRICE M. (1953) The reproductive cycle of the water shrew, *Neomys fodiens bicolor* Shaw. *Proc. zool. Soc. Lond.* **123**, 599–621

PRUITT W. (1957) A survey of the mammalian family Soricidae (shrews). *Säugetierk. Mitt.* **5**, 18–27

PUCEK M. (1959) The effect of the venom of the water shrew (*Neomys fodiens fodiens* Pennant) on certain experimental animals. *Acta theriol.* **3**, 93–104

PUCEK Z. (1959) Some biological aspects of the sex-ratio in the common shrew (*Sorex araneus araneus* L.). *Acta theriol.* **3**, 43–73

PUCEK Z. (1960) Sexual maturation and variability of the reproductive system in young shrews (*Sorex* L.) in the first calendar year of life. *Acta theriol.* **3**, 269–96

PYE J.D. (1960) A theory of echolocation by bats. *J. Laryngol. Otol.* **74**, 718–29

QUICK H.F. (1955) Food habits of marten (*Martes americana*) in Northern British Columbia. *Canad. Field-Nat.* **69**, 144–7

RABUS A. (1881) Beiträge zur Kenntnis über den Winterschlaf der Siebenschläfer. *Zool. Gart. Frankfurt.* 321–5. (Translated in *Zoologist*, 1882, Ser. 3, **6**, 161–4)

RANSON R.M. (1934) The field vole (*Microtus*) as a laboratory animal. *J. Anim. Ecol.* **3**, 70–6

RANSON R.M. (1941a) New laboratory animals from wild species. Breeding a laboratory stock of hedgehogs (*Erinaceus europaeus*). *J. Hyg. Camb.*, **41**, 131–8

RANSON R.M. (1941b) Pre-natal and infant mortality in a laboratory population of voles (*Microtus agrestis*). *Proc. zool. Soc. Lond.* A, **111**, 45–57

RAUSCH R. (1946) Collecting bats in Ohio. *J Mammal.* **27**, 275–6

REICHSTEIN H. (1957) Schädelvariabilität europäischer Mausewiesel (*Mustela nivalis* L.) und Hermeline (*Mustela erminea* L.) in Beziehung zu Verbreitung und Geschlecht. *Z. Säugetierk.* **22**, 151–82

REINWALDT E. & ERKINARO E. (1959) Zur Taxonomie und Verbreitung des Baummarders, *Martes martes martes* (Linné, 1758). *Säugetierk. Mitt.* **7**, 97–100

REMPE U. (1957) Beobachtungen über Brunst, Paarung, Tragzeit, Geburt und Kreuzungen bei Mitgliedern der Untergattung *Putorius. Säugetierk. Mitt.* **5**, 111–13

RESSOVSKY N. TIMOFÉEFF- (1940) Mutations and geographical variation. In *The New Systematics*, ed. HUXLEY J.S. Oxford, Univ. Press

REYNOLDS J.K. (1955) Distribution and populations of the European hare in southern Ontario. *Canad. Field-Nat.* **69**, 14–20

RIDGWAY R. (1912) *Color Standards and Color Nomenclature.* Publ. by author. Washington D.C.

RIECK W. (1956) Untersuchungen über die Vermehrung des Feldhasen. *Z. Jagdw.* **11**, 49–90

RIESCH A.F. VON VIETINGHOFF- (1952) Beiträge zur Biologie des Siebenschläfers (*Glis glis* L.). *Bonn. zool. Beitr.* **3**, 167–86

RIESCH A.F. VON VIETINGHOFF- (1955) Siebenschläfermarkierung im Deister. *Z. Säugetierk.* **20**, 134–5

RITCHIE J. (1920) *The Influence of Man on Animal life in Scotland.* Cambridge, Univ. Press

RITCHIE J. (1930) The protection of the grey seal. *Scot. Nat.* (1930), 33–6

ROEBUCK A. (1951) Observations on the wood-mouse (*Apodemus sylvaticus*). *Ann. appl. Biol.* **38**, 722–4

ROTHSCHILD M. (1942) Change of pelage in the stoat *Mustela erminea* L. *Nature, Lond.* **149**, 78

ROTHSCHILD M. (1958) A further note on the increase of hares (*Lepus europaeus*) in France. *Proc. zool. Soc. Lond.* **131**, 328–9

ROTHSCHILD M. & CLAY T. (1952) *Fleas, Flukes and Cuckoos.* London, Collins

ROTHSCHILD M. & MARSH H. (1956) Increase of hares (*Lepus europaeus* Pallas) at Ashton Wold, with a note on the reduction in numbers of the brown rat (*Rattus norvegicus* Berkenhout). *Proc. zool. Soc. Lond.* **127**, 441–5

ROWE F.P. (1958) Some observations on harvest mice from the corn ricks of a Hampshire farm. *Proc. zool. Soc. Lond.* **131**, 320–3

ROWLANDS I.W. (1957) The ferret (*Mustela putorius furo* L.). In *The UFAW Handbook on the Care and Management of Laboratory Animals*, ed. WORDEN A.N. & PETTER W. LANE-. London, Univ. Fed. Anim. Welfare

ROWLANDS I.W. & PARKES A.S. (1935) The reproductive processes of certain mammals. VIII. Reproduction in foxes (*Vulpes* spp.). *Proc. zool. Soc. Lond.* **105**, 823–41

ROWLEY I. & MOLLISON B.C. (1955) Copulation in the wild rabbit, *Oryctolagus cuniculus. Behaviour*, **8**, 81–4

RYBERG O. (1947) *Studies on Bats and Bat Parasites.* Stockholm, Svensk Natur

SÄLZLE K. (1936) Untersuchungen über das Farbsehvermögen von Opossum, Waldmäusen, Rötelmäusen und Eichörnschen. *Z. Säugetierk.* **11**, 106–48

SANDARS E. (1937) *A Beast Book for the Pocket*. Oxford, Univ. Press

SAUNDBY R.P. (1960) Observations on the grey seal at St Kilda in winter. *Proc. zool. Soc. Lond.* **133**, 487–90

SCHAERFFENBERG B. (1940) Die Nahrung des Maulwurfs (*Talpa europaea* L.). *Z. angew. Ent.* **27**, 1–70

SCHEFFER V.B. & SLIPP J.W. (1944) The harbor seal in Washington State. *Amer. Midl. Nat.* **32**, 373–416

SCHEFFER V.B. (1958) *Seals, Sea-lions and Walruses*. Stanford Univ. Press

SCHILLER E.L. (1952) Studies on the helminth fauna of Alaska. V. Notes on Adak rats (*Rattus norvegicus* Berkenhout) with special reference to helminth parasites. *J. Mammal.* **33**, 38–49

SCHILLER E.L. (1956) Ecology and health of *Rattus* at Nome, Alaska. *J. Mammal.* **37**, 181–8

SCHMIDT F. (1943) Naturgeschichte des Baum- und des Steinmarders. *Monogr. Wildsäuget. Lpz.* **10**, 1–258

SCHOFIELD R.D. (1960) A thousand miles of fox trails in Michigan's ruffed grouse range. *J. Wildlife Manag.* **24**, 432–4

SCHORGER A.W. (1949) Squirrels in early Wisconsin. *Trans. Wis. Acad. Sci. Arts Lett.* **39**, 195–247

SCHWARZ E. & SCHWARZ H.K. (1943) The wild and commensal stocks of the house mouse, *Mus musculus* Linnaeus. *J. Mammal.* **24**, 59–72

SCOTT T.C.S. MORRISON- (1937) A note on the distribution of the two shrews found in Jersey. *J. Anim. Ecol.* **6**, 284–5

SCOTT T.G. (1941a) A method for estimating the red fox population. *Iowa State Coll. J. Sci.* **15**, 155–9

SCOTT T.G. (1941b) Methods and computation in fecal analysis with reference to the red fox. *Iowa State Coll. J. Sci.* **15**, 279–85

SCOTT T.G. (1943) Some food coactions of the Northern Plains red fox. *Ecol. Monogr.* **13**, 427–79

SERGEANT D.E. (1951) The status of the common seal (*Phoca vitulina* L.) on the East Anglian coast. *J. Mar. biol. Ass. U.K.* **29**, 707–17

SHARMAN G.B. (1956) Chromosomes of the common shrew. *Nature, Lond.* **177**, 941–2

SHELDON W.G. (1949) Reproductive behavior of foxes in New York State. *J. Mammal.* **30**, 236–46

SHILLITO E.E. (1960) The Behaviour of the Vole, *Microtus agrestis*, with Particular Reference to Trapping Results. Ph.D. unpubl. thesis, Univ. of Exeter

SHILLITO E.E. (1963) Exploratory behaviour in the short-tailed vole *Microtus agrestis*. *Behaviour*, **21**, 145–54.

SHILLITO J.F. (1960) The General Ecology of the Common Shrew *Sorex araneus* L. Ph.D. unpubl. thesis, Univ. of Exeter

SHILLITO J.F. (1963) Field observations on the growth, reproduction and activity of a woodland population of the common shrew *Sorex araneus* L. *Proc. zool. Soc. Lond.* **140**, 99–114

SHORTEN M. (1946) A survey of the distribution of the American grey squirrel (*Sciurus carolinensis*) and the British red squirrel (*Sciurus vulgaris leucourus*) in England and Wales in 1944–5. *J. Anim. Ecol.* **15**, 82–92

SHORTEN M. (1953) Notes on the distribution of the grey squirrel (*Sciurus carolinensis*) and the red squirrel (*Sciurus vulgaris leucourus*) in England and Wales from 1945 to 1952. *J. Anim. Ecol.* **22**, 134–40

SHORTEN M. (1954a) *Squirrels.* London, Collins

SHORTEN M. (1954b) The reaction of the brown rat towards changes in its environment. In *Control of Rats and Mice*, vol. II, ed. CHITTY D.H. Oxford, Clarendon Press

SHORTEN M. (1957a) Squirrels in England, Wales and Scotland, 1955. *J. Anim. Ecol.* **26**, 287–94

SHORTEN M. (1957b) Damage caused by squirrels in Forestry Commission areas, 1954–6. *Forestry*, **30**, 151–72

SHORTEN M. (1962) *Squirrels.* M.A.F.F. Bull. No. 184 London, H.M.S.O.

SHORTEN M. & COURTIER F.A. (1955) A population study of the grey squirrel in May 1954. *Ann. appl. Biol.* **43**, 494–510

SIDOROWICZ J. (1959) Uber Morphologie und Biologie der Haselmaus (*Muscardinus avellanarius* L.) in Polen. *Acta theriol.* **3**, 75–91

SIEFKE A. (1960) Baummarder-Paarung. *Z. Säugetierk.* **25**, 178

SIIVONEN L. (1956) The correlation between the fluctuations of partridge and European hare populations and the climatic conditions of winters in South-West Finland during the last 30 years. *Pap. Game Res. Helsinki*, No. 17

SIMMS E. (1957) *Voices of the Wild.* London, Putnam

SIMPSON G.G. (1950) History of the fauna of Latin America. *Amer. Scientist*, **38**, 361–89

SIMPSON G.G. (1951) *Horses.* New York, Oxford Univ. Press Inc.

SIMPSON G.G. (1953) *Evolution and Geography.* Condon Lecture Publics. Oregon State System of Higher Education, Eugene, Oregon

SKOCZEŃ S. (1958) Tunnel digging by the mole (*Talpa europaea* Linne). *Acta theriol.* **2**, 235–49

SKOCZEŃ S. (1961a) On food storage of the mole *Talpa europaea* Linnaeus 1758. *Acta theriol.* **5**, 23–43

SKOCZEŃ S. (1961b) Colour mutations in the mole *Talpa europaea* Linnaeus 1758. *Acta theriol.* **5**, 290–3

SLUITER J.W. (1960) Reproductive rate of the bat *Rhinolophus hipposideros*. *Proc. Kon. Ned. Akad. v. Wet. Amsterdam*, **63**, 383–93

SLUITER J.W., VAN HEERDT P.F. & BEZEM J.J. (1956) Population statistics of the bat *Myotis mystacinus*, based on the marking-recapture method. *Arch. néerl. Zool.* **12**, 63–88

SMITH W.A., KENT F.L. & STRATTON G.B., ed. (1952) *World List of Scientific Periodicals Published in the Years 1900–1950*, 3rd ed. London, Butterworth Sci. Publ.

SMITH W.W. (1958) Melanistic *Rattus norvegicus* in south-western Georgia. *J. Mammal.* **39**, 304–6

'SNAFFLE' (1904) *The Roedeer.* London, E.M. Harwar

SNELL G.D. ed. (1941) *Biology of the Laboratory Mouse* by staff of Roscoe B. Jackson Memorial Laboratory, Philadelphia

SOPER E.A. (1955) *When Badgers Wake.* London, Routledge & Kegan Paul

SOPER J.D. (1919) Notes on Canadian weasels. *Canad. Field-Nat.* **33**, 43–7

SOUTHERN H.N. (1940) The ecology and population dynamics of the wild rabbit, *Oryctolagus cuniculus*. *Ann. appl. Biol.* **27**, 509–26

SOUTHERN H.N. (1942) Periodicity of refection in the wild rabbit. *Nature, Lond.* **149**, 553

SOUTHERN H.N. (1948) Sexual and aggressive behaviour in the wild rabbit. *Behaviour*, **1**, 173–94

SOUTHERN H.N. (1954) Tawny owls and their prey. *Ibis*, **96**, 384–410

SOUTHERN H.N. (1957) The harvest mouse (*Micromys minutus* Pallas, 1771). In *The UFAW Handbook on the Care and Management of Laboratory Animals*, ed. WORDEN A.N. & PETTER W. LANE-. London, Univ. Fed. Anim. Welfare

SOUTHERN H.N. & CROWCROFT W.P. (1956) Terrestrial habits of the water vole (*Arvicola amphibius*). *Proc. zool. Soc. Lond.* **126**, 166–7

SOUTHERN H.N. & LAURIE E.M.O. (1946) The house-mouse (*Mus musculus*) in corn ricks. *J. Anim. Ecol.* **15**, 134–49

SOUTHERN H.N. & WATSON J.S. (1941) Summer food of the red fox in Great Britain. A preliminary report. *J. Anim. Ecol.* **10**, 1–11

SOUTHERN H.N., WATSON J.S. & CHITTY D. (1946) Watching nocturnal animals by infra-red radiation. *J. Anim. Ecol.* **15**, 198–202

SOUTHWICK C.H. (1956) The abundance and distribution of harvest mice (*Micromys minutus*) in corn ricks near Oxford. *Proc. zool. Soc. Lond.* **126**, 449–52

SPEED M.C. (1956) An indigenous British horse. *Brit. Vet. J.* **112**, 483–90

STEIN G.H.W. (1950a) Zur Biologie des Maulwurfs, *Talpa europaea* L. *Bonn. zool. Beitr.* **1**, 97–116

STEIN G.H.W. (1950b) Grossenvariabilität und Rassenbildung bei *Talpa europaea* L. *Zool. Jb.* **79**, 321–49

STEIN G.H.W. (1950c) Uber Fortpflanzungszyklus, Wurfgrosse und Lebens dauer bei einigen, kleinen Nagetieren. *Schaadl. k. pfung.* **42**, 122–31

STEIN C.H.W. (1954) Materialien zum Haarwechsel deutscher Insectivoren. *Mitt. zool. Mus. Berl.* **30**, 12–34

STEIN G.H.W. (1956) Natürliche Auslese bei der Rötelmaus. *Z. Säugetierk.* **21**, 84–100

STEIN G.H.W. (1957) Materialen zur Kenntnis der Feldmaus *Microtus arvalis* Pallas. *Z. Säugetierk.* **22**, 117–35

STEIN G.H.W. (1958) *Die Feldmaus*. Wittenberg Lutherstadt, A. Ziemsen

STEIN G.H.W. (1960a) Schädelallometrien und Systematik bei altweltlichen Maulwürfen (Talpinae). *Mitt. zool. Mus. Berlin*, **36**, 1–48

STEIN G.H.W. (1960b) Zum Haarwechsel der Feldmaus *Microtus arvalis* (Pallas, 1779) und weiterer Muroidea. *Acta theriol.* **4**, 27–44

STEIN G.H.W. (1961) Beziehung zwischen Bestandsdichte und Vermehrung bei der Waldspitzmaus, *Sorex araneus*, und weiteren Rotzahnspitzmäusen. *Z. Säugetierk.* **26**, 13–28

STEPHENS M.N. (1952) Seasonal observations on the wild rabbit (*Oryctolagus cuniculus cuniculus* L.) in west Wales. *Proc. zool. Soc. Lond.* **122**, 417–34

STEPHENS M. (1957) *The Otter Report*. London. Univ Fed.. Anim. Welfare.

STEVEN D.M. (1953) Recent evolution in the genus *Clethrionomys*. *Symp. Soc. exp. Biol.* No. 7, 310–19

STEVEN G.A. (1934) A short investigation into the habits, abundance and species of seals on the north Cornwall coast. *J. Mar. biol. Ass. U.K.* **19,** 489–501

STEVEN G.A. (1936) Seals (*Halichoerus grypus*) of Cornwall coasts. *J. Mar. biol. Ass. U.K.* **20,** 493–506

STEVENSON J.H.F. (1959) *Mink in Britain,* 3rd ed. Exeter, Pitts

STIEVE H. (1950) Anatomisch biologische Untersuchungen über der Fortpflanzungstätigkeit des europäischen Rehes (*Capreolus*). *Z. mikr. anat. Forsch.* **55,** 427–530

STIEVE H. (1952) Zur Fortpflanzungsbiologie des europäischen Feldhasen (*Lepus europaeus* Pallas). *Zool. Anz.* **148,** 101–14

STOVES J.L. (1957) *Fibre Microscopy.* London, Nat. Trade Press

SUMNER F.B. (1932) Genetic, distributional and evolutionary studies of the subspecies of deer mice (*Peromyscus*). *Bibliogr. genet.* **9,** 1–106

SWITZENBERG D.F. (1950) Breeding productivity in Michigan red foxes. *J. Mammal.* **31,** 194–5

TAIT A.H. (1953) History of the sika. *Field,* **201,** 546

TALBOT L.M. & TALBOT M.H. (1962) Flaxedil and other drugs in field immobilization and translocation of large mammals in East Africa. *J. Mammal.* **43,** 76–88

TANSLEY A.G. (1939) *The British Isles and their Vegetation.* Cambridge, Univ. Press

TARKOWSKI A.K. (1957) Studies on reproduction and prenatal mortality of the common shrew (*Sorex araneus* L.). Part II. Reproduction under natural conditions. *Ann. Univ. M. Curie-Skłodowska,* C, **10,** 177–244

TAYLOR E.L. (1940) Pseudo-rumination in the rabbit. *Proc. zool Soc. Lond.* **110,** 159–63

TAYLOR W.L. (1946) The wild cat (*Felis silvestris*) in Great Britain. *J. Anim. Ecol.* **15,** 130–3

TAYLOR W.L. (1952) The polecat (*Mustela putorius*) in Wales. *J. Anim. Ecol.* **21,** 272–4

TAYLOR W.L. (1956) Pine martens in Britain. *Countryman, Idbury,* **53,** 277–81

TEGNER H.S. (1951) *The Roe Deer.* London, Batchworth

TELFER I.M. & WATT G. (1953) The grey seals of the Farne Islands. *Trans. nat. Hist. Soc. Northumb.* N.S., **10,** 165–84

TEMBROCK G. (1957) Zur Ethologie des Rotfuchses (*Vulpes vulpes* [L.]), unter besondere Berücksichtigung der Fortpflanzung. *Zool. Gart. Lpzg.* **23,** 289–532

TEMBROCK G. (1958a) Spielverhalten beim Rotfuchs. *Zool. Beitr. Berl.* **3,** 423–96

TEMBROCK G. (1958b) Zur Aktivitätsperiodik bei *Vulpes* und *Alopex. Zool. Jb.* (*Allg. Zool.*) **68,** 297–324

TEPLOV V.P. (1943) [The importance of the common shrew (*Sorex araneus* L.) and some other mammals in the diet of the grayling (*Thymallus thymallus* L.)]. *Zool. Zh.* **22,** 366–8

TETLEY H. (1941) On the Scottish fox. *Proc. zool. Soc. Lond.* **111**B, 23–35

TETLEY H. (1945) Notes on some specimens of the British otter. *Proc. zool. Soc. Lond.* **115,** 189–93

TETLEY H. (1945) Notes on British polecats and ferrets. *Proc. zool. Soc. Lond.* 115, 212–17

THOMAS O. (1905) Suggestions for the nomenclature of the cranial length measurements and of the cheek-teeth of mammals. *Proc. biol. Soc. Wash.* 18, 191–6

THOMPSON H.V. (1953) The edible dormouse (*Glis glis* L.) in England, 1902–1951. *Proc. zool. Soc. Lond.* 122, 1017–24

THOMPSON H.V. & ARMOUR C.J. (1954) Methods of marking wild rabbits. *J. Wildlife Manag.* 18, 411–14

THOMPSON H.V. & WORDEN A.N. (1956) *The Rabbit.* London, Collins

THURLOW W.G. (1958) The yellow-necked field mouse at Stowmarket. *Trans. Suff. Nat. Soc.* 10, 297–300

TRUE F.W. (1904) Whalebone whales of the Western North Atlantic. *Bull. Amer. Mus. nat. Hist.* 85, 1–350

TURČEK F.J. (1953) [Ecological analysis of a population of the red-backed vole (*Clethrionomys glareolus* Schreber) on Pol'ana Mountain in Slovakia]. *Práce výzk. úst. lesn. ČSR.* No. 3, 325–74

UHLIG H.G. (1955) The Gray Squirrel: its Life History, Ecology and Population Characteristics in west Virginia. Pittman-Robertson Project 31-R, Consv. Commission West Virginia. Unpubl.

URSIN E. (1956) Geographical variation in *Apodemus sylvaticus* and *Apodemus flavicollis* (Rodentia, Muridae) in Europe with special reference to Danish and Latvian populations. *Biol. Skr. Kong. Danske Vidensk. Selsk.* 8, No. 4

ÜTTENDÖRFER O. (1939) *Die Ernährung der deutschen Raubvögel und Eulen, und ihr Bedeutung in der heimischen Natur.* Berlin, J. Neumann-Neudamm

VENABLES L.S.V. (1943) Observations at a pipistrelle bat roost. *J. Anim. Ecol.* 12, 19–26

VENABLES L.S.V. & LESLIE P.H. (1942) The rat and mouse populations of corn ricks. *J. Anim. Ecol.* 11, 44–68

VENABLES L.S.V. & VENABLES U.M. (1955) *Birds and Mammals of Shetland.* Edinburgh, Oliver & Boyd

VENABLES U.M. & VENABLES L.S.V. (1955) Observations on a breeding colony of the seal *Phoca vitulina* in Shetland. *Proc. zool. Soc. Lond.* 125, 521–32

VENABLES U.M. & VENABLES L.S.V. (1957) Mating behaviour of the seal *Phoca vitulina* in Shetland. *Proc. zool. Soc. Lond.* 128, 387–96

VENABLES U.M. & VENABLES L.S.V. (1959) Vernal coition of the seal *Phoca vitulina* in Shetland. *Proc. zool. Soc. Lond.* 132, 665–9

VENABLES U.M. & VENABLES L.S.V. (1960) A seal survey of Northern Ireland 1956–1957. *Proc. zool. Soc. Lond.* 133, 490–4

VILLALOBOS C.M.J. (1947) *Colour Atlas.* El Alteneo, Buenos Aires

VINCENT R.E. (1958) Observations on red fox behavior. *Ecology*, 39, 755–7

VOS A. DE & GUENTHER S.E. (1952) Preliminary live-trapping studies of marten. *J. Wildlife Manag.* 16, 207–14

WACHTENDORF W. (1951) Beiträge zur Ökologie und Biologie der Haselmaus (*Muscardinus avellanarius*) im Alpenvorland. *Zool. Jb. (Syst.),* 80, 189–203

WADDINGTON C.H. (1939) *An Introduction to Modern Genetics.* London, Allen & Unwin

WARWICK T. (1934) The distribution of the musk rat (*Fiber zibethicus*) in the British Isles. *J. Anim. Ecol.* **3**, 250–67

WARWICK T. (1940) A contribution to the ecology of the musk rat (*Ondatra zibethica*) in the British Isles. *Proc. zool. Soc. Lond.* A, **110**, 165–201

WATSON A. (1955) The winter food of six Highland foxes. *Scot. Nat.* **67**, 123–4

WATSON J.S. (1944) The melanic form of *Rattus norvegicus* in London. *Nature, Lond.* **154**, 334–5

WATSON J.S. (1950) Some observations on the reproduction of *Rattus rattus* L. *Proc. zool. Soc. Lond.* **120**, 1–12

WATSON J.S. (1951) *The Rat Problem in Cyprus.* London, H.M.S.O. Colon. Res. Publ. No. 9

WATSON J.S. (1959) Identification of rats and mice in New Zealand. *N.Z. J. Agric.* (1959), 365–8

WATSON J.S. & BISCOE C.H. TYNDALE (1953) The apophyseal line as an age indicator for the wild rabbit, *Oryctolagus cuniculus* (L.). *N.Z. J. Sci.* **34**, 427–35

WATSON J.S. & TAYLOR R.H. (1955) Reingestion in the Hare *Lepus europaeus* Pal. *Science*, **121**, 314

WATT H.B. (1937) On the wild goats of Scotland. *J. Anim. Ecol.* **6**, 15–22

WATZKA M. (1940) Mikroskopisch-anatomische Untersuchungen über die Ranzzeit und Tragdauer des Hermelins (*Putorius ermineus*). *Z. mikr. anat. Forsch.* **48**, 359–74

WHITEHEAD G.K. (1949) Chinese water deer. *Field*, **193**, 301

WHITEHEAD G.K. (1950) *Deer and their Management in the Deer Parks of Great Britain and Ireland.* London, Country Life

WHITEHEAD G.K. (1953) *The Ancient White Cattle of Britain and their Descendants.* London, Faber

WHITEHEAD G.K. (1954a) Deer from Asia at home in England. *Field*, **203**, 663

WHITEHEAD G.K. (1954b) Epping Forest and its deer. *Country Life*, **116**, 810–11

WHITEHEAD G.K. (1960) *The Deer Stalking Grounds of Great Britain and Ireland.* London, Hollis & Carter

WIJNGAARDEN A. VAN (1954) *Biologie en Bestrijding van de Woelrat*, Arvicola terrestris terrestris (L.) *in Nederland.* Eindhoven

WIJNGAARDEN A. VAN (1957) The mammal fauna of two Betuwe landscapes. *Mammalia*, **21**, 267–300

WIJNGAARDEN A. VAN (1960) The population dynamics of four confined populations of the continental vole *Microtus arvalis* (Pallas). *Versl. Landbouwk. Onderzoek.* No. 66, 22

WILDHAGEN A. (1952) *Om vekslingene bestanden av Smånagere i Norge 1871–1949.* Drammen, J. Steenberg & Co.

WILDMAN A.B. (1954) *The Microscopy of Animal Textile Fibres.* Wool Industr. Res. Assn. Leeds

WOOD J.E. (1959) Relative estimates of fox population levels. *J. Wildlife Manag.* **23**, 53–63

WORDEN A.N. & PETTER W. LANE-, ed. (1957) *The UFAW Handbook on the Care and Management of Laboratory Animals*, 2nd ed. London, Univ. Fed. Anim. Welfare

WRANGEL H.F. VON (1939) Beiträge zur Biologie der Rötelmaus *Clethrionomys glareolus* Schr. *Z. Säugetierk.* **14,** 52–93

WRIGHT P.L. (1947) The sexual cycle of the long-tailed weasel (*Mustela frenata*). *J. Mammal.* **28,** 343–52

YAPP W.B. (1955) A classification of the habitats of British birds. *Bird Study,* **2,** 111–21

YEAGER L.E. (1950) Implications of some harvest and habitat factors in pine marten management. *Trans. 15th N. Amer. Wildlife Conf.* 319–34

YEATES G.K. (1946) *Bird Photography.* London, Faber

ZEJDA J. (1961) Age structure in populations of the bank vole, *Clethrionomys glareolus* Schreber 1780. *Zool. Listy,* **10,** 249–64

ZIMMERMANN K. (1936) Zur Kenntnis der europäischen Waldmäuse (*Sylvaemus sylvaticus* L. und *Sylvaemus flavicollis* Melchior). *Arch. Naturgesch.* N.F., **5,** 116–33

ZIMMERMANN K. (1937) Die märkische Rötelmaus, Analyse einer Population. *Märkische Tierwelt,* **3,** 34–40

ZIMMERMANN K. (1940) [1943] Zur Kenntnis deutscher Maus- und Zwerg-Wiesel. *Z. Säugetierk.* **15,** 289–98

ZIMMERMANN K. (1955) Körpergrösse und Bestandsdichte bei Feldmäusen (*Microtus arvalis*). *Z. Säugetierk.* **20,** 114–18

ZIMMERMANN K. (1957) Sind Gelbhalsmaus und Waldmaus miteinander kreuzbar? *Z. Säugetierk.* **22,** 214–17

ZIMMERMANN K. (1959a) Über eine Kreuzung von Unterarten der Feldmaus *Microtus arvalis. Zool. Jb. (Syst.),* **87,** 1 12

ZIMMERMANN K. (1959b) *Taschenbuch unserer wildlebenden Säugetiere.* Leipzig-Jena, Urania-Verlag.

ZIMMERMANN K. (1962) Die Untergattungen der Gattung *Apodemus* Kaup. *Bonn. zool. Beitr.* **13,** 198–208

ZIPPELIUS H.-M. (1957) Zur Karawanenbildung bei der Feldspitzmaus (*Crocidura leucodon*). *Bonn. zool. Beitr.* **8,** 81 4

ZIPPIN C. (1958) The removal method of estimation. *J. Wildlife Manag.* **22,** 82–90

Index

Page references in bold type are to order, family, genus and species sections in Part II; those in italics are to pages with line drawings.

453